Earthworms through the ages

BOOKS BY *William Hazlett Upson*

ME AND HENRY AND THE ARTILLERY

ALEXANDER BOTTS: Earthworm Tractors

EARTHWORMS IN EUROPE: Alexander Botts Makes the
Old World Tractor-Conscious

KEEP 'EM CRAWLING: Earthworms at War

BOTTS IN WAR, BOTTS IN PEACE: Earthworms
Can Take Anything

HOW TO BE RICH LIKE ME

EARTHWORMS THROUGH THE AGES: The Wisdom
of Alexander Botts

Earthworms
through the ages

THE WISDOM OF
ALEXANDER BOTTS

BY *William Hazlett Upson*

RINEHART AND COMPANY, INCORPORATED

NEW YORK · TORONTO

CONTENTS

MORE TROUBLE WITH THE EXPENSE ACCOUNT   3

THE TRACTOR BUSINESS IS NO PLACE FOR
   WEAKLINGS   25

"THAR'S GOLD IN THEM THAR MOUNTAINS"   51

THE PEACEMAKER   75

WORKING ON THE LEVEE   103

COÖPERATION   126

THE GREAT HIGHWAY CONTROVERSY   148

GOOD NEWS   171

HOLLYWOOD IS WONDERFUL, BUT—   193

SITUATION HAYWIRE   213

THE BOTTS PLAN FOR A LASTING PEACE   230

OUR GALLANT ALLIES   247

THE MÖBIUS STRIP   264

I WANT OUT   282

BOTTS IS BACK—WITH ALL PAPERS IN ORDER   299

Earthworms through the ages

More Trouble With the Expense Account

EARTHWORM TRACTOR COMPANY
EARTHWORM CITY, ILLINOIS
OFFICE OF THE SALES MANAGER

January 2, 1932.

MR. ALEXANDER BOTTS,
VICE PRESIDENT IN CHARGE OF TRACTOR SALES,
DEANE SUPPLY COMPANY,
MERCEDILLO, CALIFORNIA.

DEAR BOTTS: Your letter of recent date is received, and we are very glad that you are accepting our offer to reënter the sales department of the Earthworm Tractor Company.

As I have indicated in a former letter, you are to act as a traveling sales-promotion agent. I inclose a list of Earthworm tractor dealers whom we want you to visit, set down in the order in which we wish you to visit them. The first is Mr. George Grubb, Rio Pedro, California. We are writing Mr. Grubb that you will call on him in the near future.

We want you to spend a week or two with each dealer, analyzing his problems, helping him with suggestions and advice, and teaching him the various sales methods which you used in the old days as a salesman for this company, and which you have recently employed so successfully, in

3

spite of the depression, in selling tractors for the Deane Supply Company.

We will pay you four hundred dollars a month, which represents your old salary of five hundred minus the 20 per cent cut which we have been forced to make throughout our organization. We will also allow traveling expenses; and in this connection I feel that I should remind you that the good old days of extravagant expense accounts are gone. Our slogan for 1932 is: "Net profits are more important than gross volume." We are insisting that all our traveling representatives practice the most rigid economy. I inclose five hundred dollars advance expense money, and suggest that you use it sparingly.

Kindly start as soon as possible, and send us frequent reports of your progress. We have every confidence in you, and wish you the best of luck.

Most sincerely,
GILBERT HENDERSON, Sales Manager.

ALEXANDER BOTTS
SALES PROMOTION REPRESENTATIVE
EARTHWORM TRACTOR COMPANY

RIO PEDRO, CALIFORNIA,
Wednesday, January 6, 1932.

MR. GILBERT HENDERSON,
SALES MANAGER,
EARTHWORM TRACTOR COMPANY,
EARTHWORM CITY, ILLINOIS.
Via Air Mail.

DEAR HENDERSON: Well, here I am. I have started in with a rush. You will note that I already have a supply of swell official embossed stationery, which I ordered in advance, and which I am using in this, my first report, to let you know that I arrived in Rio Pedro this morning, that I called on Mr. George Grubb, and that I have already got things moving so satisfactorily that I will need a thousand dollars additional expense money right away. I want you to wire me the money as soon as you receive this letter—otherwise I may be held up in the very important undertakings which I am initiating in this region.

It certainly seems wonderful to be working once more for the good old Earthworm Tractor Company. Of course, it would be even better if I had my wife along, the way I did on the great European trip. But Gadget is pretty busy these days. Alexander Botts, Junior, and Gadget the Second are now almost three years old, and they are the finest pair of twins in the San Joaquin Valley. They are, however, a lot of work, so Mrs. Botts felt she had to stay at home.

But don't get the idea that being alone will cramp my style. I still have just as much brains and ability as ever, and I have a feeling that this new enterprise is going to be the real climax of my career. The fact that I am spending more money than you expected is a most hopeful sign, because it indicates that I am promoting far more activities than you ever dreamed of; although part of the extra expense is due to the fact that our dealer here is a pathetically moribund specimen, who does not know the meaning of the word "coöperate."

When I introduced myself to Mr. George Grubb this morning, he at once told me that I was simply wasting my time. He said that the tractor business in this region was completely shot, that he hadn't sold a single machine for six months, and that he had no sales in prospect.

"And if I can't sell tractors around here," he said, "nobody can. So you might as well take the next train out of town. I don't want to waste my time listening to a lot of ignorant suggestions from an outsider like you who doesn't understand the conditions here, and probably doesn't know anything about selling tractors anyway."

These ungracious remarks, naturally, pleased me very much. I saw at once that in working with Mr. Grubb I would run into various difficulties. And difficulties always stimulate me, because I can look forward with so much pleasure to the warm glow of satisfaction which is sure to envelop me when I have overcome them.

I proceeded to handle Mr. Grubb with all my old-time tact and adroitness. An ordinary sales representative might have been discouraged at the old guy's opening remarks, or he might have lost his temper and told him—truthfully enough—that he was an egregious ass to turn down in this loutish way a perfectly friendly and well-meant offer of assistance. But I made neither of these mistakes.

"Mr. Grubb," I said, with a pleasant smile, "your remarks are partially true. As yet, I know nothing of conditions in your territory. But I can learn. Accordingly, I plan to take a room at the hotel, stay around a few days and see if I can stir up something of interest. I might even locate a prospect for you. But whatever happens, I will not call on you or bother you in any way until I have something definite to tell you."

"You'd better not," said Mr. Grubb. "And I warn you again that you are just wasting your time. There isn't anybody around here that wants to buy an Earthworm tractor. And even if they did, they haven't got the money to pay for it. There just is no business any more at all."

"Well, I guess I'll look around, anyway," I said. "Good morning, Mr. Grubb."

"Good-by," he said.

Leaving this poor idiot sitting gloomily in his office, I walked briskly down town and began nosing about asking questions. Everybody was most pessimistic. Having noticed that business was slightly sick, they had decided it was on its deathbed. Times were terrible, they told me, and nothing was going on at all. Even the new post office, which the Government was just starting to build, was held up because the contractor had been unable to get the proper kind of stone.

When I heard this last bit of information I began to

prick up my ears. My subtle intuition told me that here there might possibly be some business for tractors. And I was right. Before long I located a rather sad and disagreeable old party by the name of Ira Button who owns a sandstone quarry about ten miles away up in the mountains, and who had contracted, for a very pleasing sum of money, to supply the stone for the monumental new post office. He had worked the quarry for several months, taking the stone out and getting it ready. Then, last week, just as he was going to start shipping it to town by motor trucks, the highway bridge over the Rio Pedro Canyon was washed out and the only road from his quarry was completely cut off. He said the state highway department would probably build a new bridge, but it would take many months to complete it. And, as the stone had to be delivered within four weeks, it looked as if poor old Mr. Ira Button was completely blowed up. So there he sat in his office, drawing little pictures on the blotter, thinking about his troubles and doing nothing at all to remedy them.

"What sort of a place is that canyon?" I asked. "Are the sides straight up and down or sloping?"

"They're sloping," said Mr. Button. "But they're a pretty steep slope."

"Is it possible for a man to climb down into this canyon and up the other side?" I asked.

"Yes."

"Very good," I said. "What you need is an Earthworm tractor. With one of these mechanical marvels you can pull loads over the roughest country. You can put your stone in a wagon, take it down into the canyon, ford the stream and drag it up the other side."

"I thought of that," said Mr. Button, "and I asked Mr. Grubb, the Earthworm tractor dealer, if it could be done."

"What did he say?"

"He said I was crazy. He said the tractor would get smashed to pieces the first trip. And he didn't want to do business with me anyway, because I have no money to pay for a tractor. I've sunk everything I own in the quarry."

"That's too bad," I said. "But you'll have plenty of money, won't you, when you deliver that stone?"

"Yes, if I deliver it."

"Did old Grubb go out and look over the ground with you?"

"No, he said he didn't have time to bother with it."

"All right," I said, "you and I are going to inspect that canyon, Mr. Button. Is that your flivver out in front?"

"Yes."

"Very good. Let's go."

We went. A drive of about ten miles brought us to the edge of the Rio Pedro Canyon—two hundred feet deep, a quarter of a mile wide, with a rapid stream in the bottom, rushing past the wreckage of the old highway bridge.

"The quarry," said Mr. Button, "is right over there on the other side, less than half a mile away. So near, and yet so far."

"All right," I said. "Let's investigate."

After spending several hours scrambling around over the rocks, I located what looked like a perfectly practicable tractor route, and made up my mind to put on a demonstration.

The banks near the old bridge are too steep even for an Earthworm, but by driving about a mile up-stream we can make a crossing just above the great Rio Pedro Falls, where the canyon is not more than a hundred feet deep, and where the banks don't have much more than a forty-five-degree slope. After crossing the canyon we will bring the stone to the end of the present road, and it will then be taken to town in motor trucks.

While we were tramping around we met another man who was looking over the canyon. He was particularly interested in the waterfall, which is about a hundred feet high, and very beautiful. He said he was coming up next

Saturday with a group of people who are going to take some moving pictures of the place.

This at once gave me another splendid idea. I told the gentleman I expected to be up there myself in a few days with a tractor, and I said I would pay him any reasonable price up to five hundred dollars for a series of shots showing the tractor and the wagon negotiating this difficult and rocky country. The moving-picture man refused to commit himself in advance, but I feel certain he will fall in with my plans.

And my demonstrations will thus kill two birds with one stone. It will sell a tractor to Mr. Button, and it will provide our advertising department with a remarkabe picture which it can send all over the country to show the skeptics exactly what an Earthworm tractor is capable of when handled by a man who really understands it.

Upon our return to town, I discovered that Mr. Ira Button has no wagon adequate for the rough work I am planning, so I ordered one to be specially made by the local blacksmith and wheelwright. It will be of unusual size and strength, but the cost will be only three hundred dollars, and the maker has promised to rush the work and have it ready by Saturday morning.

After arranging for the wagon, I called on Mr. George Grubb, our dealer, and laid the whole beautiful scheme before him; suggesting that he lend me one of his tractors and stand the expense of the wagon. But, as I had feared, he failed to become enthusiastic.

"The country around that canyon is entirely too rough for tractors, Earthworms or any other kind," he said. "And I certainly won't let you use one of my stock machines to put on any such demonstration. You would just knock the thing all to pieces. And I have no intention of paying for that fool wagon you say you have ordered. The whole plan is idiotic. This man Button can't buy a tractor. He hasn't got the money to pay for it."

"He'll have the money," I said, "as soon as he delivers that stone."

At this Mr. Button laughed in what I can only describe as a jeering manner. "If he had the faintest chance of getting that stone down here," he said, "I might trust him. But he hasn't. So, if he wants to buy a tractor from me, he'll have to pay cash—which he can't. So that's the end of it."

"Not at all," I replied. "I have been sent to help you, and I am going to help you in spite of yourself. You have some Earthworm tractors on hand here in your warehouse?"

"I have just one—a sixty-horsepower model."

"Exactly what I want," I said. "Here is my offer: I will rent this machine from you for one or more days, starting next Saturday, at twenty-five dollars a day. I will pay for the wagon I have ordered. I will haul out enough stone for Mr. Button so that he can get a first payment from the people who are building the post office. This will enable him to offer you a first payment on the tractor, and when you see how things are going, I am sure you will be only too glad to sell him the machine. In the remote contingency that he doesn't buy the tractor, the Earthworm Tractor Company agrees—through me, its representative —to return the tractor to you in perfect condition or pay you for it in full. Nothing could be more generous than that. You can't lose. What do you say? Will you rent me the tractor?"

"Well," he said, "if you want to make a fool of yourself, and if the Earthworm Tractor Company is willing to pay for your foolishness, it is all right with me."

"Very good, Mr. Grubb," I said. "I'll call for the tractor on Saturday. Good afternoon."

As it was then almost six o'clock, I came back to the hotel and ate supper. I have been spending the evening writing this report. Tomorrow and Friday I will superintend the construction of the wagon and do some more general investigating. And on Saturday the real excitement will start.

I have given you a very full account of my activities, so that you may see that my extra expenses are really a form of enlightened economy. I may not have to spend all of the thousand dollars, but I am having you send it to me anyway, just to be on the safe side. And even if I do use it all, the expenditure of these few paltry dollars will be completely overbalanced by the benefits derived from the moving picture and from the revival of the tractor business which my demonstration will accomplish.

> Most sincerely,
> ALEXANDER BOTTS.

GEORGE GRUBB
EARTHWORM TRACTOR DEALER
RIO PEDRO, CALIFORNIA

January 6, 1932.

MR. GILBERT HENDERSON,
SALES MANAGER,
EARTHWORM TRACTOR COMPANY,
EARTHWORM CITY, ILLINOIS.
Via Air Mail.

DEAR MR. HENDERSON: Your representative, Mr. Alexander Botts, has arrived. And as long as you have sent out this man to offer me unsolicited and gratuitous advice on how to run my own business, I am going to take it upon myself to give you a little advice on how to run yours.

Of all the crazy ideas ever evolved by the Earthworm Tractor Company—and there have been many—this latest scheme is the most cockeyed. It wouldn't be so bad if times were good. But you pick out the very moment when business is at its worst and I am already worried to death, and proceed to annoy me further by sending a lunatic who wants to make a disgusting exhibition of himself by performing a lot of monkeyshines all over my territory.

Mr. Botts blew in here this morning, and already has arranged to give a demonstration hauling stone over a section of mountain country which is so rough that he is sure to smash up the tractor before he can accomplish anything at all. And the purpose of this demonstration is to sell a tractor to a man who has absolutely no money to pay for it. Mr. Botts further tells me that he is going to hire a man to take moving pictures of his demonstration for advertising purposes. A sweet advertisement that will be—a picture showing an Earthworm tractor attempting to drive over a lot of rocks and bowlders, and knocking itself to pieces in the attempt.

I always try to be fair with you people, and I am coöperating with Mr. Botts as much as I reasonably can. Upon his assurance that the Earthworm Company would pay all expenses and make good any damages that might ensue, I have told him that he can use for his demonstration a sixty-horse-power Earthworm tractor which I have in stock here.

But I hate to do it. I hate to risk a four-thousand-dollar machine in this way, even if I don't have to stand the loss myself.

And I'm afraid the whole procedure will make the Earthworm tractor ridiculous in the eyes of the public. It is bad business. Instead of wasting your money on wild schemes like this, you might better reduce the price of the tractor and give your hard-working dealers a bigger discount. Think it over.

Very truly,
GEORGE GRUBB.

TELEGRAM

EARTHWORM CITY ILL
JAN 9 1932

GEORGE GRUBB
RIO PEDRO CAL

AM WIRING BOTTS TO CANCEL THE DEMONSTRATION OF
WHICH YOU DISAPPROVE AND TO CONFINE HIS ACTIVITIES
TO GIVING YOU SUCH ADVICE AND SUGGESTIONS AS YOU
DESIRE STOP OUR ONE THOUGHT IN SENDING MR BOTTS WAS
THAT HE MIGHT HELP YOU AND WE STILL HOPE AND BE-
LIEVE THAT HE MAY BE ABLE TO DO SO

GILBERT HENDERSON

TELEGRAM

EARTHWORM CITY ILL
JAN 9 1932

ALEXANDER BOTTS
CARE GEORGE GRUBB
RIO PEDRO CAL

YOUR LETTER RECEIVED BUT AM NOT SENDING THE FUNDS
YOU REQUEST STOP REFER TO MY LETTER OF JANUARY SEC-
OND NET PROFITS RATHER THAN GROSS SALES THE
WATCHWORD FOR NINETEEN THIRTY TWO STOP EXPENSES
MUST BE KEPT DOWN STOP YOU HAVE NO AUTHORITY TO
FINANCE DEMONSTRATIONS STOP THAT IS THE DEALERS
BUSINESS STOP YOU WILL AT ONCE CANCEL PLANS FOR THE
DEMONSTRATION DESCRIBED IN YOUR LETTER UNLESS
GRUBB WILL STAND ALL EXPENSE STOP YOUR JOB IS TO
ASSIST DEALER WITH ADVICE AND TACTFUL SUGGESTIONS
STOP LETTER FROM GRUBB INDICATES YOU HAVE FAILED
TO USE TACT AND HAVE GIVEN NO SUGGESTIONS WHICH
HE CONSIDERS WORTH ACTING UPON STOP WAKE UP AND
TRY TO MAKE YOURSELF A HELP RATHER THAN A HIN-
DRANCE TO MR GRUBB STOP WATCH THAT EXPENSE
ACCOUNT

GILBERT HENDERSON

TELEGRAM

RIO PEDRO CAL
JAN 9 1932

GILBERT HENDERSON
SALES MANAGER
EARTHWORM TRACTOR CO
EARTHWORM CITY ILL

YOUR WIRE RECEIVED STOP AM MUCH DISAPPOINTED IN
YOUR ATTITUDE STOP HOW DO YOU EXPECT ME TO ACCOM-
PLISH ANYTHING WHEN YOU WONT BACK ME UP WITH THE
NECESSARY FUNDS QUESTION MARK AND HOW DO YOU EX-
PECT ME TO HELP THIS GUY WITH ADVICE AND SUGGES-
TIONS WHEN HE WONT LISTEN TO ANYTHING I SAY AN-
OTHER QUESTION MARK AM GOING AHEAD WITH DEMON-
STRATION ANYWAY AND WILL SEND YOU FULL REPORT AS
SOON AS I HAVE TIME STOP IN HASTE

ALEXANDER BOTTS

GEORGE GRUBB
EARTHWORM TRACTOR DEALER
RIO PEDRO, CALIFORNIA

Saturday evening, January 9, 1932.

MR. GILBERT HENDERSON,
SALES MANAGER,
EARTHWORM TRACTOR COMPANY,
EARTHWORM CITY, ILLINOIS.

DEAR MR. HENDERSON: I inclose my bill for
$3521.64, which you owe me for one sixty-horse-power
Earthworm tractor. The amount represents the list price
of $4000, plus freight, and minus my dealer's commission.

Things have turned out exactly as I told you they
would—only worse. I had expected this wild representative
of yours to damage my tractor to some extent. But I had
not supposed he would be able to convert it into a total loss.

In case Mr. Botts has not written you of his exploits this afternoon, or in case he has attempted to excuse himself by sending you some highly adorned cock-and-bull story, I will give you a brief account of the facts as I observed them.

Owing to various outside matters of business, I did not reach my office today until two o'clock in the afternoon. When I arrived, my secretary handed me the telegram which you had sent in answer to my letter. My secretary also stated that there had been a telegram for Mr. Botts, which she had given him when he came into the office toward the end of the morning.

"Did Mr. Botts," I asked, "make any remarks after he read his telegram?"

"Yes," she replied. "He said the message gave him a big laugh. He said that his boss at the factory didn't want him to put on this demonstration, but he was going to, anyway. He said he had already agreed to buy a special wagon from the blacksmith, and he had promised Mr. Button to haul some stone for him, and he had arranged with a moving-picture man for the taking of a picture. He told me he just didn't have the heart to disappoint all these people, so he took the tractor and drove away."

Upon hearing this, I was, naturally, much displeased. I didn't want Mr. Botts using my tractor to put on a demonstration against your orders. So I at once got into my car and drove out the Rio Pedro Canyon road with the intention of stopping him. Unfortunately, I was too late.

When I reached the broken highway bridge, I stopped the car. Somewhere in the distance I heard the roar of a tractor motor. As the noise seemed to come from somewhere in the canyon, I climbed down the steep bank to the edge of the river. Then, following the direction of the noise, I walked upstream for almost a mile. Finally I rounded a bend and came in sight of the great Rio Pedro Falls. On the bank of the stream at the top of the falls, I observed Mr. Alexander Botts and my Earthworm tractor.

He was evidently preparing to drive across the stream at the very brink of the cataract.

Two motion-picture cameras, with their operators, were perched in advantageous positions on the rocky canyon wall. There appeared to be a number of people present, but I could not tell how many, as my view was limited by the fact that I was looking up from the bottom of the falls.

At once I shouted to Mr. Botts to stop, but the roar of the motor and the thundering of the waters completely drowned out my voice. I waved frantically, but no one noticed me. The walls of the canyon for some distance below the falls are sheer rock. In order to reach the top of the falls I would have had to follow the stream for almost a mile down to the neighborhood of the ruined bridge, then climb out of the canyon and return along the rim. There was no time for this.

As I watched, I saw Mr. Botts step down from the tractor, and, with the assistance of another man, place a very lifelike-looking dummy in the driver's seat. This procedure certainly showed up Mr. Botts in his true colors. He was perfectly willing to risk my tractor for the sake of his half-witted advertising motion picture, but he was not willing to risk his own worthless neck. Once more I yelled "Stop" at the top of my voice. But no one heard me. I saw Mr. Botts throw in the clutch. Slowly and steadily, with no one to guide it but the dummy driver, that tractor started moving straight across the rushing stream not more than three feet from the edge of the waterfall. The men with the moving-picture cameras seemed to be working feverishly.

At first, I thought the machine would get across all right. It held its direction straight enough, but it had been aimed a little bit wrong, so that its course, instead of carrying it parallel to the edge, brought it gradually nearer and nearer. Finally, about two-thirds of the way across, it toppled over, and with a sickening plunge disappeared into the depths of the pool at the bottom.

As the disaster was so complete, and as there was, obviously, nothing more I could do, I retraced my steps, climbed out of the canyon and drove back to town.

Mr. Botts has not yet dared to show up here at the office. If he does, I shall simply have him thrown out at once. And in the future I must insist that all business between myself and the Earthworm Tractor Company be handled direct, and not through any such outlandish emissaries as this Botts person.

In conclusion, I draw your attention once more to the inclosed bill. I shall expect your check in full payment by return mail.

> Very truly,
>
> GEORGE GRUBB.

EARTHWORM TRACTOR COMPANY
EARTHWORM CITY, ILLINOIS
OFFICE OF THE SALES MANAGER

Monday, January 11, 1932.

MR. ALEXANDER BOTTS,
CARE MR. GEORGE GRUBB,
RIO PEDRO, CALIFORNIA.
Via Air Mail.

DEAR BOTTS: Your telegram, stating that you were about to put on a demonstration in spite of my direct orders to the contrary, arrived on Saturday.

Today I have received a letter from Mr. George Grubb, telling of the disastrous consequences of that demonstration, and stating that he expects the Earthworm Company to pay for the tractor which was destroyed in the course of your highly reckless activities.

As we have not yet heard from you, we do not know exactly how many more heavy expenses you have incurred.

It is obvious, however, that you have deliberately and completely disregarded my instructions to the effect that your expense account must be kept down to a minimum, and have completely failed to accomplish anything in the way of assisting our dealer, Mr. George Grubb.

In these circumstances, it is necessary for us to advise you that your services will no longer be required by this company. If you care to submit an itemized statement of your expenses, the same will be considered by our accounting department.

Very truly,

GILBERT HENDERSON,
Sales Manager.

ALEXANDER BOTTS
SALES PROMOTION REPRESENTATIVE
EARTHWORM TRACTOR COMPANY

RIO PEDRO, CALIFORNIA,
Wednesday, January 13, 1932.

MR. GILBERT HENDERSON,
SALES MANAGER,
EARTHWORM TRACTOR COMPANY,
EARTHWORM CITY, ILLINOIS.
Via Air Mail.

DEAR HENDERSON: I meant to write you before, but I have been very busy. And it is just as well I waited, because now I can answer your snappy little letter, which has just arrived. It certainly seems like the good old days to have you bawling me out so thoroughly and so completely. I sure got to hand it to you, Mr. Henderson. You may be getting old, but you're not losing any of your vitality or any of your command of the English language. When I got to the end of the letter, and saw that you were actually pulling the old bluff of pretending to fire me, it just made me feel good all over.

It also seemed just like the dear old days to have you giving me definite instructions as to what I should do, in spite of the fact that you are so far away that you, naturally, are completely ignorant of conditions here. And I see you are still making the same old error of concentrating your attention too strongly on the size of the expense account. "Net profits rather than gross sales" is a good slogan, but you should always remember that increasing the profits may be accomplished just as well by adding to the receipts as by cutting down the expenses.

In my recent activities here in Rio Pedro, it is true that I ran up a good many expenses. But these expenses were necessary in order that we might receive even greater advantages. When I wrote you my former letter, I had everything organized on a perfectly sound basis. I had every reason to expect that, at an outlay of a few paltry hundreds of dollars, I would sell a tractor, and, by so doing, teach the opinionated and obstinate Mr. Grubb a much-needed lesson in salesmanship, and inspire him to go ahead and make further sales on his own account. In addition, I expected to get a magnificent motion picture for the use of the advertising department. Either one of these achievements would have justified the expense. So, even if no other factors had been involved, I should have probably disregarded your telegram and gone ahead with my demonstration.

But by the time that telegram arrived, I had discovered and taken advantage of certain new factors which were so favorable to my enterprise that it would have been idiotic to hold back. The discovery and utilization of these new factors was due entirely to my own energy and resourcefulness. Early last Saturday morning the blacksmith informed me that the big three-hundred-dollar wagon would be completed a little before noon. So, instead of loafing around town for several hours until it should be ready, I persuaded Mr. Button to drive me out to the canyon for a final inspection of the ground. Incidentally, we had heard that the moving-picture people were already there, and I wanted to talk to them and make definite arrangements for our picture.

When we arrived at the canyon, we discovered a very curious situation. The whole landscape was swarming with humanity. Instead of a small group taking shots of the scenery, as I had expected, there was a large outfit from one of the big studios in Hollywood, engaged in the production of a stupendous and spectacular drama of the great open spaces. Besides the producing and executive staff, there were a lot of stars and featured players, and an appalling mob of extras, including several dozen cowboys and at least five hundred wild Indians.

Leaving Mr. Button sitting in the car, I began walking around looking for the advance agent I had talked with a few days previously. But I could not find him. Either he was not there or he was lost in this great crowd. I therefore approached a gentleman who was standing beside a camera and told him I wish to have a few private movies taken. He let out a loud laugh. "You'll have to see the director about that," he said, "and from the way the old guy is carrying on this morning, there isn't one chance in a thousand he'll do anything for anybody. Boy, that lad is sore."

"Has there been some trouble?" I asked.

"I'll say there has. According to the plot of this picture, the hero and heroine escape across the canyon. The villain tries to follow them in a big tractor, and he gets swept over the falls. That's the big scene, and it looks now as if it has gone hay-wire."

"It has?"

"Yes. The director didn't want to smash up a new tractor by sending it over the falls, so he brought along an old secondhand piece of junk. And now this old tractor has broken down completely, and they can't even drive it up to the top of the falls, let alone run it over."

"Ah, ha!" I said at once. "This is a lucky break for me."

It was, indeed, a most unusual and unexpected piece of good fortune. But I wish to point out, for the benefit of certain people in the Earthworm Tractor Company who may be inclined to think that my success as a salesman is due entirely to what they call fool luck, that I never would have discovered this situation unless I had been up on my toes and chasing about the country with my eyes wide open and my mind on the alert. And I never would have been able to exploit the opportunity to its fullest extent, had I not had the skill and finesse to nurse the situation along until the time was ripe to take definite action.

Most people would have rushed to the director at once, and tried to sell him a tractor. But I decided to make a careful and cautious approach. My first move was to walk over to where the director was standing and listen unobtrusively to what was going on.

The director was a large man with a red face, and he seemed in a state of great agitation. "This is a mess," he said. "Just look at all these people standing around, drawing their salaries and doing nothing. We've got to finish up here today, and we can't do it unless we get a tractor."

Various assistants began fluttering about and explaining that it would take two days to repair the tractor, and just as long to get another one up from Los Angeles.

"There must be tractors somewhere in this God-forsaken country," he said. "And it's up to some of you guys to locate one."

"If you are looking for a tractor," I said, stepping forward, "I have one down at Rio Pedro. If you want to use it, I can bring it up here."

"How long will it take?" he asked.

"About two hours," I said.

"All right," he said. "How much do you want for it?"

"We'll discuss that when I arrive. Good-by."

I hurried back to the road and had Mr. Button drive me to town as fast as possible. When I reached Mr. Grubb's office, his secretary handed me your telegram directing me to cancel the demonstration. Naturally, I paid no attention to these instructions, and, after sending you a brief wire in reply, I took the tractor, hooked onto the big wagon which the blacksmith had just finished, and drove as rapidly as possible to the canyon; arriving about three hours after I had left.

During this time, the director—just as I expected—had worked himself up into a state of far greater anxiety and impatience than ever. Besides, I now had the tractor on hand where he could look at it and realize that it was exactly the machine he needed. All this made it possible for me to bargain with him more successfully than when I first talked to him.

In fact, I now had him where I could make him eat right out of my hand. During my absence he had sent several of his assistants down to scour the farming country around Rio Pedro, and report whether they could find a tractor. Fortunately, he had as yet heard nothing from these people. He had also tried to make the five hundred wild Indians drag the old broken-down tractor by main strength up to the top of the falls. But after an hour's work, they had moved it only a hundred yards, and gave it up as a bad job.

I was now his only hope, and he was willing to buy the tractor at two or three times the list price. I told him, however, that I did not care to sell, and I proposed an arrangement that I had thought out very carefully. First of all, I insisted that he let me haul one load of stone from the quarry around to the road, in order to show Mr. Button, the quarry man, that it could be done. I also insisted that moving pictures be taken of this trip. At first, the director kicked like a steer, because this would delay everything for about an hour. But I remained firm, and at last he agreed. The trip was entirely successful. We got several thousand feet of wonderful pictures, and the moving-picture company will send you the films, free of charge, as soon as they are developed.

After the trip with the stone was over, I took the

tractor up the canyon again. And in consideration of a payment of six thousand dollars in cash, I ran the old baby
over the big waterfall. Perhaps I was a fool to do it so
cheap. The poor director would have willingly paid more.
However, I am not the man to take a mean advantage of
someone else's misfortunes, and I am pleased to report
that the director thanked me warmly, and stated that he
was entirely satisfied with the deal.

I am even more pleased to report an additional
achievement. After the moving-picture people departed, I
went down to the foot of the waterfall to see what was left
of the tractor, and I was delighted to discover that instead
of descending upon a heap of bowlders, as at Niagara, the
waters of this cataract plunge directly into a very deep
pool. This at once gave me an idea. And, by working all
day Sunday with several of Mr. Grubb's mechanics and a
long cable and a winch from Mr. Button's quarry, we were
able to hook onto the tractor and drag it up on the bank.
A thorough examination showed, just as I had expected,
that it takes more than a drop of one hundred feet into a
pool of water to destroy a sturdy Earthworm tractor. The
radiator, part of the hood, and various minor widgets were
smashed up. But a couple of day's work and a few hundred
dollars' worth of parts purchased from Mr. Grubb have
sufficed to put the machine back in running order, apparently just as good as new.

So everything has worked out even better than I expected. I have paid old man Grubb the full list price of
four thousand dollars for his tractor, plus freight, so you
don't have to bother about the bill which he sent you. And
I have sold the machine and the big wagon to Mr. Button,
who will use them to haul out his stone. I have chosen to
regard the tractor as secondhand, placing the price, including the wagon, at three thousand dollars cash. This
money was advanced by the contractor who is building the
post office, as soon as he found out that the tractor was
actually able to bring out the stone which he needed.

Mr. Grubb seems to be the most surprised man in all Southern California. The poor sap actually didn't know, until I showed him, that an Earthworm tractor is built strong enough to negotiate this rough mountain country around here. He tells me that as soon as he can get in another machine, he will put on a demonstration for a man in the western part of the county who is engaged in a big logging operation and will probably take several machines as soon as he is shown how well they get over the hills and rocks.

Having disregarded your telegram instructing me to cancel my demonstration, I will now disregard your letter telling me I am fired, and proceed to the next job, with the feeling that I have made a reasonably auspicious start. And I think you ought to agree with me. Possibly you will not have the imagination or the artistic sensibilities necessary to appreciate the remarkable movie I have made. Possibly you may not be much impressed by the sale of the tractor to Mr. Button or by the way I have waked up Mr. Grubb. But certainly, in view of the interminable manner in which you have been harping upon the subject, you cannot fail to appreciate my expense account, which may be summed up as follows:

Received from moving-picture director............ $6,000.00
Received from Ira Button for tractor and wagon.... 3,000.00

Total Receipts.............................. $9,000.00

Paid to Mr. George Grubb, for tractor, gas, oil, spare
    parts, labor, and so on....................... $4,571.29
Paid to blacksmith, for wagon.................. 300.00
Paid to myself (traveling and miscellaneous expense) 246.37
Paid to myself, for this month's salary (I thought I
    might as well hold this out, so as to save you the
    trouble of sending me a check later. You will note
    that I have decided to raise my pay to an amount
    more nearly corresponding to what I am worth).. 500.00

Total Expenses............................. $5,617.66

Total Receipts.............................. $9,000.00

Total Expenses 5,617.66

Net profit (which you have been talking about so continually) $3,382.34

I inclose a draft for this last amount, and in conclusion I wish to suggest that if you would only hire a few more men like me, you wouldn't have to worry about whether you sold any tractors or not. You could run the whole company on the profits from the salesmen's expense accounts.

Very truly,

ALEXANDER BOTTS.

THE TRACTOR BUSINESS IS NO PLACE FOR WEAKLINGS

EARTHWORM TRACTOR COMPANY
EARTHWORM CITY, ILLINOIS
OFFICE OF THE SALES MANAGER

Tuesday, February 2, 1932.

MR. ALEXANDER BOTTS,
TYLERVILLE HOTEL,
TYLERVILLE, WISCONSIN.

DEAR BOTTS: According to your schedule, you should be arriving in Tylerville day after tomorrow. In a former letter, you will remember, we requested you to call on our dealer in Tylerville, Mr. A. H. Smith, of the Smith Tractor Company, Incorporated, and assist him in putting on an intensive selling drive. Recent developments, however, make it necessary for us to alter these instructions.

Mr. Smith has written us that the building which housed his business has burned, and that his affairs are in very bad shape. His contract as dealer for the Earthworm Tractor Company expires in two weeks, and he says he will be unable to renew it.

An implement dealer by the name of John Yerkes, in Tylerville, has written us that he would be glad to take over the dealership which Mr. Smith is giving up.

Instead of consulting with Mr. Smith, therefore, you will make a thorough investigation of Mr. Yerkes and any other possible candidates for the dealership, and sign a contract for the coming year with the man who seems to you the most promising.

Incidentally, I may say that Mr. Yerkes' letter has impressed me most favorably. He sounds like a good practical man, with plenty of force and energy.

I inclose several copies of Form CX-447-G—our standard dealer's contract.

Very sincerely,
GILBERT HENDERSON,
Sales Manager.

ALEXANDER BOTTS
SALES PROMOTION REPRESENTATIVE
EARTHWORM TRACTOR COMPANY

TYLERVILLE HOTEL,
TYLERVILLE, WISCONSIN.
Thursday evening,
February 4, 1932.

MR. GILBERT HENDERSON, SALES MANAGER,
EARTHWORM TRACTOR COMPANY,
EARTHWORM CITY, ILLINOIS.

DEAR HENDERSON: I arrived in town this afternoon, and found your letter awaiting me. Right away I got busy. I inquired at the local chamber of commerce and elsewhere, and found that Mr. Yerkes is the only man in town who is in a position to take over and successfully carry on the dealership which Mr. Smith is giving up.

Before offering Mr. Yerkes the job, however, I decided I would have a look at this Smith guy. I had met him once several years ago, and I remembered him as one of our most successful dealers.

"Perhaps," I said to myself, "old man Henderson's idea that we ought to drop him in the garbage can this way is just as cockeyed as some of his former ideas." So I went around and called on Mr. Smith. I asked him what was the matter. And I am very glad that I did.

The poor fish has certainly been having rotten luck. His business is completely bankrupt, and he himself seems on the verge of a nervous breakdown. Honestly, Henderson, his story was pitiful. The way he talked about his dear old grandfather almost had me in tears. And before I knew what I was doing, I had promised to help him. At first sight, the case appears hopeless. To meet his immediate obligations he will have to borrow fifty thousand dollars on no security. And this isn't all. If he borrows the money, he will have to pay it back sometime, and it doesn't look to me as if he ever could.

But difficulties such as these never discourage Alexander Botts. I am leaving this afternoon for Chicago, where I will attempt to negotiate the necessary loan. If I fail, which is more than likely, the Earthworm Tractor Company will have to advance the fifty thousand dollars. Otherwise we can't keep Mr. Smith as our dealer.

I am sure that you will be delighted to know about this generous piece of rescue work. My address in Chicago will be the Blackstone Hotel.

Most sincerely,
ALEXANDER BOTTS.

EARTHWORM TRACTOR COMPANY
EARTHWORM CITY, ILLINOIS
OFFICE OF THE SALES MANAGER

Friday, February 5, 1932.

MR. ALEXANDER BOTTS,
BLACKSTONE HOTEL,
CHICAGO, ILLINOIS.

DEAR BOTTS: Your letter is received, and I am not in any way delighted to know about "this generous piece of rescue work." I don't wish to seem harsh or unfeeling. And I deeply regret the fact that Mr. Smith's business has failed. But you must realize that the Earthworm Tractor Company cannot pay your salary and expenses while you rush about the country attempting to negotiate a large unsecured loan for a completely bankrupt gentleman who has already notified us that he has severed his business connection with us. Your suggestion that the Earthworm Company might lend Mr. Smith fifty thousand dollars is absurd. This company is a business concern, not a philanthropic organization.

You will return to Tylerville at once, and follow out my instructions regarding the investigation of Mr. John Yerkes.

Very truly yours,
GILBERT HENDERSON,
Sales Manager.

ALEXANDER BOTTS
SALES PROMOTION REPRESENTATIVE
EARTHWORM TRACTOR COMPANY

BLACKSTONE HOTEL,
CHICAGO, ILLINOIS.
Saturday, February 6, 1932.

MR. GILBERT HENDERSON, SALES MANAGER,
EARTHWORM TRACTOR COMPANY,
EARTHWORM CITY, ILLINOIS.

DEAR HENDERSON: Your letter of yesterday is here, and there is one thing about it that pleases me very much. When I wrote you that I thought you would be "delighted to know about this generous piece of rescue work," I had, all the time, a sort of a hunch that perhaps you would not be delighted at all. Your letter proves, in a very pleasing way, that I was right. It confirms an opinion I have had for a long time—to the effect that practically all my hunches are correct. And it encourages me to go ahead and act upon a very distinct hunch which has recently entered my mind.

This new hunch is a sort of vague feeling that in business, as well as elsewhere, we always get along better if we act in a large, generous and open-hearted way—looking always at the idealistic, inspirational and humanistic aspects of a problem, and refusing to stultify ourselves by a narrow preoccupation with crassly materialistic details.

Such being the case, it is obvious that I will have to follow out my original plan in this Smith matter, in spite of your orders to the contrary. But do not get the idea that I am blaming you in any way for giving me these orders. In fact, I will admit that the fault, if any, is entirely mine. My letter to you from Tylerville had to be cut short so that I could catch the train for Chicago. I did not have time to give you the details of my interview with Mr. Smith. Consequently, when you wrote me, you did not know the facts of the case. And it was perfectly natural for you to write without any real comprehension of what you were saying.

At present, fortunately, I have plenty of time. The banker whom I came to see has gone out into the suburbs somewhere for the week-end, so it will be necessary for me to remain here until he gets back on Monday or Tuesday. This will be no hardship, however, as my room here at the hotel is very comfortable, not to say luxurious. And, as I loll about comfortably on the elegant upholstery of a large armchair, I will give you an account of my visit to poor old Mr. Smith, and explain exactly why I am right in this matter and why you are wrong.

Mr. Smith's business offices had, as you know, burned down. So I called on him at his home—a handsome brick house amid pleasant surroundings in the outskirts of Tylerville. The room in which he received me was elegantly furnished and pleasing to the eye, but Mr. Smith himself was indeed a pitiable spectacle. I had remembered him, from my brief acquaintance of years ago, as a most admirable person with handsome features and a commanding presence. But all this was now changed. Before me I saw a weak and trembling creature, with a furtive expression, a nervous shiftiness of eye, and a general hangdog air of discouragement and defeat. If you had been there, Henderson, you would have felt just as sorry for him as I did. And your warm heart would have at once prompted you to do everything you could to help him.

As soon as I had introduced myself, Mr. Smith began a long and tedious discussion of his troubles. And out of his rambling remarks I was able to piece together the salient facts of the case—which are, briefly, as follows:

Mr. Smith's business is carried on through the Smith Tractor Company, a corporation in which he owns practically all the stock. The company's main asset is—or rather was—a handsome building which cost three hundred thousand dollars, and which housed the tractor salesrooms and offices. The building was mortgaged to the local building-and-loan association; the final payment of fifty thousand dollars being due next week. Besides this, the local national bank held the company's note for ten thousand—also due next week. Mr. Smith did not have the sixty thousand to make these payments—the tractor business has been a bit slow lately—but he was sure he could get an extension, or borrow the money somewhere, as the building was worth so much more than the loans, and was well insured.

And then, without warning, Mr. Smith was visited by a series of astounding misfortunes. His bookkeeper, whom he loved and trusted like his own son, fell in love with a girl who worked as assistant cashier at the building-and-loan office. They got so warm and confused about each other than they both forgot all about business. The bookkeeper forgot to mail the check that Mr. Smith gave him for the fire insurance, and his head was so full of poetry that he paid no attention to the notices that came in from the insurance company. The building-and-loan association never uttered a peep, because it was the job of the assistant cashier to check the insurance on property on which they held mortgages; and the assistant cashier, poor girl, was so busy thinking about moonlight and roses that she, naturally, couldn't keep her mind on her work. All of which was, I suppose, perfectly natural and according to recognized principles of biology, but it was certainly tough on poor old Mr. Smith.

Well, the happy, though demented, pair got married a week ago Wednesday and left for Kansas City, where the bridegroom had found himself a new and better job. So that was all right for them. But the next day—Thursday—Mr. Smith's building burned down. And on Friday he was hit in the face with the news that there was no insurance, and that his company was in the hole with debts of sixty thousand, and assets, including the building lot and a few things saved from the fire, of about ten thousand.

This regrettable situation was in no way the fault of

Mr. Smith. It would be unfair to claim that he should have realized the state his bookkeeper was in, and checked up on him more closely. No mere tractor man can be expected to grasp all the psychological and fiscal implications of a love affair between a bookkeeper and an assistant cashier.

The disaster was simply a case of bad luck. What happened was that the three Fates, or possibly a couple of other sinister goddesses of misfortune, sneaked up on Mr. Smith when he was not looking, and just naturally gnawed the seat right out of his pants.

And even this was not all. When the poor man realized his condition, he began rushing around to the banks, hoping to get an extension on his loans, or else to borrow enough to meet his payments. But everybody sized him up as busted beyond hope, and nobody would give him any accommodation at all. None of his friends would help him. And this final misfortune just tore the remains of his pants right off, removing in addition all that was left of his courage and morale.

At the time I visited him, he could see nothing but the dark side of things. "I am ruined," he said. "And, what is worse, I am disgraced. I am no better than a common thief. I have borrowed other people's money, and I can't pay it back. When I look at that picture up there, I feel so ashamed I almost want to shoot myself."

He pointed to an oil portrait on the wall. It showed an elderly gentleman with side whiskers.

"Who is the old bozo?" I asked.

"That is my grandfather," said Mr. Smith. "He came here to Tylerville in the 70's, and went into business. And before he died—ten years ago—he became known all over this part of the state. He was as solid and dependable as the United States Government. He always paid his debts. His word was his bond. And when he made a promise he always kept it. He established the reputation of the Smith family in this community. And now I have ruined that reputation. I don't see how I can stand the disgrace."

"Don't be a sap," I said. "It wasn't your fault your bookkeeper fell in love and picked out the wrong sweetie. Besides, all these debts are in the name of the Smith Tractor Company, aren't they?"

"Yes."

"And the company is incorporated?"

"Yes."

"Then you are not personally responsible for the debts at all, are you?"

"Legally I'm not. But morally I am. I own the company. So the only way I can save my reputation is to save the company. If I could save it by putting in all my personal property, I would. But I haven't enough."

"How much have you?" I asked.

"About twenty-five thousand dollars in cash and securities, and this house—it cost seventy-five thousand, but nobody seems to want to buy it."

"Have you tried to sell it?"

"I sure have. I've seen real-estate agents, and I've put advertisements in papers all over this part of the country. But there is no demand for a place like this. It's too big. People want small houses these days. The only offer so far is ten thousand, and that's probably the best I'll get. So, even if I sold out completely, I'd still owe fifteen thousand. I can't see where there is any hope for me. You had better give the dealership to Yerkes. I hear he would be glad to take it. So just forget about me. I'm nothing but a failure and a dead beat. When I think about my grandfather——"

"For Pete's sake," I said, "forget about your grandfather. He has nothing to do with the case. He can't get you out of this hole. And you'd better forget this weak-minded, idealistic scheme of selling out your private assets to pay a lot of corporation debts. Try to be practical and optimistic, and look on the bright side of things."

"But there isn't any bright side."

"Oh, yes, there is. You've got me here to help you. And I'm one of the best little helpers in the whole United

States. I'm going around to see these bankers myself. I'm
going to raise the fifty thousand dollars you need. It will
be in the form of a long-term loan. That will give you time
to get your nerve back. You can keep on with your Earthworm Tractor dealership, and before you know it you'll
have every cent paid off."

"You can't do anything with those bankers," said Mr.
Smith. "I talked to them all one afternoon, and they
wouldn't even listen."

"What it takes to talk to bankers, I've got," I said.
"So just sit tight and don't do anything till you hear from
me. And I won't sign up Mr. Yerkes without seeing you
first. Good afternoon."

Leaving poor old Mr. Smith in a state of nervous
collapse in his handsome residence, I went over and talked
to the officers of the building-and-loan association. I told
them that if they carried Mr. Smith a little longer they
might get paid in full, but if they forced him into bankruptcy, he would be ruined so completely that they would
get practically nothing. This seemed to me a very reasonable argument. But they replied that they had carried him
long enough, that he was ruined anyway, and that they
were going to collect what little they could and let it go
at that. They also declined to accept any responsibility for
the lapsing of the insurance, pointing out—truthfully
enough, I suppose—that the insurance was primarily Mr.
Smith's responsibility.

On the whole, however, they acted so dumb that I
finally gave them up as a bad job, and went over to the
national bank. Here I learned that nothing could be done
without the authority of the president—and the president
had gone off to Chicago to spend a week at a bankers' convention. This, naturally, made it necessary for me to go to
Chicago myself. I returned to the hotel, wrote a brief letter
to you, and caught the late afternoon train.

I wish to point out that this trip to Chicago is not an
extra expense—as insinuated in your letter—but a distinct

saving to the Earthworm Company. If I had stayed in Tylerville, I would have had to waste a whole week waiting for this guy to get back. As it is, I will finish up the whole business in a few days. And the saving would have been even greater had it not been for this week-end in the suburbs.

When I called at the hotel where this bank president was supposed to be staying, I found that, instead of giving the bankers' convention his undivided attention, he had gone off to spend several days with some friends on the North Shore. It would, of course, be a tactical blunder to bother him on his vacation. So there is nothing to do but wait until his return.

And now that I have explained everything so completely and so lucidly, you will, of course, realize that I am handling this thing in exactly the right manner. However, do not get too optimistic. There is always a remote chance that this bank president may turn me down.

And it might not be a bad idea if you were to see the president of the company and tell him to arrange things so that, if we should happen to need it, he can let us have fifty thousand dollars on short notice.

Most sincerely,
ALEXANDER BOTTS.

EARTHWORM TRACTOR COMPANY
EARTHWORM CITY, ILLINOIS
OFFICE OF THE SALES MANAGER

February 8, 1932.

MR. ALEXANDER BOTTS,
BLACKSTONE HOTEL,
CHICAGO, ILLINOIS.

DEAR BOTTS: I regret to inform you that your handling of the Smith affair is becoming more and more unsatisfactory to this company. I have tried to be patient with you, but my patience is almost exhausted. I wanted you to go back to Tylerville and get busy at once on the job which has been assigned to you. Furthermore, I want you to handle this job in a common-sense manner—getting rid of all this mawkish and sickly sentimentality.

Kindly remember that you are working for the Earth-worm Tractor Company. You are to pick out a dealer in Tylerville for this company. And in picking out a dealer, there is only one thing to consider: You must choose the man who will best serve the interests of the company.

Looking at the matter from this point of view, you should realize that Mr. Smith is completely out of the question. He has resigned; he does not want the job. Furthermore, he completely lacks the material resources with which to carry on. The Earthworm Company will not even consider advancing him any money, and, even if he gets a fifty-thousand-dollar loan from a bank, he will still be deeply in debt, and we absolutely cannot afford to depend on a man whose financial condition is so shaky.

Finally, we don't want a man who is so lacking in strength of character. Your recent letter, describing your interview with Mr. Smith, bears out this lack very clearly. Obviously, the man is a weakling. Instead of facing his troubles in a manly way, he is apparently sitting around, whining pitifully, moaning about his grandfather, and do-ing nothing at all to help himself. He is not the type of man we want for an Earthworm dealer. The tractor busi-ness is no place for weaklings.

I shall expect to hear, in the very near future, that you are back on the job again with all your old-time good sense and energy.

> Very truly,
> GILBERT HENDERSON,
> Sales Manager.

ALEXANDER BOTTS
SALES PROMOTION REPRESENTATIVE
EARTHWORM TRACTOR COMPANY

BLACKSTONE HOTEL,
CHICAGO, ILLINOIS.
Tuesday, February 9, 1932.

MR. GILBERT HENDERSON,
SALES MANAGER,
EARTHWORM TRACTOR COMPANY,
EARTHWORM CITY, ILLINOIS.

DEAR HENDERSON: Your letter of yesterday is received, and you will doubtless be pleased—this time I have a hunch you really will be pleased—to hear that I am starting for Tylerville this afternoon. I am leaving Chicago, partly because you seem to want me to—after all, you are the guy that hired me, and I suppose your orders are entitled to some consideration—and partly because my business here is finished up anyway. The president of the Tylerville National Bank got back to his hotel here in Chicago this morning, and I had an interview with him. On the whole, it was rather unsatisfactory.

This bank president turned out to be one of the coldest, most inhuman old money grubbers I have ever met. Besides which, he is a hypocrite—a man who attempts to justify his avariciousness and greed by spewing forth a lot of sanctimonious talk about high principles. When I suggested that he might extend Mr. Smith's note and lend him an additional fifty or sixty thousand dollars, he refused for what he called moral reasons.

"Mr. Botts," he said, "you are asking me to do something which is basically unethical. You are asking me to extend credit to a man who does not deserve credit. You seem to forget, Mr. Botts, that our whole economic structure is based on credit. And credit is based on the payment of debts. This is the first and most important principle of business. As long as people believe that a debt is something which must be paid, our business life is on a sound basis. But as soon as people begin to think that a debt is something to be wiggled out of, disaster stares us in the face."

"All of which sounds very fine," I said, "but it doesn't mean anything. What we are interested in here is not a lot of vague, general principles. We are interested in the concrete case of poor old Mr. Smith."

"Exactly. Mr. Smith owes my bank ten thousand dollars, and he owes the building-and-loan association, in which I am a stockholder, fifty thousand. He tells us he is not going to pay these debts. By defaulting in this way, Mr. Smith not only ruins his own credit, he also undermines the foundations of business in general. And any man who lends him more money under such circumstances is guilty of condoning and encouraging a very dangerous tendency."

"You've certainly got a wonderful flow of language," I said. "But didn't it ever occur to you that there is such a thing as humanity in business? And since when is it unethical to help a human being in distress? Besides, Mr. Smith is a good egg. He would pay these debts if he could. But he can't. And it isn't really his fault. You can't very well blame him because that poor sap of a bookkeeper went crazy and forgot to renew the insurance."

"I am not interested in excuses," said the bank president. "In my opinion, one of the chief troubles with the world today is the fact that there is such a large and increasing number of debtors who are using up all their energy, not in honestly attempting to pay their debts but in whining around, advancing all manner of plausible reasons why they should not pay, and even attempting to cure their troubles by borrowing more. As a matter of public duty, therefore, I must absolutely refuse to do anything that might aid or abet this vicious practice. Good afternoon, Mr. Botts."

"All right," I said, "if that's the way you feel about

it, I'll not insist on casting any more pearls. Good afternoon, Mr. Shylock."

With this snappy farewell, I strode jauntily from the
room, concealing my natural irritation. I will frankly admit
that I was pretty sore. But in spite of the fact that this
filthy banker would do nothing, and in spite of the fact
that you people in the Earthworm Company are so completely unsympathetic, I do not regret my efforts in behalf
of Mr. Smith. It will always be a source of satisfaction to
me that I did the best I could.

And now I will bow to the inevitable, and go back to
Tylerville to investigate Mr. John Yerkes.

Most sincerely,

ALEXANDER BOTTS.

ALEXANDER BOTTS

SALES PROMOTION REPRESENTATIVE

EARTHWORM TRACTOR COMPANY

TYLERVILLE HOTEL,

TYLERVILLE, WISCONSIN.

Wednesday evening,

February 10, 1932.

MR. GILBERT HENDERSON,

SALES MANAGER,

EARTHWORM TRACTOR COMPANY,

EARTHWORM CITY, ILLINOIS.

DEAR HENDERSON: As soon as I reached Tylerville, late this afternoon, I called on Mr. Yerkes. And I
will have to admit that your favorable impression of him,
based on the letter which he sent you, is undoubtedly
correct.

From an emotional and sentimental point of view, I
hate to see Mr. Smith getting washed down the sewer. But
you are right in saying that this affair must be decided
from a strictly business point of view. We must get the man

who will best serve the interests of the Earthworm Tractor Company. And Mr. Yerkes seems to have the three qualifications which you so logically set forth in your letter as being essential. He is very eager to get the job, and will undoubtedly push our business here with great vigor and efficiency. He has ample capital. And finally, he has all the strength of character, optimism and virility which poor old Mr. Smith so conspicuously lacks.

But the thing that impressed me the most about Mr. Yerkes was the truly noble way in which he agreed with my opinion of that mephitic reptile, the president of the Tylerville National Bank. During my conversation with Mr. Yerkes I told him some of the idiotic remarks the bank president had made to me in Chicago. And I had also repeated, with justifiable pride, a few of the snappy replies I had handed the old crab.

"You are a man after my own heart!" Mr. Yerkes said. "Only I'm afraid you didn't give it to him hot enough. You should have heard me the last time I told him what I thought of him."

"So you have had trouble with him too?"

"Plenty. You wouldn't believe it, but he once tried to get me to pay him a debt I didn't owe."

"How could he expect to get by with anything as raw as that?"

"Oh, it's a long story. A few years back I had a run of bad luck—lost a lot of money in Florida real estate and other things—and the first thing I knew my implement business here had gone busted on me. I had to let it go through bankruptcy. The creditors got twenty cents on the dollar—and they were lucky at that. Fortunately, the business was incorporated, so they couldn't touch my private assets. I had plenty of funds to get started again, and in about three years I was more prosperous than ever. It was a good come-back, and I don't mind saying I'm proud of the way I managed things. But it certainly made this bank president sore."

"You mean he hated to see anybody besides himself making any money?"

"Yes. And he had a fool idea that I had done him dirt in some way. You see, when my company went busted, his bank was the principal creditor. It like to drove him crazy, getting only twenty cents on the dollar. And when I was back on my feet again, he wrote me a nasty letter asking me to pay the balance, with interest. Can you tie that? He actually expected interest too."

"And you wrote him a letter telling him where to get off?"

"Wrote him a letter, nothing. I went down there personally. I took the letter, and I waved it in his face, and I said, 'Did you write this?' 'Yes,' he said. So I says, 'What's the idea? Don't you know you got no legal claim on me at all?' And he says, 'That's true. But now you've got money, you ought to pay your back debts just the same. It's a moral obligation.' "

"He's always drooling out that pious apple sauce about morals," I said. "What did you tell him next?"

"Believe me, I told him plenty. I just poured it onto him. 'The laws of this great country,' I says, 'tell me I don't have to pay you. But you think you know better. Is that showing a proper respect for the law? Is that good citizenship? Is that what you call good morals?' "

"A neat crack," I said. "What answer did he make?"

"Well, sir, he didn't have a word to say. I had him, and he knew it. So I went right on. I said, 'The law is just, and enlightened, and based on human values. It provides the corporation form of doing business so a man's commercial losses can't ruin him personally. It provides bankruptcy proceedings, so a man can get rid of his debts and make a fresh start. Even in international finance, it is now admitted that government debts must be adjusted on the basis of capacity to pay. And here you are talking as if we lived in the dark ages. If a man once gets in debt, you want to grind him down and keep him down forever. I bet you would even like to have debtors' prisons again.' "

"I bet he would, at that," I said.

"So then," Mr. Yerkes continued, "I told him he had no cause for complaint anyway. I said, 'You bankers charge so much interest on all your loans that you have more than enough to cover the ones that go bad. If you didn't have a few losses, your profits would be all out of reason. You've got more money than I have anyway. So why should I, for no reason at all, turn over a lot of my hard-earned cash to a guy like you that is already lousy with wealth? Answer me that!"

"And did he answer you?" I asked.

"No. He just set there. So I bawled him out a bit more. And finally I took the letter he had sent me, and I threw it in his face. 'You can take that,' I says, 'and you know what you can do with it.' Then I walked out."

"Swell!" I said. "I sure wish I had been there to hear you."

I was so pleased with Mr. Yerkes' account of the way he had showed up this bank president for the slimy bum that he is that I wanted to sign a dealer's contract with him right away. But I had promised Mr. Smith I would see him before I placed the contract elsewhere. So I told Mr. Yerkes that I would give him a definite answer about the dealership tomorrow afternoon. We then shook hands in a most cordial fashion, and I came back to the hotel, arriving just in time for supper.

I will see Mr. Smith tomorrow morning, and I shall hope to get everything fixed up with Mr. Yerkes in the afternoon, so that I may leave for the next job before night.

Most sincerely,
ALEXANDER BOTTS.

ALEXANDER BOTTS
SALES PROMOTION REPRESENTATIVE
EARTHWORM TRACTOR COMPANY

TYLERVILLE HOTEL,
TYLERVILLE, WISCONSIN.
Thursday noon,
February 11, 1932.

MR. GILBERT HENDERSON,
SALES MANAGER,
EARTHWORM TRACTOR COMPANY,
EARTHWORM CITY, ILLINOIS.

DEAR HENDERSON: When I called at Mr. Smith's handsome residence this morning, I found the whole place locked up and apparently deserted. I went to the house next door, where I found an elderly lady who told me a most pitiful tale.

"Poor Mr. Smith!" she said. "His house has been sold, and he and Mrs. Smith and the two children have moved away. It's a very sad case. They are such fine people. They have been our neighbors for years. And now they are being driven out of their home—which seems so cruel and unjust. Of course, I am just a woman, and probably I don't understand such things, but I can't see why—just because Mr. Smith failed in business—they should take away his home and throw the whole family penniless into the streets."

"I don't understand it myself," I said. "I know something of Mr. Smith's affairs, and I understand that Mr. Smith's house would be safe from his creditors. But, evidently, I was mistaken. How does Mr. Smith seem to be standing the shock?"

"He is putting up a very brave appearance. But, inwardly, he must be in despair. Really, it's pitiful."

"Yes," I agreed, "it is. When did the Smiths move? And where did they go?"

"They left two days ago," said the lady, "and I understand they have rented a miserable little shack over on the other side of the railroad. And even that isn't the worst of it. Apparently Mr. Smith has lost every cent of his money, and, in order to eke out a bare living, he will have to humiliate himself by doing manual labor."

"What sort of manual labor?"

"It's most extraordinary. He has been going around to all his old friends, including myself, and asking for the job of running our furnaces in the winter and taking care of our lawns in the summer. We have all been dreadfully embarrassed at the idea of employing an old friend for such menial tasks. But as long as he needed the work and asked for it, we have agreed to give it to him. It's a wretched situation."

"It surely is," I agreed. "Can you tell me where I can find this unfortunate gentleman?"

She gave me the address. I thanked her and departed. After twenty minutes' walk, I found myself at Mr. Smith's new residence. It was in a rather cheap section of town, not far from the freight yards. But it did not quite deserve the description of "a miserable little shack." It was a small, inexpensive, but rather cute bungalow. I walked up to the door with some hesitation. I rather dreaded an interview with this miserable man. But when Mr. Smith answered my knock, I saw at once that his former neighbor had been right when she said he was putting up a brave appearance. As a matter of fact, his appearance was so remarkably brave that I could hardly believe I was talking to the same man who, only last week, had been so downcast, so miserable, and so filled with despair.

"Good morning, Mr. Botts," he said, shaking hands enthusiastically. "Come in." His manner was cordial and friendly, and he seemed to be fairly bubbling over with enthusiasm and good nature. He led me into a small and rather cheaply furnished room.

"I am glad," I said, "to see you looking so cheerful, Mr. Smith."

"Why shouldn't I be cheerful?" he answered. "I have just had a wonderful piece of good luck. You remember what a ghastly mess I was in when you came to see me last week?"

"I certainly do."

"At that time," Mr. Smith went on, "I didn't think I could ever get out of it. And then, the day after your visit, the miracle happened."

"What happened?" I asked.

"A wealthy gentleman in Milwaukee saw one of the newspaper advertisements in which I offered my house for sale. He wanted a place in this part of the country. He was a fast worker. He came. He saw. He bought. And, instead of ten thousand, which was the best previous offer, this bozo paid twenty-five thousand for the whole place, includ-all the furnishings, except my grandfather's portrait and a few personal belongings. As soon as the deal went through, I sold all my other assets and paid up every dollar owed by the Smith Tractor Company. I tell you, Mr. Botts, it was wonderful. Never in all my life have I been so happy."

"But it leaves you absolutely flat, doesn't it?"

"No. After everything was fixed up, I found I had $37.42 left over, so I am that much ahead of the game. Besides, I still have my grandfather's portrait. So everything is fine."

"Just the same," I said, "I should think it would be rather distressing to you to have to move out of your lovely home into this place. How does the rest of your family feel about it?"

"They are behaving swell," said Mr. Smith, with a somewhat self-satisfied smile. "For the first time in years, my wife is doing all the cooking and housework, and she claims she likes it. My two sons are continuing in school, and entirely on their own initiative, they have decided to help the family finances by starting up a magazine-subscription business. You don't know how good this makes me feel. I never realized, until just lately, what a fine family I have."

"Is it true," I asked, "that you are planning to take care of lawns and furnaces for a living?"

"Exactly," said Mr. Smith. "The work doesn't pay very much, and eventually, of course, I may get into something better. But for the present it will do very well. The rent of this house here is very low, and we'll have enough to live on, simply, but very comfortably. So, you see, there's nothing to regret about this whole business, and there is everything to be thankful for."

"Well, maybe so," I said. "It's true that you might be a whole lot worse off. But I can't understand why you should be so thankful about things."

"Don't be a boob," said Mr. Smith. "Who wouldn't be thankful in my position? I've paid all my debts. I don't have to worry any more. I don't have to go whining and slinking around. When I go down town, I can hold up my head and strut around as proud as I want. And when I meet any of these birds who made the mistake of thinking I was going to be a low-down bankrupt and defaulter, I can laugh right in their faces. I can thumb my nose at them."

"I hope," I said, "that when you meet the president of the national bank you will use both hands and plenty of wiggling of the fingers."

"But I don't want to thumb my nose at him. He has acted too decent."

"What?" I said. "That old, frozen codfish?"

"Oh, yes. He's not really so bad as you think. He came around last night, after he got back from Chicago, and told me that I had worked this thing out in exactly the right way. He said he was very much pleased by the whole business."

"Of course, he was pleased," I said. "There's nothing

gives that guy greater joy than seeing a man sold out and left flat. And the flatter the better."

"No," said Mr. Smith, "you're wrong about that. The old boy was actually sorry I'd lost everything, and he said that if I wanted to go on with the tractor business, he would finance me."

"In what way?"

"We would form a new company. He would supply all the capital and take half the stock. I would run the business and get the other half of the stock, plus five thousand dollars yearly as salary. It seems to me that's a pretty liberal offer."

"Yes," I admitted, "it's a swell offer. But I can hardly believe he made it. When I talked to him, he wouldn't even risk five cents on you."

"But that was when he thought I wasn't going to pay my debts. Now he knows I have paid them, and he also knows I put in a lot of my personal assets that I was not legally required to contribute. At present, he says, my credit is just as good as anybody else's cash. And he says he is not making this offer with the idea of helping me. He claims it is a purely business affair. He is always glad to invest his money in a good, safe business which promises to make him a handsome profit."

"Probably that's it," I said. "He's perfectly selfish, after all. But from your point of view, it looks to me like a good proposition. What did you tell him?"

"I thanked him and told him I could not accept."

"Why not?"

"In the first place, I very much doubted if you people would renew my contract. You've practically decided to give it to Mr. Yerkes, haven't you?"

"I had intended to," I said, "and Yerkes is very anxious to have it. But I haven't made any definite promises."

"You'd better give it to him," said Mr. Smith, "because, on the whole, I think I'd rather not take it, even if it was offered to me. I've had so much worry lately that I need a vacation. I think I'll stay out of any sort of executive business job—for a while, at least. This taking care of furnaces and lawns will mean a certain amount of physical work, but it will be a rest for my mind. I'm actually looking forward to it with pleasure. So don't worry about me, Mr. Botts. Now that I'm out of debt, I'm really on top of the world. I don't have to ask any favors from anybody. And I can look my grandfather's portrait right in the eye and tell myself that I am just as good a man as he was."

"Well, if that's the way you feel about it, Mr. Smith," I said, "there's nothing much more I can say, except that I am very glad indeed to see you are taking this thing in such a fine spirit. Good-by and good luck to you."

"Good-by," said Mr. Smith, "and give my best wishes to Mr. Yerkes."

I walked back to the hotel, and I have been spending the rest of the morning writing this report. As it is now lunchtime, I will close. This afternoon I will see Mr. Yerkes, and get this business finished up.

Very truly,

ALEXANDER BOTTS.

TELEGRAM

EARTHWORM CITY ILL

10 AM

FEB 12 1932

ALEXANDER BOTTS TYLERVILLE HOTEL
TYLERVILLE WIS
HOLD UP NEGOTIATIONS WITH YERKES STOP AFTER READING YOUR TWO LATEST REPORTS I AM INCLINED TO THINK WE OUGHT TO URGE SMITH TO TAKE CONTRACT

GILBERT HENDERSON

ALEXANDER BOTTS
SALES PROMOTION REPRESENTATIVE
EARTHWORM TRACTOR COMPANY

TYLERVILLE HOTEL
TYLERVILLE, WISCONSIN.
Friday noon,
February 12, 1932.

MR. GILBERT HENDERSON,
SALES MANAGER,
EARTHWORM TRACTOR COMPANY,
EARTHWORM CITY, ILLINOIS.

DEAR HENDERSON: Your telegram has just arrived, and it is too late. The contract has already been signed. But when I explain all the circumstances, I am sure you will agree that I have acted wisely.

Yesterday noon, after I had written you about my visit to Mr. Smith, I decided it might be well, before proceeding further in this matter, thoroughly to weigh and consider the various new factors which had entered the case. Accordingly, instead of calling on Mr. Yerkes at once, I retired to my room and gave myself up to a prolonged period of deep meditation and thought. And it gives me great pleasure to report that I finally arrived at a singularly brilliant idea which cuts through all the fogs and uncertainties of this dealership question, and makes the whole proposition as clear as day. This idea is so unusual that not one man in ten thousand would have thought of it. But it is so simple, when once it has been stated, that even a guy like you will understand it and recognize its truth and validity.

In evolving this idea I started with your proposition that this is strictly a business affair, in which sentiment has no place. In picking a dealer here, we must choose the man who will best serve the interests of the Earthworm Tractor Company. Having adopted this principle, I took up your

assertion that "the tractor business is no place for weaklings." And, after a long process of careful analysis and
logical reasoning, I reached the conclusion that this second
idea was correct.

I then compared Mr. Yerkes and Mr. Smith. And it
was at once evident that the magnificent way Mr. Yerkes
talked up to the bank president indicated a remarkable
amount of strength and virility. On the other hand, the
pathetic manner in which Mr. Smith talked of his troubles
and harped on his grandfather indicated nothing but weakness and lack of force.

An ordinary man would have decided at once in favor
of Mr. Yerkes. But I did not. I kept on doggedly and per-
sistently turning the matter over in my mind—thinking,
analyzing, considering. And at last, after four hours and
twenty minutes of the most intense mental activity, the big
idea burst upon me. I realized, with a sudden flash of inspiration, that the way these men talk is of no more importance to us than a pinch of bug dust—the only thing that
matters is the way they act. Looking at it from this point
of view, it was clear that Mr. Smith, in spite of his sentimental gabblings, had really done something when he paid
off his debts. And this led me right on to the astounding
conclusion that the real weak sister was the virile and impressive talker who had been perfectly satisfied to let his
creditors get along with twenty cents on the dollar.

I was, naturally, delighted that my original hunch in
favor of Mr. Smith was thus confirmed by purely intellectual reasoning. And I have been surprised and amused to
learn, from your telegram, that you—probably by accident
—have also hit upon the correct point of view.

As soon as I reached my inspired decision, I dropped
the rôle of cloistered scholar and became the man of action.
I rushed over to Mr. Smith's house. I told him that the
Earthworm Tractor Company could not get along without
him. I brushed aside his plea that he wanted a vacation
among the furnaces and lawn mowers. And I am overjoyed

to announce that, after considerable argument, he gave in and signed the contract, which I inclose herewith.

Very truly,
ALEXANDER BOTTS.

"THAR'S GOLD IN THEM THAR MOUNTAINS"

ALEXANDER BOTTS
SALES PROMOTION REPRESENTATIVE
EARTHWORM TRACTOR COMPANY

Dow's Gulf, Vermont.
Monday evening,
June 6, 1932.

MR. GILBERT HENDERSON, SALES MANAGER,
EARTHWORM TRACTOR COMPANY,
EARTHWORM CITY, ILLINOIS.

DEAR HENDERSON: It gives me great pleasure to report that I have started my activities in this town with even more than my usual energy. Although I arrived only this morning, I have already become deeply involved in the promotion of a gold mine.

In case you should wonder why a man who was sent out primarily to infuse new life and selling enthusiasm in the Earthworm-tractor dealers of the country should turn to mining, I will explain that this new activity is necessary in order to stimulate and revivify Mr. George Dow, who is our dealer in this territory, and also one of the laziest yokels I have ever run across.

Honestly, Henderson, he is as sleepy, as dumb and as contented as a superannuated Holstein cow. When I called on him this morning at his office, he languidly invited me to take a chair and then sat down himself, arranged his long, skinny legs on the desk, stuck an old pipe in his mouth, and settled himself as if he was going to take a nap. He was too lazy even to light the pipe.

"How's business?" I asked.

"Can't complain," he said.

"Selling any tractors?"

"No."

"Got any on hand?"

"Yes. I got two sixty-horse-power models in the warehouse."

"How long since you've sold a tractor?"

"I don't know. I guess the last sale I made was about a year ago—maybe a year and a half."

"That's terrible," I said. "I had no idea things were so bad up in this country. But you can cheer up, Mr. Dow, for the Earthworm Tractor Company has sent me out to help you dealers. I am ready to assist you in any way I can; and if we get together and attack this situation with energy and enthusiasm, I feel sure we can achieve some real results."

At this, Mr. Dow smiled in what might be described as an amused and tolerant manner. He was a rather likable old bozo, maybe sixty years old, and he had a lot of pleasant-looking little wrinkles around his eyes.

"Well, well," he said, "it does beat all how you young chaps are always rushing around, full of energy and excitement. But when you're as old as I am, my boy, you will learn to take things more calmly."

"Possibly," I said, "you are taking things too calmly. If you don't get out and buzz about a bit, how can you expect to pull yourself out of this depression?"

"But there isn't any depression here," he said. "In Vermont we don't have these crazy booms that you have in the big cities, and we don't have big depressions either. We just live along quiet and sensible. At the moment it is true that business is rotten and times are rather hard. But it doesn't bother me at all."

"What?" I asked. "Business is rotten, and it doesn't bother you?"

"Certainly not. I've got everything I need. I have a nice house at the edge of town here, a splendid vegetable garden, a couple of cows, a fine flock of hens, a little orchard, and a woodpile big enough to last all next winter. I have about five thousand dollars in the bank—and I intend to keep it there. Most of my neighbors are fixed the same way, so we none of us have to worry very much about hard times. Of course, there are a few people who are out of luck and have nothing at all, but we have them with us even when times are supposed to be good. In some ways I am better off than the average."

"I thought you just said you hadn't sold a single tractor for over a year."

"Yes, but I have a little garage and filling station that I run in connection with my tractor agency, and this business is still going on—after a fashion."

"Is it making any money?"

"No, but it's not losing any, either. And I'm paying the help enough to live on. Another fortunate thing is that my son, who has been taking a course in mining engineering down at Columbia, has just graduated, so I won't have any more expense for his college course. He hasn't been able to get a job, so I have told him to come home and stay with his father and mother, where the cost of living is almost nothing. He will be here in a day or two. There are plenty of good chairs in the office here, and room enough for another pair of feet on the desk, so he and I can just sit around and discuss the weather and politics and so on, and thumb our noses at this much-advertised business depression."

Having finished these remarks, Mr. Dow stretched

himself contentedly and settled down even deeper into his comfortable swivel chair. It seemed to be up to me to make some adequate reply. And this was difficult, because, although Mr. Dow's line of argument was completely cockeyed, it nevertheless had a certain plausibility about it. If he actually had everything he needed already, and was completely satisfied, possibly there was no logical reason why he should start tearing around and trying to rake in more cash. For a moment he almost had me converted to his point of view. But, naturally, a high-powered salesman like myself, whose whole business is to inspire pep and energy, cannot afford to listen to any such insidious propaganda as Mr. Dow was putting out.

"Your whole point of view is wrong," I said. "To hear you talk, anybody would think you had given up even trying to sell tractors."

"Of course I have," he said. "Why should I waste my time trying to sell tractors when there isn't anybody around here at the present time that needs any such thing?"

"But there must be a few possible customers. How about the farmers?"

"They are all feeling too poor."

"Any lumbering going on in these mountains?"

"There used to be, but there isn't any more."

"Any industries that could use tractors?"

"No. We used to have a pulp mill and several sawmills. And a long time ago we even had a gold mine. But they all shut down."

"You say there used to be a gold mine? I didn't know they had such things in Vermont."

"Oh, yes," said Mr. Dow. "There has always been a certain amount of mining in the Green Mountains—iron, copper, gold, silver, and so on. But they're not doing anything these days—can't compete with the big Western production. This particular gold mine belongs to me."

"It does?"

"Yes, I inherited it from my father. He opened it up

back in the 70's, and sank about all the money he had in it.
If you look out the window there, you'll see a little tumble-
down shed up on the side of the mountain. That shed is
at the mouth of the mine."

"I see it," I said. "Is there really any gold there?"

"Oh, yes. There's a little. But not enough so my father
could make it pay. He went completely busted."

"And you've never tried to work it yourself?"

"Absolutely not. I don't know anything about mining,
and I don't want to. As I told you before, I'm perfectly
happy and contented, and I intend to remain so. I'm not
going to risk any of my money in any speculative enterprise,
whether it's gold mining or high-powered tractor-selling
campaigns, or anything else."

"Well," I said, "maybe you're right. But don't get
the idea that a tractor-selling campaign necessarily takes a
lot of money. The important thing is plenty of energy and
persistence. There must be some place around here where
we can sell tractors. Is there any road building going on?"

"Yes, the local road commissioner is putting in several miles of driveway through a tract of woods that has
been bequeathed to the town as a park. It's quite a big job.
There's a lot of grading and cut-and-fill work. The commissioner is spending about fifteen thousand dollars—which
was left for this purpose by the man who bequeathed the
park."

"Is the commissioner using tractors?"

"No."

"All right. We'll sell him a few."

"We can't. He's doing the whole thing by hand labor
—picks and shovels and wheelbarrows."

"I'll soon argue him out of that idea," I said. "Just
wait till I show him how much labor he'll save by getting
rid of his medieval implements and doing the job as the
Lord intended—with Earthworm tractors."

"But he doesn't want to save labor."

"Why not? Is he crazy?"

"No. He's just trying to be public-spirited. He is building the road without machinery so as to provide work for all of the town's unemployed who want it—which means about twenty men. Besides helping these people, the commissioner feels he is benefiting the whole town by keeping all the money right here."

"A swell benefit that is to the town as a whole," I said. "All that guy is doing is subsidizing inefficiency. He may be handing out a little temporary relief to a few unfortunates, but he is cheating all the rest of the town by giving them only about a quarter as much road as they are entitled to from the money he is spending."

"Maybe you're right," said Mr. Dow, "but you'll never make the road commissioner see it that way. He has made up his mind that he is the guardian angel of the unemployed, and nobody can tell him any different. He's just as stubborn as I am."

"In that case," I said, "he must be a tough customer. But there must be some way to get to him."

"I'm afraid not," said Mr. Dow. "He'll never buy a tractor as long as there are men in this town who want work and can't get it."

At this point I suddenly got one of those keen and practical ideas which so often come to me in difficult situations. "I know how we can handle this thing," I said. "It is very simple. All we have to do is get rid of the unemployed."

"Drown them in the river or something?"

"No. Give them jobs."

"Doing what?"

"Anything. You might, for instance, open up your gold mine and hire all these men away from the road commissioner. Then he would have to buy a tractor."

"Maybe so. But where would I come out? I'd be paying wages to twenty men and nothing to show for it."

"You would have a lot to show for it," I said. "You would sell a four-thousand-dollar tractor, on which your commission would be eight hundred dollars. That would carry your pay roll for a week and still show you a handsome profit. At the end of the week—after you had sold the tractor—you could shut down."

"And turn all those men loose again without any jobs?"

"Oh, they would be all right," I said. "The road commissioner would probably hire them back. He has enough money to buy a tractor and hire these men besides. But you might find you could make enough out of the mine to keep running for quite a while."

"And eventually go busted like my father did."

"No," I said. "If you were a deep student of political economy, such as I am, you would know that this is a peculiarly auspicious time to run a gold mine."

"In spite of the depression?"

"Because of the depression," I said. "Production costs —labor and supplies and everything—are low. And the product, gold, automatically sells at par. You would have a much better chance than your father had."

"Well, I don't know," said Mr. Dow. "I'm not a student of political economy, like you, but I do know that in the 70's, when my father was working this mine, prices were even lower than they are today. And gold was selling at a premium, because all the money was paper, which was not redeemable in specie. It looks like my father had a better chance than I would have."

"At first sight," I admitted, "it might look that way. And as you are not a student of political economy, I can't go into the matter deeply enough to show you where you are wrong. But, regardless of theoretical considerations, I am convinced that it would be of tremendous practical benefit both to yourself and to the tractor business if you would take a chance on this gold-mining proposition."

"I wouldn't even consider it," said Mr. Dow. "I've told you before that I don't know anything about gold mining—and I don't want to know anything about it."

"You said your son has just graduated in mining engineering, and has no job. Why not let him run this mine?"

"And bankrupt the whole family? I should say not."

"Your son will be home in a day or so, won't he?"

"Yes."

"It wouldn't hurt anything to talk the thing over with him?"

"No, I suppose not."

"All right then," I said, "I won't bother you any more about it right now, but when your son arrives we will get together and decide what to do."

"It don't sound good to me," said Mr. Dow.

"Perhaps you will change your mind later," I said. "And now I think I'll be getting back to the hotel for lunch. I'll see you again this afternoon or tomorrow. Good-by."

I left the old guy sprawled out languidly in his office chair with his feet in the same position on top of the desk. As I walked along toward the hotel I kept turning this gold-mine idea over and over in my mind, and the more I thought about it the better it seemed. By the time I reached the hotel, I had made up my mind to make a little private investigation of the mine as soon as possible. As I am fairly ignorant about such matters, I decided I would need expert advice. On the chance that I might possibly run across something, I asked the hotel clerk whether there was such a thing as a mining engineer in town, and if not, where would be the nearest place I could find one.

The clerk did not even seem to know what a mining engineer was. He doubted if any such thing could be found in town, or even in Rutland or Burlington. He said, however, he would make inquiries. After thanking him I went in to lunch.

Half an hour later, when I came out of the dining room, the clerk called me and introduced a very courteous and pleasant-spoken gentleman by the name of Mr. Bailey Bryant. It appeared that Mr. Bryant was from New York, and had arrived at the hotel two or three days before to take advantage of the excellent fishing in the mountain streams of the neighborhood. He had heard the hotel clerk inquiring for a mining engineer, and as that was his profession he had stepped forward to offer his services.

This was indeed a piece of splendid good luck, and a striking example of how fortune seems to favor a man like myself who is always on the alert and ready to grasp any opportunity that presents itself.

At once I took Mr. Bryant aside, explained the whole situation completely and frankly, much as I have set it forth in this letter, and asked him if he would look over the mine and give me his opinion on it. He replied that he would be delighted, and we started to walk up the mountain to the little shed which Mr. Dow had pointed out to me.

On the way Mr. Bryant gave me a number of fascinating reminiscences of his gold-mining experiences in South Africa, in California and in Alaska. Seldom have I met a more brilliant conversationalist. As I am a very good judge of men, it did not take me long to realize that in spite of his modest manner Mr. Bryant possessed an unusually powerful intellect and was a real authority in his field.

When we reached the mine we discovered that it was a small tunnel, perhaps six feet in diameter, cut horizontally into the solid rock of the mountain. Mr. Bryant, with admirable foresight, had brought an electric flash light. Although the tunnel was partially obstructed by fallen rocks and rubbish, we had no trouble in penetrating to its end, which was perhaps a hundred yards from the opening.

My companion subjected the rock walls to the most minute and painstaking examination, while I stood by in a state of suppressed excitement—eager to ask questions, but holding on to myself so as not to interrupt the train of his thought. From time to time he loosened small fragments of stone, examined them with a lens and put them in his pocket. He seemed particularly interested in the rock at the end of the tunnel, and here he took three or four samples. After perhaps half an hour, we returned to the opening.

"This is most interesting," he said. "As a careful scientist, I naturally hesitate to commit myself absolutely, but I do not mind telling you that every indication points to the fact that the work on this mine was stopped at the very moment when the richest ore was about to be uncovered."

"You really think so?" I asked.

"That is my opinion," he said. "Look. Here is a specimen from about the middle of the tunnel. Ordinary Barre granite with a trace of mica. Possibly a little gold in it, but obviously not much."

"It certainly is not much to look at," I said.

"No," he agreed, "but now cast your eye on this, which came from the end of the tunnel." He held up a piece of whitish stone. "Pure quartz, and in a formation completely analogous to that of the great Comstock lode in Nevada. It is most interesting."

"Then you really think it would pay to work this mine?"

"Before giving you a definite answer, I should have to make a more complete survey. It will be necessary for me to blast off a little more rock at the end of the tunnel, so as to uncover the richer ore which I hope to find just back of the present face. Then, after making a chemical and microscopic examination of the ore, I would be in a position to give you a very definite opinion based upon solid scientific facts."

"Would you be willing," I asked, "to make this examination for me?"

"Certainly," he replied. "You understand, of course, that I will have to charge you for it. I have been glad to give you my unofficial opinion free, but for a regular professional report I would have to ask my regular professional fee, which is a hundred dollars."

"Holy Moses!" I said. "A hundred dollars?"

"That," he said, "is my regular fee."

"Well," I said, "I guess that's perfectly reasonable for expert advice from an important guy like you, but I don't know just how I am going to pay it. I can't afford the expense myself. And I'm afraid the company wouldn't let me get away with it on the expense account. Mr. Dow really ought to pay it himself. But he's so tight with his money that I don't believe we could talk it out of him—unless, of course, it turned out that the mine was a real bonanza like you think it is. And listen. That gives me an idea. How would you like to gamble on this—double or quits?"

"What do you mean?" he asked.

"If it turns out that this thing is a big money maker, I'll guarantee you two hundred dollars—double your fee. In that case I'm practically sure I can get that much out of old man Dow. Almost anybody would pay two hundred dollars for a real gold mine. So I'm willing to take a chance, and, if he won't pay you, I will. On the other hand, if we don't find this rich ore you're looking for, we'll call it quits and you get nothing. How about it?"

"Fair enough," said Mr. Bryant. "Every mining engineer is a gambler at heart, and I'm no exception."

We shook hands on the bargain and returned to the town, where Mr. Bryant left me. He said he would get the supplies he needed and return to the mine to make his investigations, and he courteously declined my offer of assistance, saying that he could work better and concentrate more effectively when he was alone.

I spent the remainder of the afternoon seeing if I could discover any further opportunities for possible tractor sales. I ran into nothing, however, that looked in any way promising.

This evening I have been writing this report. I have just seen Mr. Bryant in the lobby. He reports that his investigations have proceeded very satisfactorily, and he wishes me to bring Mr. Dow up to the mine tomorrow morning so that we can all look over the ground together. When I asked him whether his report would be as favorable as he had hoped, he merely smiled and said that he would prefer to say nothing until tomorrow.

I have just called up Mr. Dow and arranged to go with him to the mine in the morning. So the stage is all set, and I have high hopes.

I have given you this very full account of my activities, so that you can see I am pulling off a very remarkable and brainy piece of work here, and so that there will be no question about allowing the two hundred dollars in case I should have to put it in my expense account.

Very sincerely,

ALEXANDER BOTTS.

ALEXANDER BOTTS
SALES PROMOTION REPRESENTATIVE
EARTHWORM TRACTOR COMPANY

DOW'S GULF, VERMONT.
Tuesday, June 7, 1932.

MR. GILBERT HENDERSON,
SALES MANAGER,
EARTHWORM TRACTOR COMPANY,
EARTHWORM CITY, ILLINOIS.

DEAR HENDERSON: What a day this has been— what a day! When I wrote you yesterday, I was expecting something pretty good, but never in my wildest dreams had I anticipated anything so sensational and so glorious as what has actually come to pass. But I must try to begin at the beginning and relate my wonderful news in an orderly manner.

This morning Mr. Bryant, Mr. Dow and I walked up to the mine. Mr. Bryant maintained his quiet and sophisticated reserve, but there was about him a subtle air of optimism which both stimulated me and aroused my curiosity. Mr. Dow was goodnatured, but inclined to scoff at the whole expedition. I had told him that my friend was a mining engineer who had kindly consented to look over his mine and give him an opinion as to its value. As for myself, I was in such a flutter of anxiety and suspense that I could hardly wait to hear Mr. Bryant's verdict.

When we reached the mouth of the tunnel, Mr. Bryant gave us a brief description of the geological formation in which the mine was located, and then explained the various factors which had caused him to believe that there might be a very rich vein of what he called auriferous quartz immediately beyond the end of the tunnel. This explanation was couched in scientific language—which I will not repeat, partly because I can't remember it, and partly because you guys at the tractor factory couldn't understand it anyway. After giving us the low-down on these theoretical matters, Mr. Bryant told us what he had done the previous afternoon.

"I got some tools and a couple of sticks of dynamite at the hardware store," he said. "Then I came up here, drilled a hole into the rock face at the end of the tunnel, and set off a small charge. The results"—and here he smiled in a mysterious and highly dramatic manner—"were so favorable that I think they can be appreciated by almost anyone. If you will step this way I will show you something that you will have no trouble in comprehending, no matter whether you have any technical training or not."

Snapping on his electric flash light, he led us through the tunnel to its extreme end. At once I noticed that the blast he had spoken of had exposed a fresh surface of rock. It was white quartz.

"Look at it a little closer," said Mr. Bryant.

Mr. Dow and I did so. And what I saw made my heart start beating and pounding in a way that it has not done for years. All over the surface of the rock, embedded in the seams and crevices, were thousands of glittering, shining yellow particles. Some were as small as grains of the finest powder. Others were the size of peas, and a few were actually as large as small acorns. It was some minutes before I could speak.

"Is it," I asked—"is it really gold?"

"Yes," said Mr. Bryant, "it is gold—and as remarkable a vein as I've seen for years." He turned to Mr. Dow. "Permit me to congratulate you," he said. "You are many times a millionaire."

It was quite evident from Mr. Dow's expression that this great discovery had knocked his intellect into a confused and dizzy whirl. He leaped forward and began clawing little chunks of the beautiful yellow metal out of the rock and turning them over and over in his hands. His naturally cautious nature prevented him from completely accepting the obvious facts, but, at the same time, he was rapidly becoming drunk at the sight and the feel of the gold, and at the thought of the incredible riches that now were his.

"I can hardly believe it," he kept saying. "I can hardly believe it. Is it really true that I am a millionaire?"

"Well," said Mr. Bryant, "the great Comstock Lode yielded something over three hundred million dollars."

"Three hundred millions dollars!" gasped Mr. Dow.

"Three hundred million dollars," repeated Mr. Bryant. "And the geologic formation here is strikingly similar to the Comstock formation—which is a fact of great scientific interest. Of course, I do not claim that this vein will turn out as well. It might yield much more, but, on the other hand, it might not run more than fifty or a hundred million."

"Well," said Mr. Dow, "even if it was only one million dollars, that would be quite a bit of money." He continued clawing out little pieces of the metal. Apparently he couldn't wait even a moment, and he wanted to get the stuff into his hands as fast as possible.

I began to get the fever myself, and it occurred to me that possibly I had handled this thing wrong. The investigation of the mine had been my idea in the first place, and with a little more forethought I might have managed so that I would have owned a substantial share.

Mr. Bryant, the engineer, was the only one of us who maintained a normal calmness. "I would suggest," he said to Mr. Dow, "that you say nothing about this to anyone until you have checked over your title to the land and made absolutely sure that no one else has even a shadow of a claim on it. Furthermore, you may want to buy additional land, in case investigation should indicate that you do not own the entire deposit."

"That certainly is a good idea," said Mr. Dow. "You have a real head on you, Mr. Bryant. How would you advise me to go about working this mine?"

"That," said Mr. Bryant, "will have to be decided after a thorough investigation of all the factors involved. Unfortunately, I won't be able to stay long enough to see the mine put on a permanent operating basis. I'm up here only for a short vacation, and pressing business will make it necessary for me to return to New York very soon. But, if you wish, I can stay around for three or four days to advise you and get you started right."

"That would be fine," said Mr. Dow. "That would be wonderful. You don't know how I appreciate this, Mr. Bryant. How can I ever repay you for what you have done?"

"Well," said Mr. Bryant, "my fee for this preliminary examination, as agreed upon by Mr. Botts and myself, is two hundred dollars. That will include my time for yesterday and today. For each additional day, starting tomorrow, I will charge you my usual rate of one hundred dollars a day."

The mention of this rate of payment served to arouse momentarily Mr. Dow's deeply ingrained New England thrift. "A hundred dollars a day is a lot of money," he said.

"Yes," agreed Mr. Bryant pleasantly, "but not a

great deal in comparison to a three-hundred-million-dollar gold mine."

"You're right," said Mr. Dow, "and you will have to excuse me for seeming so small-minded. As a matter of fact, I guess your charges are pretty small, and I will be delighted to pay them. They will be a mere drop in the bucket as compared to the gold in this mine. But I was just wondering—have you really analyzed this stuff in here? Are you absolutely sure it's actually gold, and not just copper or something? Wouldn't it, perhaps, be a good idea to get some real chemist to analyze it for us, so we'd be certain? I have a cousin that teaches in the chemistry department of Middlebury College, which is only about thirty miles away across these mountains. I could take a sample over and he could tell me all about it."

"If you ask me," I said, "I would say that you would just be wasting your time. Mr. Bryant is a professional mining engineer. He has worked in mines all over the world. And he knows his gold, and his silver, and his copper, and his tin, and everything else. If he says it's gold, that's what it is. What more could you learn from a fool college professor?"

At this point Mr. Bryant spoke up and showed what a truly broad-minded man he is. "Mr. Dow is perfectly right," he said. "To a man of my experience, it is evident that this material is gold. It is my business to know about such things, and I do know. I am certain. But it is perfectly natural for a man like Mr. Dow to have his doubts. And it is reasonable, in a matter of so much importance, that he should check the facts carefully. I should very much prefer that he get an independent opinion. In fact, I was going to suggest it myself. Here, take this."

He reached into his pocket, drew out a small pasteboard box and handed it to Mr. Dow.

"What's this for?" asked Mr. Dow.

"It is something to carry the gold which you have been pulling out of that rock."

By this time Mr. Dow had a whole handful of small nuggets. He put them in the pasteboard box. Mr. Bryant snapped a rubber band around it and handed it back.

"There you are," he said. "My advice would be that you step into your car, drive over to Middlebury and get your cousin to analyze that gold right away. While you are gone I will start an examination of this entire mountainside with a view to determining the possible extent of this deposit of auriferous quartz."

"It's a good idea," said Mr. Dow. "I'll start right away."

"And remember," cautioned Mr. Bryant, "don't breathe a word of this to anyone. Don't tell your cousin any more than you have to, and impress it upon him that the matter is to be kept secret."

"You can trust me," said Mr. Dow.

We all returned to the town, and Mr. Dow drove away in his car. Mr. Bryant invited me to accompany him on his geologic expedition, explaining laughingly that he was afraid to leave me sitting around the hotel lobby, for fear I might be tempted to spread the great news. We had a very interesting day, tramping about the mountains. As I have said before, Mr. Bryant is one of the most charming conversationalists I have ever met. And the information which he gave me about the various rock formations was not only educational but highly interesting and enjoyable.

We got back to the hotel late in the afternoon, and soon afterward Mr. Dow arrived from Middlebury. He seemed even more agitated than in the morning, and as soon as the three of us were alone in my room he actually began dancing around the floor, gibbering at us like an idiot.

"It's all true!" he said. "My cousin analyzed it, and it's gold! Think of it! Real gold! And there's millions of dollars' worth in that mountain! And it all belongs to me! It all belongs to me!"

The old guy raved along, gloating over his good fortune in such a disgusting manner that I could not help being slightly annoyed—especially as I was to have no share in all this money that he was yawping about so loudly. At the same time I could get a little cynical amusement out of the change that had taken place in Mr. Dow's character. He had completely lost that quiet, philosophical manner, that quiet contentment with the simple life, which had been so evident at our first meeting. The sudden appearance of this vast amount of filthy gold had turned him into as greedy and material-minded a man as I had ever met. Ah, well, I thought to myself, all these things are no direct concern of mine. I came here for the purpose of promoting a few tractor sales, and it looked as if I were going to do it.

After a short conference we decided upon a definite plan of action for the next few days. Mr. Bryant is going to write to various firms in different parts of the country, asking their prices on machinery to be used in working the mine. The ore is so rich that the mine could be run at a profit with the crudest possible equipment, but Mr. Bryant pointed out that the greatest profits could only be realized through the use of the most up-to-date machinery. While waiting to hear from the manufacturers, Mr. Bryant will continue his geologic investigations.

Mr. Dow is going over tomorrow morning to hire away practically all the road commissioner's workmen. With these men and one of the two tractors which he has on hand, he is going to start building a road to the mine so that the heavy ore-crushing machinery, when it arrives, may be moved up without delay. He will tell his men that the road is to be used for getting out logs, and will carefully guard the secret of the great gold strike. As for myself, I will take the second of the two tractors which Mr. Dow has on hand, and start giving a demonstration to the road commissioner.

Thus you see that everything promises to work out splendidly. I am still somewhat confused by the magnitude of the events which have been transpiring, but I trust I have given you a reasonably clear account of them. Kindly keep all this news about the gold mine strictly confidential. We do not wish the discovery to leak out at this time.

Very sincerely
ALEXANDER BOTTS.

ALEXANDER BOTTS
SALES PROMOTION REPRESENTATIVE
EARTHWORM TRACTOR COMPANY

DOW'S GULF, VERMONT.
Thursday night,
June 9, 1932.

MR. GILBERT HENDERSON,
SALES MANAGER,
EARTHWORM TRACTOR COMPANY,
EARTHWORM CITY, ILLINOIS.

DEAR HENDERSON: Two days have passed since my last letter and there is nothing much to report except that everything is going along as planned. The great gold discovery is still a secret. Mr. Bryant is continuing his geologic researches. Mr. Dow is hard at work on his new road. He has two lawyers searching the titles of his land. And he is so smug and self-satisfied that he is positively obnoxious.

As for myself, I have been spending the last two days demonstrating the tractor to the road commissioner. This gentleman is a little sore at the high-handed way in which Mr. Dow has hired most of his men away from him. But he is a reasonable guy, holds no grudge against me, and is so favorably impressed with the tractor that I think he will decide to buy it in a day or so.

No more at present.

Very truly,
ALEXANDER BOTTS.

ALEXANDER BOTTS.
SALES PROMOTION REPRESENTATIVE
EARTHWORM TRACTOR COMPANY

DOW'S GULF, VERMONT.
Friday, June 10, 1932.

MR. GILBERT HENDERSON,
SALES MANAGER,
EARTHWORM TRACTOR COMPANY,
EARTHWORM CITY, ILLINOIS.

DEAR HENDERSON: I regret to report that affairs here are not progressing in exactly the way I had expected. In fact, it now appears that in certain important matters I was so completely and absolutely mistaken that it is most embarrassing for me to explain what has occurred. However, it is always my policy to be perfectly frank. So in this case I will go ahead, following my usual custom, and tell you the whole distressing truth.

I spent this morning and most of this afternoon uneventfully enough, demonstrating the tractor on the road commissioner's cut-and-fill job. The commissioner himself was not present, being in town on some other business, but I went ahead just the same. At five o'clock I returned to town and stopped in at the post office to buy some stamps.

And here, without any warning whatsoever, I received what I can only describe as a very severe shock. As I turned away from the stamp window my eye was suddenly attracted to a picture which was posted on the bulletin board. This picture was a printed reproduction of a photograph, and it showed with great clearness the handsome and distinguished features of Mr. Bailey Bryant, the mining engineer from New York.

Above the picture were the words, "Wanted, For Grand Larceny, Uttering Counterfeit Notes, Using the Mails to Defraud, Obtaining Money Under False Pretenses, and Forgery." Beneath was a long list of names:

"John Bailey, alias John Bryant, alias Bailey Spencer, alias Spencer the Spieler, alias Peter Livingston, alias Pete the Prestidigitator." After a full physical description, there followed further information: "This man is well educated, is a good talker on almost all subjects, has a most pleasing personality, and is remarkable for his versatility and for the variety of his swindles. Is an accomplished amateur magician and has, on several occasions, robbed jewelers by substituting an empty box for one containing valuable gems. Has posed at various times as physician, clergyman, Army officer and college president." The notice ended with a request that anyone apprehending this person should place him under arrest and communicate with a gentleman called Mulrooney down in New York.

You can well imagine the astonishment and consternation which filled my mind. At once I removed the notice from the bulletin board, folded it up, put it in my pocket and hurried over to Mr. Dow's office. Mr. Dow greeted me and introduced me to his son, who had arrived the day before from Columbia.

"Mr. Dow," I said, "I have very grave news for you. I have just discovered certain facts which lead me to believe that our friend, Mr. Bailey Bryant, is not the sort of man we think he is. In fact, I'm beginning to suspect that there may be something faintly cockeyed about this whole gold-mining enterprise."

"Yes," said Mr. Dow, "the same thought occurred to my son and myself this morning."

"This morning?" I asked.

"Well, my son began to be suspicious as long ago as yesterday afternoon. As soon as he got home I told him the great news, but he was not so enthusiastic as I had expected. It seems that last fall, without telling me anything about it, he had examined the mine, gathered up a few samples of the ore, and taken them to New York with him to be analyzed. The analysis showed a certain amount of gold, but there was nothing to indicate even the possibility of any such rich deposits as we had run across. So yesterday my son went up to the mine, collected a few of those little golden nuggets and made some tests on them. They turned out to be nothing but brass."

"This is terrible," I said. "Did you tell Mr. Bryant about it?"

"At that time," said Mr. Dow, "Mr. Bryant was up in the mountains somewhere on one of his geological expeditions. In his absence we made a few inquiries around town."

"And what did you find?"

"We found that he had bought some brass pipe and a cheap shotgun at one of the hardware stores. Then he had visited a blacksmith and had him melt up the brass pipe and pour it out so that it formed a lot of small, irregular globules. He had also paid a visit to a dentist."

"You mean he was having trouble with his teeth?"

"No, he bought five dollars' worth of gold, and had the dentist melt it up and pour it out in little chunks very similar to the brass which the blacksmith had worked on. All this we found out yesterday. This morning we got Mr. Bryant in the office here and told him that we had the goods on him, and his game was up."

"What did he say?" I asked.

"At first he was very smooth, and pretended he didn't know what we were talking about. But when he saw that we had him right and proper, he owned up."

"He explained everything to you?"

"Yes," said Mr. Dow. "And some of it was pretty good. Especially what he had to say about you."

"Good Lord," I said, "what did he say about me?"

"He said that up to the time he met you he hadn't intended to pull anything crooked in this town at all. He was here partly for some fishing and a little vacation, and partly to get away from what he described as a rather unfortunate situation down in New York. But when he saw you he said you were such a perfect example of a born easy mark that he couldn't resist taking you for a ride."

"Well," I said sadly, "he certainly succeeded. He took me on a whole cruise. And I'm not sure that I understand even yet just how he managed everything."

"He told us," said Mr. Dow, "that he was going to be paid only in case the mine turned out to be worth something. That is why he arranged such a spectacular set-up. He wanted to make the mine look as good as possible. After he had uncovered a new face of rock with dynamite, he shot all that brass into it with his shotgun."

"But what about that sample that your cousin analyzed?"

"Apparently Mr. Bryant's hand is quicker than my eye. While he was putting a rubber band around the box I had filled with brass, he slipped it up his sleeve or something, and then handed me back another box with the dentist's gold in it."

"And to think," I said, "that I actually believed that guy, and swallowed everything he told me. I certainly owe you my most abject apologies. I thought I was helping you, and all I have done is to put you to a lot of trouble and expense over a mine that isn't worth a nickel."

"It isn't as bad as that," said Mr. Dow's son. "The mine is no such bonanza as you thought. But the analysis of the ore, which I made in New York last winter, shows that there actually is a small amount of gold present. In my grandfather's day the mine was a failure. But now, by putting in a little modern machinery and using the cyanide process, I'm certain that we can work it with a small but steady profit. I had intended to ask my father to finance the thing and let me run it, but he is so cautious that he never would have consented unless you and Mr. Bryant had got him started. As it is, he has to go on. He can't back out now."

"Why not?" I asked.

"He has already built a road halfway up to the mine.

And he promised all those men he hired from the road commissioner that he would give them work for the rest of the
year. So he has to go on—and it's a very good thing."

I looked at Mr. Dow, Senior, to see what he thought
of this. He was all stretched out in his office chair with his
feet up on the desk, and his whole attitude expressed the
same languid contentment which had been so noticeable on
the day I first met him.

"Yes," he said, "the whole business suits me fine. For
a while you had me all excited and het up over the idea of
being a millionaire. And that is all wrong for a man of my
age who has always been used to peace and quiet. If the excitement had kept up much longer I would have just naturally worn myself out and come to an unfortunate and prema-
ture end. As it is, I can sit around as usual with nothing
in the world to worry me. On the other hand, I'm grateful
to you because——"

"Why should you be grateful to me?" I asked.

"Because I had perhaps been getting a little too quiet
and contented, and you have shaken me up enough to get
me started on this gold mine. It will make a very nice little
business for my son. It has already provided employment
for a number of people here in town. And besides that, it
has been of some assistance to the tractor business. I saw
the road commissioner this afternoon and he told me he
wants to buy the machine which you have been demonstrating. So everything is fine, and my thanks are due to both
yourself and Mr. Bryant."

"By the way," I said, "what did you do with that guy?
You didn't pay him anything, did you?"

"No. He agreed with us that, under the circumstances,
we owed him nothing."

"But I suppose you know he's wanted down in New
York." I showed him the notice I had brought from the
post office.

"Well, well," said Mr. Dow. "My son and I had not
seen this. If we had known about it, I suppose it would

have been our duty to turn him over to the police. But as it was, we had no grudge against him and we let him go. He took the noon train for Canada. And on the whole, I'm glad he got away. It was a lucky thing for us he came to town. And I can say the same thing regarding you, Mr. Botts."

"I hope," I said, "that you're not classing me with Mr. Bryant. Certainly, you don't believe that I'm a crook?"

"Oh, no, indeed," said Mr. Dow. "Anybody as slow-witted as you couldn't be a crook. We realize perfectly that you are completely honest and that you meant well. And as a matter of fact you have, in your awkward way, helped us and our business a great deal. So we thank you from the bottom of our hearts."

As I could not think of any good answer to these various cracks of Mr. Dow's, I wished him and his son good afternoon as politely as I could and returned to the hotel. I am leaving tomorrow for the next job.

As ever,
ALEXANDER BOTTS.

THE PEACEMAKER

ALEXANDER BOTTS
SALES PROMOTION REPRESENTATIVE
EARTHWORM TRACTOR COMPANY

Hanging Garden Hotel, Babylon, Missouri.
Thursday evening, July 28, 1932.

MR. GILBERT HENDERSON, SALES MANAGER,
EARTHWORM TRACTOR COMPANY,
EARTHWORM CITY, ILLINOIS.

DEAR HENDERSON: I arrived here this after-noon, called at once on our local dealer, Mr. Ben Garber,

and ran into such an unfortunate situation that I have decided to stick around several days, if necessary, to
straighten it out. I know that ordinarily you don't want me
to spend that much time on a small dealer. But this is a
special case—as you will realize when I give you the melancholy facts as set forth by Mr. Garber.

"Last spring," he told me, "I had a swell prospect
by the name of Peabody, and another by the name of Snodgrass—both of them wheat farmers who actually had
plenty of money. I was just on the point of selling each one
of these men an Earthworm tractor and an Earthworm
combined harvester. And then the Earthworm Tractor
Company butted in and gummed the whole deal."

"How?" I asked.

"By sending out an idiotic pamphlet called Partnership Buying. This pamphlet says that in many cases it is
foolish for a farmer to buy a whole tractor all for himself
—especially if he doesn't have enough work to keep it
busy all the time. It says the thing to do is to have a group
of farmers buy one machine in partnership. And it also
says that when a tractor is sold to grain growers of established credit, the usual down payment should be waived and
no money at all demanded until after the harvest. Honestly,
Mr. Botts, I never saw such a bunch of hog wash. Have
you read this pamphlet?"

"Yes," I said, "I have read it."

"Well," continued Mr. Garber bitterly, "Mr. Peabody and Mr. Snodgrass—my two prospects—read it too.
It was sent out to the whole mailing list. And right away
they fell for the idea. I told them it would never work.
I told them they could never agree on which one of them
would use the machine when, or who would pay for how
much of what repairs. But they wouldn't listen."

"So you sold them a machine in partnership?"

"I had to, or else lose the sale entirely. They combined with a third wheat grower—a widow woman called
Hopkins—and bought one outfit consisting of a tractor and

harvester. Terms: Nothing down, and the rest after the harvest—if I can get it, which I probably can't."

"Why can't you?" I asked.

"Because they are all fighting like cats and dogs. Everything has gone wrong. Two of the owners—Snodgrass and Mrs. Hopkins—have already used the machine for harrowing and cultivating. It is now in my shop here being tuned up for the harvest. The wheat will be ready to cut next week. If it isn't cut on time, part of it may be lost—it's apt to fall down, or dry out and shatter. Each one of the three tractor owners will need six days to cut his wheat. So each one demands the machine for all next week."

"Doesn't the partnership agreement say when each one is to have it?"

"Oh, yes. They adopted the plan recommended in that lovely pamphlet. It is all to be decided by majority vote. But there is no majority. Peabody claims he should get the machine now because the other two have already used it. Mrs. Hopkins talks about chivalry, and says she should be favored because she is a woman. And Snodgrass is a big, ill-natured brute who is just naturally stubborn and ornery. Each one of the three votes for himself, and says if he can't have the machine when he wants it, he won't pay one cent on it, and he'll sue the other two owners and me for damages."

"They're crazy," I said.

"Don't I know it?" said Mr. Garber.

"You could sue them," I said, "and make them pay. After all, they bought the tractor, didn't they?"

"Yes, but I can't afford a lawsuit. It would be too expensive—and bad for business. I can't afford to lose that money either. And I certainly can't afford to take the tractor back, now that it is secondhand. So there is only one solution. The Earthworm Tractor Company, by sending out that pamphlet, got me into this mess, and the company will have to get me out. It will have to take back this used machine and pay me the full list price for it."

"Holy Moses!" I said. "The company would never do that. Besides, it isn't necessary. All you have to do, Mr. Garber, is leave the whole thing to me. I will fix everything up."

"How?" asked Mr. Garber.

"By the use of diplomacy. Tomorrow morning I will go out and visit these three tractor owners. I will talk to them gently but firmly. By the use of remorseless logic I will show them that they are wrong. And by the use of tact and subtle suggestion, I will persuade them to get together in a reasonable way and work out a fair plan for the use of the tractor."

"What sort of a plan?" he asked.

"I will decide that as I go along. I will feel my way, and thus arrive at a perfect solution. They will then be completely satisfied. They will keep the machine and pay for it, and everything will be swell."

"It would be swell if you could do it. But you can't. I have already argued with these people till I am exhausted. And it does no good. They are all as stubborn as mules."

"Mr. Garber," I said, "for years my chief business with the Earthworm Tractor Company has been adjusting difficulties. I am an expert in the art of persuasion. I am a natural-born peacemaker. You just wait and see."

"All right," he said. "If you want to waste your time, it's O.K. with me."

He then told me how to find the three tractor owners. They all live on the same road to the north of here—Mr. Peabody nearest town, Mrs. Hopkins just beyond, and Mr. Snodgrass farthest out. I jotted down this information, and then wished Mr. Garber good afternoon and came over here to the hotel.

Tomorrow I will get busy on the diplomatic negotiations. Naturally, I can't expect to establish a permanent and lasting peace among three people who own one tractor.

But I hope I can patch things up so they will get through the harvest and pay Mr. Garber. And, in the meantime, I would suggest that you suppress that pamphlet before it wrecks any more deals.

Incidentally, just who was the saphead that wrote this literary masterpiece? I wouldn't have supposed there was anyone in the Earthworm Tractor Company so dumb as to think that any group of people anywhere could successfully coöperate in the ownership of a tractor.

Yours as ever,
ALEXANDER BOTTS.

TELEGRAM

EARTHWORM CITY ILL
JULY 29 1932

ALEXANDER BOTTS
HANGING GARDEN HOTEL
BABYLON MO

YOUR JOB IS PROMOTION OF NEW SALES STOP SUGGEST THAT YOU DON'T WASTE ANY MORE TIME ON MINOR QUARRELS BETWEEN DEALER AND TRACTOR OWNERS STOP THIS IS PRIMARILY THE DEALERS AFFAIR STOP PARTNERSHIP BUYING IS A PERFECTLY SOUND IDEA STOP I WROTE THAT PAMPHLET MYSELF STOP IF GARBER USED A GOOD IDEA ON THE WRONG PEOPLE THAT IS HIS RESPONSIBILITY NOT YOURS

GILBERT HENDERSON

ALEXANDER BOTTS
SALES PROMOTION REPRESENTATIVE
EARTHWORM TRACTOR COMPANY

Hanging Garden Hotel, Babylon, Missouri.
Friday, July 29, 1932.

MR. GILBERT HENDERSON,
SALES MANAGER,
EARTHWORM TRACTOR COMPANY,
EARTHWORM CITY, ILLINOIS.

DEAR HENDERSON: Your telegram is here. And it gave me something of a jolt to learn that you wrote that pamphlet yourself. If I had known this, possibly I would not have criticized it so freely. But you will understand that I feel no malice against you personally. As a matter of fact, I was much pleased at the frank and honest way in which you admit that you are the author. It is a great comfort to me to know that I am working for a man who takes full responsibility for his mistakes, and never attempts to shift the blame onto anyone else.

I thoroughly agree with your idea that it is unwise to use up too much time on a small dealer like Mr. Garber. I will be on my way as soon as possible. However, I have got myself rather deeply involved in Mr. Garber's troubles, and it will be necessary for me to stay for another day, at least. I am sure that you will agree with me in this as soon as I have explained what I have done so far.

This morning—Friday—I rented a car at one of the local garages and drove out to visit the three partnership tractor owners. I called first on Mr. Snodgrass, who lives the farthest out. He turned out to be a very large, tough-looking baby—every bit as disagreeable as Mr. Garber had said. I found him just ready to start for town with a truckload of vegetables. When I announced that I wished to discuss the tractor situation, he told me, in a very vulgar manner, that he had no time to bother with a lousy city slicker. And, before I could explain that I was neither a city slicker nor infested with any sort of parasites, he drove off and left me.

At first I thought of chasing after him. But he seemed to be in such an unresponsive state of mind that I finally decided to let him go until some more auspicious time. Accordingly, I drove slowly down the road to the farm belonging to the Widow Hopkins. And here I met a very friendly reception.

Mrs. Hopkins is about thirty years of age, very good-looking, and most appealingly feminine. Since the death of her husband, about four years ago, she has been making a very brave fight to run the farm.

As soon as she learned that I was from the Earthworm Tractor Company, she smiled at me very prettily, and said that she knew I must be a wonderful mechanic. When I admitted that I was not so bad, she insisted that I must look at an electric paint gun which had broken down just as one of her hired men was starting to use it to spray whitewash on some of the farm buildings. I immediately took the whole thing to pieces, cleaned and adjusted the working parts, and in less than an hour had it working perfectly. Of course, it was a very simple repair job, but Mrs. Hopkins thought it was wonderful.

"You don't know how you thrill me, Mr. Botts," she said. "I am always just overcome with admiration for a man who is strong and masterful, and knows how to do things."

This appreciation gave me such a warm glow of satisfaction that I decided to operate the gun myself. So I relieved the hired man and worked all the rest of the morning, whitewashing a large henhouse, two pigpens and a corncrib. Mrs. Hopkins said it was the best job of whitewashing she had ever seen.

And the whole thing was a very clever move on my part. Mrs. Hopkins not only invited me to lunch—serving up the most succulent viands—but she was so pleased with me that she was ready to discuss the tractor situation on a basis of complete friendliness and mutual confidence. In consequence, I was able to uncover certain very important facts which Mr. Garber's clumsy efforts had failed to reveal.

In talking with Mrs. Hopkins, I first checked up the facts which had been given me by Mr. Garber, and I found that they were substantially correct. Mrs. Hopkins, in spite of her affable manners, was just about as stubborn as Garber had said. She was willing to coöperate, but only in case she could cut her wheat first. She realized that the other two owners were also demanding first whack at the machine, and she admitted that, if the problem was to be solved, somebody would have to give in.

When I suggested the possibility that we might work on Mr. Snodgrass, she said that she was completely disgusted with the man, and would prefer not to have any dealings with him at all. As I had just had a sample of Mr. Snodgrass' boorishness, I was inclined to agree with her. Accordingly, we passed on to a discussion of Mr. Howard Peabody. And at once I ran into some brand-new information.

"How do you and Mr. Peabody get along?" I asked.

"In general," she replied, "very well indeed. In fact, I am really fond of Howard. We have known each other a long time. He is, on the whole, a gentleman. He is refined. He is genteel. And he is well-mannered. But just at the moment I am a little provoked at him."

"About this tractor business?" I asked.

"It is partly that. You see, he came over here yesterday, and he offered to back down and let me have the tractor to do my harvesting first."

"What? He offered to let you have the tractor first?"

"Yes."

"Splendid!" I said. "That means it is all settled."

"I'm afraid not," she said.

"Why not?" I asked. "You and Peabody are a majority. If you vote together, you control the situation."

"But I'm not going to vote with Mr. Peabody. I told him I couldn't agree to his plan."

"Why not?"

"Because I was provoked at him."

"I don't understand," I said. "You mean you got sore because he offered to let you have the tractor?"

"It wasn't that. If he had just offered me the tractor and stopped there, it would have been all right. It was what he said afterwards that I didn't like."

"And just what did he say afterwards?"

"I don't know whether I ought to tell you."

"You'd better. I'm trying to help you. So I have to know the facts."

"Well," she said, "if you must know, Mr. Peabody asked me to marry him."

"What?" I said. "He asked you to marry him?"

"I don't see why you have to act so surprised," she said. "Am I so repulsive that nobody would want me?"

"My dear lady," I said, "you misunderstand me. I should think everybody would want you. Why, if I was not already happily married and the father of twins ——"

"Really, Mr. Botts ——"

"What I mean," I said, "is that I was surprised to learn that Mr. Peabody had so much sense. But I still don't understand why you should be provoked at him, as you say. If he wants to marry you, why shouldn't he ask you? It doesn't hurt you any. You don't have to accept him unless you want to."

"Oh, I didn't object to his proposing to me. As a matter of fact, I was flattered. I was delighted."

"Well, what is the matter?"

"I didn't like what he said beforehand."

"And what did he say beforehand?" I asked.

"I just told you. He said he would let me use the tractor first. The two things went together. If I would marry him, he would let me have the tractor. If I wouldn't marry him, he said I could just whistle for the tractor—those were his very words. It was most insulting."

"I don't see why," I said.

"Of course it was insulting," she said. "He put the whole thing on such a low plane. What he was doing was asking me to sell myself to him for a paltry piece of machinery."

"It is not so paltry," I said. "An Earthworm tractor is a real masterpiece of engineering. But I can see how you feel about it."

"I feel very much hurt," she said. "If he had really cared anything about me, he would have offered me the tractor without any humiliating conditions."

"Mrs. Hopkins," I said, "I understand your attitude perfectly. And I am very glad you told me all the facts in the case. I feel that I am now in a position to solve all your difficulties. I will go right over and see Mr. Peabody, and I am sure that I can persuade him to let you have the tractor without any reservations or conditions."

"That would be just wonderful," she said. "Do you really think you can do it?"

"Trust me," I said. "I will go at once."

"But aren't you going to finish the whitewashing?" she asked.

"I thought I had."

"Oh, no. There is still the horse barn."

"Very well," I said. "I will whitewash the horse barn."

"That is really very dear of you," she said. "And I wish I could watch you do it. But I have arranged to drive over into the next county to visit some relatives. And I want to get started right away. I'll be back early tomorrow morning—in case you have any news for me. You won't mind if I go off and leave you?"

"That will be quite all right," I said.

I helped her get the car started, and, after she had driven away, I put in several hours squirting whitewash about the horse barn. I will have to admit that this irked me a little. It seemed to me that the widow was imposing upon my good nature a little too much. But I did not want to do anything that would endanger the *entente cordiale* which had sprung up between us. So I worked bravely along, and did a good job. Toward the end of the afternoon I finished up and drove over to call on Mr. Howard Peabody.

I found him just finishing the chores. He was alone; the hired man, who usually looked after the farm, and the hired man's wife, who took care of the house, were both away on a visit. Mr. Peabody was such a timid-looking little guy that I could not understand Mrs. Hopkins' fondness for him. Mrs. Hopkins, you will remember, had told me that she was much more partial to men like me, who are strong, masterful and can do things. It just goes to show that you never can tell about a woman.

I started in on Mr. Peabody by introducing myself as a representative of the Earthworm Tractor Company, and also an old family friend of Mrs. Hopkins. At first he seemed a bit suspicious. So I spent about fifteen minutes ladling out the old apple sauce—telling him what a privilege it was to meet him, and what a really swell guy he was. This had the desired effect of convincing him that I was a person of rare judgment, and a man to be trusted. I then got down to the business in hand.

"Mr. Peabody," I said, "I have come to tell you that Mrs. Hopkins is very fond of you. When you asked her to marry you, she was highly flattered. She was delighted. She would have fallen on your neck—except for one thing."

"And what was that?"

"She misunderstood your attitude. She thought you were proposing an ignoble commercial deal by which you would swap the tractor for her hand in marriage."

"Well," said Mr. Peabody, in a rather whining tone of voice, "that was the idea, in a way."

"But not in the way she understood it," I said. "She

actually believed you were asking her to sell her warm, living body, in a most sordid manner, for a piece of cold, lifeless machinery. And I am sure, Mr. Peabody, you never even thought of such a thing."

"Well, not in those exact words, anyway."

"You see," I said. "It is all a misunderstanding. And it can be fixed up very easily."

"How?"

"You and I will go to town right away. We'll get the tractor and harvester from Mr. Garber. We'll bring them out here. And tomorrow morning when Mrs. Hopkins gets back from a little trip she is making we'll take them over and deliver them to her with no conditions attached. This will give her a concrete proof of your unselfish devotion. Then, after she has used the machinery for a few days, you can ask her any favor you want and she will grant it."

Mr. Peabody was doubtful. "I would hate to lose the tractor and the lady both," he said.

"Listen," I said. "Does it stand to reason that any mere woman, if you give her half a chance, could hold out very long against a man like you?"

Mr. Peabody smiled. "I guess you are right," he said. "We'll go after that tractor right away."

"Now you're talking," I said.

We both got into my car. We started for town. And, as we drove along, I reflected that I had handled this thing pretty well. I had every reason to suppose that events were rapidly moving toward a successful conclusion. It soon appeared, however, that I was wrong.

As we approached the outskirts of town, we observed, rolling along toward us, an Earthworm tractor pulling an Earthworm combined harvester. As we passed the tractor, we observed that it was driven by Mr. Snodgrass. A few rods farther on I stopped the car.

"There is something funny going on here," I said. "What does old Snodgrass think he is doing with that tractor?"

"How should I know?" said Mr. Peabody.

I looked back over my shoulder. The tractor and the harvester were rolling slowly but steadily along the road.

"We might go back and ask him," I said, "but he is a rather hard guy to talk to."

"He is," agreed Mr. Peabody.

"If we want to get the real dope on this," I continued, "it might be better to talk to Mr. Garber."

I started up the car and speeded on into town. We found Mr. Garber in his office.

"Is that the partnership tractor that Mr. Snodgrass is driving out of town?" I asked.

"It is," said Mr. Garber.

"What's the idea?" I asked. "Who told him he could have it?"

"I did."

"Why?"

"Well, it's like this: He came in here a little while ago. He had been peddling vegetables around town all day. He made me a proposition. He said that if I would turn the outfit over to him so that he could do his harvesting first, he would pay me spot cash for his one-third share, and he would take his chances arguing it out with the other two owners. So I let him have it."

"You had no right to do that," I said. "Didn't you know that the use of the tractor was to be decided by majority vote? And didn't you know that I was out working on these people and fixing up an agreement with them?"

"Yes, but I knew you wouldn't have any luck. And a real cash payment in days like these looks awful good. I couldn't afford to let it get away."

"You poor, simple-minded oaf," I said.

"What?" he asked.

"You poor, simple-minded oaf," I repeated. "I had this thing all fixed up. And now you have to go and spoil it all. But it may not be too late. . . . Come on, Mr. Peabody, let's get after that guy and take the machine away from him."

"I'm afraid we can't," said Mr. Peabody. "And we want to be awful careful. Snodgrass is a big guy and he's pretty rough. If we bother him too much, he might beat us up or something."

"Come on!" I said.

I dragged him down the stairs and into the car, and started after old Snodgrass. We caught up to him just beyond Mr. Peabody's front gate. I drove right past him, parked at the side of the road, got out, and waved my hand for him to stop. He stopped. I walked up beside the tractor.

"My good man," I said, "I will have to ask you to get off that tractor. Mrs. Hopkins and Mr. Peabody—a majority of the owners of this machine—have come to an agreement regarding its use. Mrs. Hopkins is to have it first. Mr. Peabody second. And you third. Consequently, you will have to turn the machine over to me so that I can deliver it to Mrs. Hopkins. If you refuse, I warn you that we will have to use force."

During the course of this speech, Mr. Snodgrass occupied himself by glaring at me as ferociously as possible and interjecting various witless remarks that he had probably learned at the talking movies, such as, "Oh, yeah?" and, "Says who?" and, "You and what six other guys?" When I had finished, he merely opened the throttle and drove on. I followed along behind the tractor for a short distance, shouting out various remarks. But he paid no attention. Finally I rejoined Mr. Peabody, who had remained seated in my car.

He was inclined to be sarcastic. "So you are the hero who was going to take the tractor away from the tough guy," he said. "It seems to me you are pretty weak. If I had been talking to him, I would have made him get right off that seat and walk home."

"Well, why didn't you?" I said. "You were right here all the time."

"I didn't want to interfere with you," he said, "after all the big talking you had done about how you were going to handle things. And now you haven't accomplished anything at all."

"Oh, yes, I have," I said. "There are more ways than one of getting a man off a tractor. What did you think I was doing when I was walking along behind the machine there?"

"It looked to me," he said, "as if you were handing out a lot of words that didn't mean anything to a man that wasn't listening."

"I was doing more than that," I said. "I was opening up the little drain cock in the bottom of the gasoline tank."

"What was the idea of that?"

"By this time," I said, "that tank is empty. In another couple of minutes the small amount of gasoline in the vacuum tank will be used up. The machine will stop. Mr. Snodgrass will discover that he has no fuel. And he will have to go off somewhere looking for more. Then we'll take charge of the machine and drive it away. But first we'll have to have some gasoline, and there may not be enough in this car. Have you got any at your place?"

"Yes," said Mr. Peabody. "But we can't do anything like this. Suppose Snodgrass should come back and catch us? He might get violent."

"All right," I said. "Let him."

I swung the car around, drove back to Mr. Peabody's place, entered the front gate and stopped in front of the barn.

"I don't like this at all," said Mr. Peabody.

"Where's that gasoline?" I asked. "In the barn?"

"No," he said. "My insurance won't let me keep it in there. It's in the root cellar."

He led me around beside the barn to a sort of hatchway. We went down a flight of brick steps. Mr. Peabody unlocked a large padlock, swung open a heavy, insulated door, like the kind they use on ice boxes, and snapped on an electric light. We stepped into a fairly good-sized underground brick vault. The place was evidently intended for storing root crops and other vegetables, but at this season of the year it was largely empty. There were several baskets of peaches, several piles of old newspapers and magazines, and a certain amount of miscellaneous junk. In one corner was a large drum of gasoline and a number of empty five-gallon oil cans. We filled up one of these cans.

"Now," I said, "we want to keep under cover until that guy gets out of the way. And we want to have some place where we can get a view of what's going on. How about the haymow?"

"All right," he said.

We carried the gasoline into the barn and set it in an empty stall. Then we climbed up a long, shaky ladder and floundered over the hay until we reached a small front window. From here we had a view of the road for quite a way in each direction. I was delighted to observe that the tractor and harvester were stalled about a quarter of a mile up the line.

"Look!" I said. "He seems to be walking around the machine. He is trying to find out what's the matter. Ah, ha! He's leaving. He's coming down the road this way. He'll walk right past here on his way to town."

"This is terrible!" said Mr. Peabody, in a weak little voice. "Maybe he's after us. Maybe he'll come right in here. I'm going to hide."

And then, believe it or not, the poor little shrimp began burrowing into the hay. In less than a minute he was completely covered up.

I remained at the window, cautiously peeking out. Mr. Snodgrass drew nearer. And, sure enough, when he reached the front gate he turned in.

"By the way," I said, speaking in a low tone of voice, "does this bum know where you keep your gasoline?"

A scared little whisper came up out of the hay. "Probably he does. He has been in here quite a few times."

"Did you lock up that cellar?" I asked.

"I'm afraid not. I was in too much of a hurry."

"Good Lord!" I said. "If he gets gasoline here, he'll start right back to the tractor, and we won't have time to make a get-away. I'm going down to lock that place up."

"You'd better not," whispered Mr. Peabody. "If he gets you, he might kill you."

"Shut up!" I said.

I crawled across the hay, went down the long, shaky ladder as fast as I could, hurried out of the barn and looked around.

There was no sign of Mr. Snodgrass. I rushed around the corner of the barn, leaped down the brick stairs, slammed shut the big door, pushed the hasp over the staple and snapped the big padlock in place.

Then, as I turned around and mounted the steps, there occurred a very peculiar phenomenon. I had a distinct feeling that I was hearing things. It almost seemed as if lusty shouts, muffled by the thick ice-box door, were issuing from the depths of the root cellar. I began to wonder what had happened to Mr. Snodgrass, and, after a brief examination of the premises failed to reveal his presence, it suddenly occurred to me, as a remote possibility, that he might be inside the cellar. If this were the case, it would be my duty to let him out. I think I once heard somewhere that it is against the law to lock a man up without a warrant or something.

But, as I thought the matter over, I decided that I had no real reason for supposing that the man was in there at all. I had not seen him enter. I had not looked inside when I shut the door. And the faint sounds of shouting which I had thought I heard were probably mere hallucination. It is well known to scientists that even perfectly normal individuals, such as myself, may have slight temporary derangements of the functioning of the auditory nerve which give rise to such effects.

I decided that, on the whole, I had no responsibility in this matter whatsoever.

I had a perfect right to lock that door. I had done so with the consent of the owner. If Mr. Snodgrass had entered the cellar, it was for the purpose of stealing gasoline. If he got caught, that was his hard luck.

And it wouldn't do him any real harm, anyway. The place was large; he would have plenty of air. The temperature within was pleasantly cool as compared to the hot summer weather outside. He had a good electric light and plenty of old newspapers and magazines to read. If he got hungry, there were several bushels of peaches. What more could he ask?

I walked around in front of the barn. From here the muffled shouts were inaudible. I climbed up into the mow and finally succeeded in coaxing Mr. Peabody out of the hay.

"It's all right," I said. "The cellar is safely locked and Mr. Snodgrass has gone."

"Where? To town?"

"How should I know? He has gone somewhere to look for motor fuel. So it is up to us to get busy."

After much persuasion, I got Mr. Peabody down the ladder. We put the gasoline in the car and I drove up the road to the tractor. I primed the vacuum tank, closed the drain cock, poured the gasoline into the tank, and then drove the tractor and the harvester off the road, across one of Mr. Peabody's fields and into a dense clump of bushes, where it was effectively hidden.

All this time Mr. Peabody had been very fidgety. He appeared to be in a panic for fear Mr. Snodgrass might come back and beat him up. At first I thought of mentioning my vague suspicion that Mr. Snodgrass might possibly be locked up in the root cellar. But I decided not to. If he were really there, it would be, on the whole, better for our purposes if he remained there until after we had driven the tractor over to Mrs. Hopkins' in the morning. And I was afraid that if I mentioned the matter to Mr. Peabody he would insist on opening the door at once on the theory that the big brute would be less dangerous at that time than after a whole night of captivity. It also seemed inadvisable to let Mr. Peabody spend the night at his farm. He might go into the root cellar after some of those peaches.

To guard against this possibility, I invited him to spend the night with me at the hotel in town.

My argument was that it would be unwise for him to stay at the farm alone. Mr. Snodgrass might show up at any moment, I said, and get violent. And I am happy to say that Mr. Peabody agreed with me.

So I brought him back to town with me. We had supper together. And since then, I have been writing this report in the lobby, while Mr. Peabody has been hiding up in my room.

So you see everything is going along fine. I have met with various difficulties, but I have overcome them all. And I expect to have everything finished up so that I can leave here on the noon train tomorrow—thus carrying out your desire that I do not spend too much time on these smaller dealers.

I will get this report on the night train, so that you will receive it in the morning.

Very sincerely,
ALEXANDER BOTTS.

TELEGRAM

EARTHWORM CITY ILL
JULY 30 1932

ALEXANDER BOTTS
HANGING GARDEN HOTEL
BABYLON MO

YOUR REPORT IS HERE AND I DISAPPROVE HIGHLY YOUR WHOLE COURSE OF ACTION STOP IT IS BAD ENOUGH FOR

YOU TO WASTE YOUR TIME PLAYING THE PART OF CUPID
BUT WHEN YOU LOCK UP ONE OF OUR CUSTOMERS AND RUN
OFF WITH HIS TRACTOR YOUR CONDUCT IS HIGHLY DANGER-
OUS AND COMPLETELY UNWARRANTED AND INEXCUSABLE
STOP YOU ARE HEREBY ORDERED TO SEE THAT SNODGRASS
IS RELEASED AT ONCE AND YOU WILL THEN LEAVE BABYLON
BY THE EARLIEST POSSIBLE TRAIN

GILBERT HENDERSON

ALEXANDER BOTTS
SALES PROMOTION REPRESENTATIVE
EARTHWORM TRACTOR COMPANY

Hanging Garden Hotel, Babylon, Missouri,
Saturday noon, July 30, 1932.

MR. GILBERT HENDERSON,
SALES MANAGER,
EARTHWORM TRACTOR COMPANY,
EARTHWORM CITY, ILLINOIS.

DEAR HENDERSON: What a day this has been!
Yesterday was fairly exciting, but today has been positively
frantic.

Early this morning I drove Mr. Peabody out to his
farm. Everything was quiet and serene—except Mr. Peabody, who seemed a bit nervous. I avoided the neighborhood
of the root cellar, and steered Mr. Peabody away from it.
I stayed right with him while he fed the stock and did the
other chores. Then I dragged him over to where we had
left the tractor and harvester. I cranked up, we both
climbed aboard, and I drove out to the widow's farm.

When we arrived, I drew up beside the road, directly
opposite the house, and right at the edge of a ten-acre
wheat field. As I stopped, Mrs. Hopkins opened the door
of the house and looked out. I cut off the motor, and told
Mr. Peabody to run over and speak his little piece and ask
the lady where she wanted us to put the machine.

So far everything had gone well, but just at this moment there arose a new and most annoying complication. As the roar of the motor died away, I heard a distant noise as of someone yelling. Looking back, I saw a man running toward us along the road from the direction of Mr. Peabody's farm. The man was a couple of hundred yards away, but he was approaching fast. He was waving his arms and shouting angrily. I recognized at once who it was. It was my old friend Mr. Snodgrass.

It became necessary for Captain Botts to think fast. And I did. It occurred to me almost immediately that Mr. Snodgrass might be a bit irate, and that he might so far forget himself as to try to take the tractor away from us. I decided, therefore, that it would be just as well to fix the machine so he could not get very far with it. I leaped nimbly to the ground. I opened the drain cock in the fuel tank, just as I had done yesterday. And the remains of our five gallons of gasoline went splashing down over the rear end of the tractor. As I climbed back into the seat, Mr. Snodgrass drew up alongside of us. Just as I had feared, his state of mind was not exactly genial. If he had not been so out of breath from running, I believe he would have climbed up and tried to throw us both off the seat. As it was, he merely addressed a few remarks to Mr. Peabody.

"I've got you now, you rat," he said. "So you thought you could lock me up and steal my tractor, did you? Well, I fooled you. I cut my way through that door with my pocket knife. And now I'm going to have my innings. You're going to state's prison for most of the rest of your life for robbery and kidnaping. And I'll take that tractor right now. Get off that seat!"

"Really, Mr. Snodgrass," I said, curling my lip in a scornful smile, "I must ask you to keep your shirt in its accustomed place. We know nothing about your being locked up. And Mr. Peabody has a perfect right to this tractor. He will tell you so himself. . . . Speak up, Mr. Peabody, and tell this guy where he gets off at."

But Mr. Peabody did not speak up. Unfortunately for him, he was on the side of the tractor nearest Mr. Snodgrass—so close to the huge brute that he was completely cowed. He just sat there, all drawed up like a scared rabbit and unable to emit even the most feeble squeak.

"Come on, Mr. Peabody, pull yourself together," I said. "Be nonchalant. Blow some smoke in the big bum's face, and show him you're not afraid of him." I handed over a cigarette and a box of matches. Mr. Peabody accepted them mechanically, put the cigarette in his mouth, lit it, and threw the match back over his shoulder.

Well, it was just too bad. There was a sudden puff of flame behind us, and immediately the entire rear end of the tractor seemed to be on fire. Mr. Peabody leaped off one side of the machine, practically into the arms of Mr. Snodgrass, while I went bounding down the road and off into the wheat field. And this was not so good either. That wheat was dead ripe, and very dry. And I was no sooner in it than I found it was blazing and crackling furiously all around me. Two or three vigorous jumps got me out of the fire, but it spread so rapidly that I had to keep right on running to save myself from being burned up.

After I once got started, it was impossible for me to go back to the road. I had to continue straight ahead. And the fire, driven along by a moderate breeze, kept right behind me. I went up a small ridge, down the other side, and, finally, just as I was about to drop from exhaustion, I reached a back road which ran along the far side of the wheat field. Here the fire stopped, and there seemed little danger that it would spread in other directions. This particular ten-acre patch of wheat was gone, but the flames were held in on all sides by roads, and by woods and cornfields, which at this time were not dry enough to burn.

After resting myself for a few minutes, I started back. I attempted to circle around the still-smoldering wheat field. But I was so weary that my mind was a bit confused. While passing through a small patch of woods I must have lost my sense of direction. I staggered along through woods and cornfields for at least an hour, and finally reached a road which led me, not to the widow's farm, but directly into the little town of Babylon. In some ways this was rather fortunate, as it gave me a chance to go to the Hanging Garden Hotel, and get myself washed up.

When I entered the lobby, the desk clerk handed me your telegram. I opened it with great eagerness. In my somewhat discouraged state of mind, a rousing message of encouragement and confidence from my chief would have been a great help. You can imagine my disappointment when your communication turned out to be nothing but a good swift kick in the pants.

With greatly lowered vitality I wandered over to the office of our dealer, Mr. Garber. I hoped that he might have some news, and possibly a few words of good cheer. It turned out that he had some news, but absolutely nothing in the way of good cheer. Various reports about the fire had reached him from people who had come to town over the road which led past the widow's farm. And his nerves were very much on edge.

"So you are the guy," he said, "who called me a simple-minded oaf for letting Mr. Snodgrass take the tractor! And what do you do? You kidnap Mr. Snodgrass, who is one of my customers. You steal the tractor. And then you burn it up, along with a whole field of wheat belonging to Mrs. Hopkins, who is another of my customers."

"It was all an accident," I said.

"Accident or no accident," he said, "you and I are through with each other. You can just get out of this office, and out of town. And you can stay out. If you don't, I'll call in the sheriff and have you put in jail for arson and other misdemeanors and felonies."

"Very well," I said, "I'm on my way."

I withdrew in a dignified manner. And then I decided that I might as well go out and have a look at the remains of the tractor. By this time I was not as optimistic as I had once been as to the possibility of straightening out the affairs of the three tractor owners. But it seemed to me that it was still my duty to do anything that I could. I couldn't make things any worse, and there was a faint chance that I might be able to make them a little better.

I had a taxi man take me out to Mr. Peabody's farm. The owner was not there. I dismissed the taxi, climbed into the rented car—which I had left in Mr. Peabody's barn—and drove up the road. As I approached the Hopkins place, I decided to take no chances with Mr. Snodgrass. I would talk to him from the car, and I would keep the motor running so that I could make a quick getaway in case he got violent.

But when I arrived at the scene of the tragedy, there was nobody in sight but poor little Mr. Peabody. He was seated, the picture of dejection and despair, on the charred and blackened seat cushion of the tractor. His eyes were fixed on the remains of what had once been a pretty nice field of wheat.

I drove up beside him.

"Good morning," I said. "Is Mr. Snodgrass around anywhere?"

"No," said Mr. Peabody. "He has gone to town."

I stopped the motor. And then Mr. Peabody started in to tell me what he thought of me.

"A swell friend you turned out to be," he said. "You were going to fix everything up." He smiled bitterly. "Well, I guess you've fixed it. But if old Snodgrass thinks he can put over anything as raw as this, he'll find out he's mistaken. I'll sue him. I'll get the money back."

"What money?" I asked.

"That check he made me give him. He has probably cashed it by now. But he can't get by with it. It was highway robbery. And Mrs. Hopkins came out here, and she just stood around and never lifted a finger to help me. She'll be sorry she acted this way. I wouldn't marry her now if she came to me on her bended knees."

"I don't understand," I said. "What happened?"

"I couldn't help myself," said Mr. Peabody. "Old Snodgrass claimed I started the fire."

"Well, you did, didn't you?" I said.

"You spread the gasoline all around. And you gave me the match. So it's really your fault. But Snodgrass blamed it all on me. He said I was the one who had ruined the tractor, and I would have to stand the loss. He made me buy out his share and Mrs. Hopkins' share. He took me by the neck and shook me all around. So I had to do what he told me. I wrote him a check for the full price of the tractor and the harvester."

"And what did he do with it?"

"He took it to town. He said he was going to cash it right away and pay Mr. Garber in full."

"What?" I said. "Mr. Garber is getting paid in full? Say, this is wonderful. This is marvelous."

"Yes. Just as marvelous as finding a dead cat in your soup. I suppose I ought to be giving three cheers and waving a flag. I pay the full price, and I get a burned-up wreck."

"Maybe it is not so bad," I said. "Let's look the old baby over."

I got out of the car and made a rapid inspection. The harvester was untouched. I looked over the tractor. The seat cushion and the paint at the rear end had been pretty well ruined. Aside from this, there was no damage at all. It takes more than a small gasoline fire on the outside to do any real damage to a machine that is almost entirely steel and iron.

I drained several gallons of gasoline out of my car and put them in the tank. Then I cranked up the tractor motor. It ran fine.

"Mr. Peabody," I said, "there is nothing the matter with this machine. Fifty cents' worth of paint and a couple of dollars for a new seat cushion will make it just as good as new. You are a lucky man, Mr. Peabody."

"Well," he admitted, "I seem to be a lot better off than I thought I was."

"You are in fine shape," I said. "With a farm like yours you need a tractor and harvester all for yourself."

"I guess maybe that is right."

"Of course it is," I said. "So now you can just drive your machine on home. Thanks to me, you are sitting pretty."

"Thanks to you in a pig's eye," he said. "If I'm sitting pretty, it is due to pure bull luck. After all the monkey-shines you have been pulling around here, it is a wonder we both aren't in jail. I can't imagine why I was dumb enough to even let you come in my front gate. But you can be sure I never will again. Good-by."

With these words he started up the machine, swung around and drove down the road toward his farm. As I stood watching him, I heard a cheery voice behind me. "Well, well! If it isn't Mr. Botts himself, the big paint-gun expert!" I turned around. It was Mrs. Hopkins. "I came out to see what was going on," she said. "Is Mr. Peabody's tractor all fixed up now? Is he going to have a big repair bill?"

"The machine was hardly hurt at all," I said. "The total repairs won't amount to more than two or three dollars."

"That's fine," she said. "So now everybody is happy."

"I am glad you are not sore at me, Mrs. Hopkins," I said. "And I can assure you that I am sorry your wheat got burned up."

"I am not worrying about the wheat," she said. "It was only ten acres. And I have a lot more. Besides, I have something else to think about that is much more important."

"You don't say?"

"Yes, Mr. Botts. And it's so important that I just can't keep it to myself. I'm going to be married."

"Are you sure?" I asked.

"Of course I'm sure."

"Well, that's fine," I said. "But, from what he told me, I sort of got the idea that Mr. Peabody had changed his mind."

"Mr. Peabody! That little shrimp! He has nothing to do with the case. I'm going to marry Mr. Snodgrass."

"What? The big gorilla?"

"Really, Mr. Botts. You do say the oddest things."

"Well," I said, "you change your mind so quick I can't keep up with you. Yesterday you said you didn't want to have anything to do with Mr. Snodgrass. You said you were completely disgusted with him."

"Of course I was disgusted with him—because he wouldn't pay any attention to me. Ever since he bought that farm and moved in two years ago, I have been just crazy about him. He is so big, so strong, so virile. He is a regular superman—the perfect answer to a poor widow's prayer. I kept trying to strike up a friendship with him, but he would never respond at all. And that is why I got disgusted with him. I didn't know then that he really wanted to be friendly, but that he was just too shy."

"He didn't seem very shy to me," I said.

"Oh, he's bold enough with men. But with women, Mr. Botts, he is just like a great, big, awkward boy. You know, he has been secretly in love with me all the time, but he was too timid to say so. He wanted to take my part in all these discussions about the tractor, but he was too bashful. So he finally got hold of the machine, and he was going to bring it out to me. Isn't it just too cute for words?"

"Yes," I said, "a very whimsical situation indeed."

"Even then, he wouldn't have dared tell me how he felt about it. So it is probably just as well that you and Mr. Peabody went crazy and stole the tractor and everything. Because when he saw my wheat field burning up, he was so sorry for me and so angry at Mr. Peabody that he forgot all his bashfulness. Oh, it was wonderful,

Mr. Botts. I was so proud of the masterful way in which he handled the situation. He shook Mr. Peabody as a terrier shakes a rat. He made him pay for the machine. Then he was going to make him pay for the wheat. He was just like a raging lion. But when I said that we did not want to be too hard on Mr. Peabody, he deferred to my wishes as gently as a lamb. It just shows how much power I have over him. And it certainly gave me a thrill. And then he came in the house, and his bashfulness held off long enough for us to get engaged, and then he took the check and went to town in my car, and we're going to be married next week and—— Look! Here he comes now."

I glanced down the road. A car was rapidly approaching.

"Well," I said, "I guess I'll be on my way. Good-by and good luck to you."

As I climbed into my car, Mr. Snodgrass drove up, leaped out of the car and walked over to Mrs. Hopkins.

"It is all fixed up," he said. "I paid Garber for the old tractor and harvester, and I've bought a brand-new tractor and harvester for us. It will be delivered tomorrow." At this point he caught sight of me. "So you are the man," he said, "that helped Peabody lock me up and steal the tractor and burn up Mrs. Hopkins' wheat! I've a good mind to knock your block off."

He advanced toward me in a menacing manner, but Mrs. Hopkins held him back.

"Don't hurt poor little Mr. Botts," she said. "He means well. And most of the time he's harmless—in spite of the fact that he seems to be crazy."

"All right," said Snodgrass. "But he had better get away from here before I change my mind."

"I'm leaving right now," I said. I turned the car around and started for town.

And, as I drove along, I couldn't help but congratulate myself on the complete success of my activities. Think of it—a bitter fight settled, a very pretty romance started, and two complete tractor-harvester outfits sold where only one had been partially sold before. I tell you, Henderson, it just makes me feel good all over.

As ever,
ALEXANDER BOTTS.

WORKING ON THE LEVEE

ALEXANDER BOTTS
SALES PROMOTION REPRESENTATIVE
EARTHWORM TRACTOR COMPANY

MEMPHIS, TENNESSEE,
Saturday, August 20, 1932.

MR. GILBERT HENDERSON,
SALES MANAGER,
EARTHWORM TRACTOR COMPANY,
EARTHWORM CITY, ILLINOIS.

DEAR HENDERSON: I arrived in Memphis this morning, called at once on our local dealer, Mr. Fitz William, and ran into a piece of news which so filled my bosom with joy that it like to shot all the buttons off my vest.

Mr. Fitz William says that the Federal flood-control people are on the point of spending millions of dollars for the building of many miles of levees in the Yazoo-delta region along the Mississippi River to the south of here. In other words, while the hot sands of the desert of depression are drifting drearily over most of the country, there is, in this region, an amazing oasis of prosperity. And this oasis ought to be a swell place to sell tractors.

At the moment, the best prospect seems to be a local

contractor by the name of Jim Slanker, who has just been awarded a two-million-yard levee-building contract. He is said to be in the market for twenty-five sixty-horse-power tractors and ten elevating graders, besides a lot of shovels, drag lines and other equipment.

Mr. Slanker lives here in Memphis, but he has gone down into the Yazoo delta, south of Greenville, to a small place called South Gumbo, Mississippi, which is the site of the levee he is to build. Mr. Fitz William, at my suggestion, is shipping a six-horse-power Earthworm tractor and an Earthworm elevating grader to South Gumbo. And he and I are starting down ourselves this afternoon to put on a demonstration.

This begins to look like the good old days. We got a chance to sell twenty-five tractors and ten graders! You will agree with me that it sounds almost like a fairy tale.

My address for the next few days will be South Gumbo, Mississippi.

> Hastily but joyfully,
> ALEXANDER BOTTS.

NIGHT TELEGRAM LETTER

> EARTHWORM CITY ILL
> AUG 22 1932

ALEXANDER BOTTS
SOUTH GUMBO MISS

DELIGHTED WITH YOUR LETTER STOP IN THE PRESENT HARD TIMES A SALE OF TWENTY FIVE TRACTORS WOULD MAKE ALL THE DIFFERENCE BETWEEN CONTINUING FACTORY PRODUCTION AT CURRENT REDUCED RATE OR LAYING OFF MORE MEN AND PARTIALLY SHUTTING DOWN STOP IN VIEW OF THE GREAT IMPORTANCE OF THIS DEAL I AM PLANNING TO COME DOWN TO MISSISSIPPI IN A FEW DAYS TO TAKE CHARGE PERSONALLY

> GILBERT HENDERSON

ALEXANDER BOTTS
SALES PROMOTION REPRESENTATIVE
EARTHWORM TRACTOR COMPANY

SOUTH GUMBO, MISSISSIPPI,
Tuesday Evening,
August 23, 1932.

MR. GILBERT HENDERSON,
SALES MANAGER,
EARTHWORM TRACTOR COMPANY,
EARTHWORM CITY, ILLINOIS.

DEAR HENDERSON: Your telegram has come, and it is my painful duty to inform you—with all due respect for your high character and excellent intentions—that it would, on the whole, be much better, in my opinion, for you to stay up there in the office where you belong, and not try to come down here and start monkeying with a situation that you don't know anything about. In case you might be inclined to doubt the wisdom of my advice, I will give you a brief account of my activities for the past few days, explaining all the trouble I have had, and clearly setting forth the reasons why the present unfortunate situation can best be handled by me without any outside interference.

Mr. Fitz William, our Memphis dealer, and I arrived here at South Gumbo day before yesterday. The town is nothing but a railroad station and two or three houses, set in the midst of the desolate swamps and canebrakes along the Mississippi River. We found Mr. Jim Slanker at his newly established construction camp not far from the station. He is a great big bozo, more than six feet tall, heavily built, and with a voice like the whistle on the factory at Earthworm City. His chin carries a beard of several days' growth, and his hip is decorated with a large revolver in a holster.

The camp has just been started, but already there is

quite a force of men at work—engineers and surveyors going over the site of the levee, mechanics setting up equipment, and a gang of Negro workmen putting up bunk
houses and tool sheds. When we arrived, old Jim was boss-
ing around a bunch of these workmen in a way that was
slightly louder and more hard-boiled than a regular-army
first sergeant.

Waiting for a lull in the proceedings, we introduced
ourselves. Old Jim at once said he would be very glad
to see our tractor, and invited us to stay at his camp. Like
most of these tough babies, he is hospitable and big-
hearted. And we would have got along fine except for one
thing.

This one fly in the ointment was Mr. Fitz William,
our dealer from Memphis. Before he got through, this guy
pretty near ruined all our chances. It wasn't that he deliberately tried to ball things up, or that he did any one
thing that was so bad.

The whole trouble was that he is a white-collar man
from the city, and when he found himself down in the
swamps with a bunch of hard-boiled dirt movers, he was
lost. Everything he did was just a little bit wrong. And
all the time that I was attempting—by means of my natural
tact and intelligence—to get us in strong with old Jim
and his organization, this guy was gradually but steadily
queering everything.

In the first place, he insisted on telling everybody exactly who he was, which wouldn't have been so bad except
that he gave them his full name, which turns out to be
Edwin Reginald Fitz William. Can you tie that?

Then he started in wearing the damndest clothes—
which some store in Memphis sold him as the proper thing
for roughing it in the great outdoors. The outfit included
a cute little Norfolk jacket, golf knickerbockers, shiny
riding boots, a white shirt with a high stiff collar, and a
Tyrolean hat with a little feather in it. As far as his costume

was concerned, this feather was the last straw—or, perhaps, quill.

But even so, he might have got by if he hadn't talked so much. The tractor and the grader were delayed somewhere in shipment, and didn't arrive until late this afternoon. For two days we had nothing much to do. And Mr. Edwin Reginald Fitz William insisted on tagging around after old Jim Slanker, prattling endlessly about the advantages of Earthworm tractors and graders. I kept telling him that Jim was busy and didn't want to be bothered. I pointed out that the demonstration we were going to put on would be far more convincing than any mere line of talk. But he would not listen to me.

Old Jim held onto himself for a long time. Evidently he did not want to get rough with a man who was a guest at his camp. But his irritation kept increasing. Twice on Monday afternoon he quietly advised Edwin to shut up. Early this morning—Tuesday—he told him fairly loud that he had better shut his face. And just before lunch, he not only yelled at him in a very loud voice and told him to shut his face but also pushed him out of the office and slammed the door.

This kept the poor sap quiet for several hours. But when the tractor and the grader finally arrived on a freight car, late this afternoon, he rushed up to Jim's office to announce the glad news. And, in spite of the fact that Jim was busy with one of his engineers, he started a long oration about all the wonderful things the tractor was going to do tomorrow.

So Jim just took him by the collar, stuck the end of his gun into his back, marched him down to the station, put him on the evening train for Memphis, and told him that, if he ever showed his nose around here again, he would shoot him just like a rabbit. And as the train pulled out, old Jim turned to me and said that I could stick around as long as I behaved myself.

"But," he added, "if you ever bring down any more

of these babbling white-collar friends of yours, I will throw you out, just like Fitz William."

So that was that. And now I think you can appreciate my consternation when I received—a few minutes after Mr. Fitz William's departure—your telegram announcing that you were coming down here. And I think you will understand my insistence that you stay right where you are. The presence, for only two days, of one white-collar man has almost ruined my chances here. The arrival of another would cause the entire deal to blow up with a loud report.

And even if you were going to be a help instead of a hindrance, your presence would be totally unnecessary. I am perfectly competent myself. Considering the circumstances, I have accomplished a whole lot already. Of course, up to this time, all my efforts to get in strong around here have been neutralized by the egregious asininities of the sap from Memphis. On the other hand, however, I have not aroused any active antagonism. And now that the big annoyance has gone home, my pleasing personality will begin to get in its work. The demonstration of the tractor and grader, which I expect to start tomorrow morning, will naturally be a tremendous help. And before long I shall doubtless have old Jim eating out of my hand.

But even this is not all. In addition to my direct approach to Mr. Jim Slanker, I have already started a cautious reconnaissance with a view to making a sort of flank attack.

This plan is based on my previous experience with a great many other hard-boiled bozos. I have found that these people always have a soft spot somewhere. The tougher they are, the more apt they are to have someone closely associated with them upon whom they lean for advice and counsel. Perhaps you remember old man Higginson in Omaha. Several of our bright salesmen had been chasing him for years—and they never got anywhere, because he wouldn't buy anything without the O. K. of his chief mechanic, who was such a shy, retiring lad that none of the boys knew he existed until I came along and put over a sale by working on him instead of on the old man.

Of course, it is not always the chief mechanic. Sometimes you have to see the guy's wife. Sometimes he has a woman secretary who is hired to run the office, but who also runs pretty much the whole business, including the boss. Sometimes, of course, the boss makes all his own decisions without consulting anybody. But in the case of Mr. Jim Slanker, I have a very strong hunch—and my hunches are almost always right—that there is somebody in his organization who has the inside track and can make or break this sale.

As soon as I discover this power behind the throne, I will start working on him, or her, as well as on the old man, and the sale will go through as easy as a toenail through a sock.

There isn't even any competition from rival tractor companies; up to this time, no other salesmen have penetrated this far into the swamps. So all you have to do, Henderson, is stop worrying and leave everything to

Your thoroughly competent representative,
ALEXANDER BOTTS.

P. S. I hope you won't be offended at my telling you so positively not to come down here. My advice is based on a sincere desire to further the best interests of the Earthworm Tractor Company. And all my remarks have been made in a spirit of the greatest possible friendliness. No one, Henderson, has a greater admiration for your sterling qualities than I. And there is no one who appreciates more fully your brilliancy and efficiency as the executive head of the sales department of the Earthworm Tractor Company.

But you have got to admit that your proper place is at the factory. Your natural sphere of operations is the office, not the field. You spend so much time in a swivel chair that you are just a pants polisher, a white-collar city slicker and, as such, totally lacking in that adaptability which is so necessary for a man who expects to succeed in the field.

I, on the other hand, am the ideal field man—the quintessence of adaptability. When I am in the swamps, I am just like a little duck. When I am in the Rockies, I am like a mountain goat. And when I am in the Arizona Desert, you could not tell the difference between me and a Gila monster. Furthermore, when it comes to handling tough guys like Jim Slanker, I am there. So you had better just stay home, Henderson, and leave this job down here to a bozo that understands it.

NIGHT LETTER TELEGRAM

EARTHWORM CITY ILL

AUG 25 1932

ALEXANDER BOTTS
SOUTH GUMBO MISS

YOUR LETTER RECEIVED STOP DONT WORRY ABOUT MY BEING OFFENDED STOP I KNOW EXACTLY HOW YOU FEEL STOP WHEN I WAS A SALESMAN MYSELF IN THE OLD DAYS I USED TO HAVE THE SAME DISTRUST OF THE MAN WHO WAS THEN SALES MANAGER STOP DONT WORRY ABOUT MY SPOILING THINGS IF I COME DOWN STOP I DONT CLAIM TO BE SO ADAPTABLE THAT PEOPLE WOULD MISTAKE ME FOR A DUCK GOAT OR GILA MONSTER BUT BEFORE I WAS SALES MANAGER I SPENT MANY YEARS IN THE FIELD AND SUCCESSFULLY HANDLED MORE TOUGH GUYS THAN YOU HAVE EVER SEEN STOP HOWEVER I AM VERY BUSY HERE AND IF YOU ARE ABSOLUTELY SURE YOU CAN SWING THIS DEAL I MAY NOT COME DOWN STOP WILL LET YOU KNOW DEFINITELY IN A FEW DAYS

GILBERT HENDERSON

ALEXANDER BOTTS
SALES PROMOTION REPRESENTATIVE
EARTHWORM TRACTOR COMPANY

METHODIST EPISCOPAL HOSPITAL,
VICKSBURG, MISSISSIPPI,
Saturday, August 27, 1932.

MR. GILBERT HENDERSON,
SALES MANAGER,
EARTHWORM TRACTOR COMPANY,
EARTHWORM CITY, ILLINOIS.

DEAR HENDERSON: Your telegram was forwarded from South Gumbo, and has reached me down here at the hospital. I wanted to write to you before, but I have not been feeling so good. Today, however, for the first time, I am pretty comfortable. So I will now give you all the news.

On Wednesday morning I put on my scheduled tractor and grader demonstration, using one of Mr. Slanker's mechanics as tractor operator. Everything went swell. As we rolled along through the canebrake, plowing up the tough gumbo soil and casting it onto the site of the new levee, I could see that both Mr. Slanker and the operator were deeply impressed. Neither one of them had ever before seen our new and improved models at work.

The real excitement, however, came during the noon hour, in the form of an incident which proves that I was right when I told you in a former letter that this is a tough country, and no place for a city slicker.

At exactly twelve o'clock I stopped the tractor, and Jim Slanker and the operator and I sat down to eat our lunch beside a big two-yard steam shovel, which had been opening up a drainage ditch, and which had just stopped work for the noon hour. We had hardly seated ourselves before there suddenly appeared, on the other side of the steam shovel, four men from the gang who had been working at the camp. They were huge, gorillalike creatures. They were drunk. And they were in an ugly mood. Two of them had knives. The others had pick handles. Advancing in a compact group, they began a highly threatening and somewhat incoherent demand for higher wages.

Now, it is a basic principle down here in the swamps that a contractor must never show any weakness or stand for any foolishness from his workmen. If he does, his prestige is gone and he is done for. It was obviously up to Jim Slanker to do something. And he did. He was the only one of us who was armed, and he promptly pulled out his gun and ordered the four gorillas to go back where they belonged.

Unfortunately, however, they were too drunk to know what they were doing. They kept slowly advancing upon us, coming around from behind the huge dipper of the shovel, which was resting on the ground. Again Jim shouted a warning. They paid no attention. It seemed only a question of seconds before he would start firing.

At this critical juncture—and I may say that of all the junctures I have experienced, this was by all odds the most critical—I suddenly got an idea. In less than a second I figured out a comprehensive plan for the handling of this dangerous situation. And almost in the twinkling of a gnat's eyelash, I not only put this plan into action but carried it through to a triumphant conclusion. Truth compels me to admit that immediately afterward I blundered into an idiotic and disgusting anticlimax. But that does not alter the fact that the main part of the show was a real honey—one of the cleverest and most sensational performances which has ever been pulled in the entire history of the dirt-moving business.

And the whole thing was so charmingly simple that it was over in less than one-tenth of the time it takes to tell it. I sprang to my feet. I cast from me the remains of the ham sandwich on which I had been gnawing. Quickly but silently I climbed into the cab of the shovel, where a glance at the gauge showed me that the steam pressure was O. K. Standing at the controls, I watched the four menacing workmen. They were all bunched up together. They scowled. They threatened. They advanced. They moved around in front of the dipper.

And then I launched my attack. With a single flip of the wrist I sent the huge dipper lunging forward, neatly scooping them up; and then, swinging the dipper, with them in it, high in the air, I brought it to rest at a point about forty feet above the surface of the ground.

Jim Slanker and the operator were so astounded by this sudden change in the situation that they seemed unable to comprehend what had happened. So I called out to them, assuring them that everything was now all right.

"You don't have to worry any more," I said. "I have got those babies where they can't hurt anybody. All you have to do is talk to them in a fatherly manner, and I think they will see the error of their ways."

At this point, four bewildered faces appeared, looking over the rim of the dipper. And never have I seen people change so completely in such a short time. My little gesture with the steam shovel had produced a psychological as well as a physical effect. The suddenness and unexpectedness of the thing had been such a shock to the four victims that all the fight was gone out of them. They were helpless, and they knew it. The dipper was too high for them to jump out, and they were in such a state of nervous collapse that they didn't dare try to crawl down along the boom. In other words, they were completely humbled, ready to beg for forgiveness and do anything that Jim Slanker asked them. My modest effort had been crowned with complete success.

As I stepped down from the steam shovel, I was so filled with pride and admiration for myself that I fear I did not pay sufficient attention to where I was stepping. And this, as it turned out, was just too bad. My foot slipped, and I fell heavily to the ground. The drop was not more than three feet, but my foot got doubled under me in some way, and as I landed I sustained an injury which later turned out to be a broken ankle. It was a most distressing and idiotic ending for my great and heroic exploit.

Jim Slanker acted splendidly. Leaving the operator to deal with the four workmen, he rushed me in his car all the way down here to the hospital at Vicksburg, and he did not return to South Gumbo until the broken bone had been set and I had been put to bed.

There is not much more to tell. The doctor says the fracture is a simple one, and will heal up as good as new. By this time I am comfortable enough, but I will have to stay in bed a week or two longer. This is, naturally, very annoying, as I ought to be back at South Gumbo.

However, I have a feeling that everything will come out all right, in spite of my absence. Yesterday I got a letter from Jim Slanker saying that his operator is continuing the demonstration. Mr. Slanker wants to run the tractor for at least a week longer in order to find out whether it can keep on moving dirt at the same rate at which it started out.

Mr. Slanker says that his operator finally released the four men, after giving them a terrific bawling out. He says they were so cowed that he is sure they will never make any trouble again.

Incidentally, Mr. Slanker is highly grateful for my part in the affair. "If it had not been for you," he writes, "I would have had to shoot those bums. And shooting is always messy; it makes a lot of trouble, excites the rest of the help, and causes a lot of extra work digging graves. I was too dumb to think of anything else. But you have brains. And any guy who can go up against four of these critters, drunk and waving knives and pick handles, and, by using a steam shovel, handle them gently and almost tenderly, yet with complete firmness—any guy that can do that is a real man. So I take off my hat to you, Mr. Botts."

In closing, I may say that I consider this a very touching tribute. I think I will save Mr. Slanker's letter for my grandchildren.

No more at present.

As ever,

ALEXANDER BOTTS.

TELEGRAM

EARTHWORM CITY ILL
AUG 29 1932

ALEXANDER BOTTS
METHODIST EPISCOPAL HOSPITAL
VICKSBURG MISS

SORRY TO HEAR OF ACCIDENT AND HOPE EVERYTHING IS GOING WELL STOP WISH YOU HAD NOTIFIED ME SOONER STOP I AM LEAVING AT ONCE FOR SOUTH GUMBO TO TAKE CHARGE OF DEMONSTRATION STOP WILL GO BY WAY OF MEMPHIS AND SEE FITZ WILLIAM STOP PLEASE WIRE ME THERE ANY INFORMATION YOU FEEL MIGHT BE HELPFUL STOP IN A FORMER LETTER YOU MENTIONED THE POSSIBILITY THAT THERE MIGHT BE SOMEONE IN SLANKERS ORGANIZATION WHO WOULD HAVE DECISIVE INFLUENCE WITH HIM IN THIS DEAL STOP PLEASE LET ME KNOW WHAT YOU FOUND OUT AND ADVISE WHAT YOU THINK WOULD BE MY BEST PLAN OF ACTION

GILBERT HENDERSON

TELEGRAM

VICKSBURG MISS
AUG 29 1932

GILBERT HENDERSON
CARE EDWIN REGINALD FITZ WILLIAM
MEMPHIS TENN

I GOT FULL DOPE ON SLANKERS ORGANIZATION BEFORE I LEFT SOUTH GUMBO STOP THE PERSON FOR YOU TO SEE IS

MISS FLORA HIGGINS MR SLANKERS SECRETARY WHO IS IN CHARGE OF HIS MAIN OFFICE IN MEMPHIS STOP GET IN TOUCH WITH HER AT ONCE AND STAY WITH HER UNTIL YOU HAVE HER COMPLETELY SOLD ON EARTHWORM TRAC- TORS AND GRADERS

ALEXANDER BOTTS

TELEGRAM

MEMPHIS TENN
SEPT I 1932

ALEXANDER BOTTS
METHODIST EPISCOPAL HOSPITAL
VICKSBURG MISS

ARRIVED IN MEMPHIS DAY BEFORE YESTERDAY STOP HAVE SPENT MOST OF MY TIME SINCE TRYING TO SELL MISS FLORA HIGGINS ON THE IDEA OF EARTHWORM EQUIPMENT BUT WITHOUT ANY TANGIBLE RESULTS STOP I AM BEGINNING TO HAVE VERY GRAVE DOUBTS AS TO THE WISDOM OF THIS COURSE STOP ARE YOU ABSOLUTELY SURE ABOUT THIS WOMANS INFLUENCE IN DECIDING ON TRACTOR PURCHASE STOP DO YOU STILL ADVISE MY REMAINING HERE AND FOL- LOWING THIS LINE STOP WIRE REPLY

GILBERT HENDERSON

TELEGRAM

VICKSBURG MISS
SEPT I 1932

GILBERT HENDERSON
CARE EDWIN REGINALD FITZ WILLIAM
MEMPHIS TENN

YOUR TELEGRAM RECEIVED AND I HASTEN TO ASSURE YOU THAT I HAVE ABSOLUTELY NO DOUBTS WHATEVER REGARD- ING MISS HIGGINS INFLUENCE ON SLANKER STOP I CANNOT HOWEVER GIVE DEFINITE ADVICE AS TO YOUR COURSE OF ACTION WITHOUT KNOWING EXACTLY WHAT YOU HAVE

ACCOMPLISHED SO FAR STOP PLEASE SEND ME A FULL AND
DETAILED ACCOUNT OF EVERYTHING YOU HAVE DONE STOP
I WILL THEN BE IN A POSITION TO TELL YOU WHAT TO DO
NEXT STOP FOR THE PRESENT WOULD ADVISE THAT YOU
CONTINUE PRESENT TACTICS MAKING EVERY EFFORT TO
GET MISS HIGGINS ON OUR SIDE   ALEXANDER BOTTS

Sept. 1, 1932.

MR. ALEXANDER BOTTS,
METHODIST EPISCOPAL HOSPITAL,
VICKSBURG, MISSISSIPPI.

DEAR BOTTS: Your telegram is received, and I
may say that I do not share your complete confidence in
this scheme of selling tractors to a hard-boiled dirt mover
by working through his woman secretary. When you first
proposed this idea, I was somewhat skeptical. But I realized that you had pretty thoroughly gone over the ground
down here, and that you should, therefore, have a better
grasp of the situation than a newcomer. So, with considerable reluctance, I decided to follow your advice. The results, up to this time, have not been reassuring.

However, I will follow your suggestion and give you
a brief account of what I have done, and then I wish you
to write me at once, explaining definitely all the facts which
led you, in the first place, to believe that Mr. Slanker's
secretary would have a deciding influence in this deal. And,
after I have described the discouraging aspect of things
here, I want you to let me know whether you still think
it advisable for me to continue this line of action.

I arrived in Memphis day before yesterday—Tuesday—and spent practically all the afternoon at Mr.
Slanker's office showing Miss Flora Higgins pictures and
diagrams of our tractors and graders, and explaining their
advantages.

Miss Higgins was cordial enough—in fact, she was
almost too cordial—but she did not make a favorable im-

pression on me. Just as you said, she is in full charge of the office here—not only that, she seems to be the entire office force—and she is young, and energetic, and good-looking. But it is hard for me to believe that she would have much influence on a man who is thinking of buying a lot of expensive machinery. She just doesn't have the brains.

All the time I was showing the pictures and explaining the specifications, her attention kept wandering to other matters. About the only contribution she made to the subject under discussion was to say that she thought the tractor was "just too darling for words," and the grader was "as cute as a bug's ear." Most of her conversation had to do with her various boy friends, the parties and dances she had attended in the past and was expecting to attend in the fuure, and her ambition to go to Hollywood and become a motion-picture actress. Finally, she invited me to go to a party with her that night. Not wishing to seem lacking in cordiality, I accepted—though not without considerable misgiving.

The party turned out to be even worse than I had feared. She brought along a group of her more or less half-witted boy and girl friends, and we put in a rather noisy but incredibly tedious evening at a distinctly low-grade speakeasy. Somehow, a man like myself, who is almost fifty years old, is married and has three grown children, seems to be out of place raising whoopee with the younger generation. However, I did the best I could. When the party broke up, everybody seemed to expect me to pay the bill, and so I did. It was $76.50, including tips.

Well, that would be all right, if it actually helped put over this deal. But I am not at all sure that it will. And my doubts are getting stronger all the time. Yesterday, and again today, I wanted Miss Higgins to come out with me to see a tractor demonstration which Fitz William has arranged to put on for her benefit. But I couldn't even get hold of her to tell her about it. Honestly, I am at a loss to know what she does with all her time—spends it with her worthless boy friends, perhaps. She is hardly ever at the office. I called there twice yesterday and once this morning, and each time the place was closed up.

Finally, late this afternoon, I found her in. But all I got out of it was another fool invitation. She wants me to go on a party tomorrow night where, she says, I will meet members of some of the most aristocratic families in Memphis. She claims that she herself belongs to one of the important old families; she says they used to be very rich, but lost all their money during the Civil War. For this reason, she says, it is perfectly thrilling for her to meet a man like me who has so much money and is such a dear about spending it.

The more this woman talks, the less I like her. But she is so insistent about my attending this party that I have finally agreed. I only hope that you were right about her having the inside track with old Slanker; I would certainly hate to think I was sacrificing myself in vain. I can't imagine how this fool woman could have any legitimate influence over a man like Slanker, but maybe she has something on him, so that she can scare him into doing what she wants. I hope so, anyway.

Please answer this letter at once, and give me the complete and authentic dope on this business. Maybe you had better wire me; I'll go crazy if I keep up this foolishness much longer.

Yours,
GILBERT HENDERSON.

TELEGRAM

VICKSBURG MISS
SEPT 2 1932

GILBERT HENDERSON
CARE EDWIN REGINALD FITZ WILLIAM
MEMPHIS TENN

DELIGHTED WITH YOUR LETTER STOP KEEP RIGHT ON STOP
YOU ARE GOING SWELL

BOTTS

CARE MR. E. R. FITZ WILLIAM,
EARTHWORM TRACTOR DEALER,
MEMPHIS, TENNESSEE,
September 3, 1932.

MR. ALEXANDER BOTTS,
METHODIST EPISCOPAL HOSPITAL,
VICKSBURG, MISSISSIPPI.

DEAR BOTTS: Never, in all my experience in the tractor business, has anyone given me a line of advice so completely worthless as what you have been handing out the past few days. I don't like to be too hard on a man who is in the hospital, but a broken ankle does not excuse you for losing your brains. Every bit of information you have given me has turned out to be absolutely and completely wrong. And it is now up to you to do something—and do it quick—to get us out of the mess which you are responsible for. As a result of my believing your inaccurate statements and following your stupid advice, it now appears that we have got in so wrong with Mr. Slanker that this whole tractor deal may fall through. Incidentally, you have caused me a tremendous amount of annoyance and personal inconvenience, not to mention expense.

The party which Miss Higgins gave last night was

much worse than the other one. We went to a speak-easy that was much more disgusting. The members of our party were much louder. And the bill was considerably higher— amounting in this case to $121.25, including tips. But even that was not the worst of it.

Immediately after I had paid this outrageous sum, the establishment was raided by the police, and all the guests, including myself, were taken to the station house, where we were forced to spend the few hours that remained of the night. In the morning, the judge, after giving us a most insulting talk, turned us all loose.

By slipping out in a hurry, I was able to shake off Miss Higgins. But later in the morning she called me up at Mr. Fitz William's office to request a loan of fifty dollars. She said that Mr. Jim Slanker had made a rush trip up from South Gumbo to find out what had happened to a number of important letters he was expecting. When he found that all his mail had been lying around the office for two weeks, he was pretty sore—which Miss Higgins considered most unreasonable. She admitted that it was her business to forward these letters, but she said he ought to realize that anyone is liable to make a mistake.

He also accused her of neglecting all her other duties, and she says she excused herself by telling him that she was looking after his interests by spending all her time with Mr. Henderson, of the Earthworm Tractor Company. His answer to this was a remark to the effect that "this guy Henderson had better not show up around here again, if he does, I'll knock his block off."

After making this statement, Mr. Slanker told her she was fired, paid her off, marched her out of the office, locked the door, and left for South Gumbo. Miss Higgins went on to tell me that, although she is perfectly furious at Mr. Slanker, she is, in some ways, rather glad to lose her job. She is tired working, and this will give her a chance to take a little vacation trip up to St. Louis to visit one of her girl friends who has recently married. It appears that the girl friend's husband has money, so Miss Higgins thinks she can live on them very comfortably for weeks to come. But it will take a certain amount of cash to get up to St. Louis—hence the request that I lend her fifty dollars. In refusing this request, I made it pretty clear that we were through with each other forever. So I don't have to bother about Miss Higgins any more—thank the Lord.

But there still remains the mess which she leaves behind here. And what a mess! This woman, whom you in your ignorance believed to be so important, and upon whom, following your advice, I wasted more than three days' time and more than two hundred dollars in cash, is now fired in a way that indicates she never did have any importance. And this is not all. In passing out of the picture, the dizzy dumb-bell bleats around in such a foolish way that she contrives to get me in wrong, and make me look completely ridiculous in the eyes of this important prospect, Mr. Jim Slanker.

The whole thing leaves me in a quandary. I, naturally, hesitate to go down to South Gumbo at the present time. Any attempt which I might make to approach Mr. Slanker would be so handicapped by Miss Higgins' advance publicity about me that I should probably accomplish more harm than good. But something has to be done. And, as long as you are responsible for all this trouble, you will have to do it.

Broken leg, or no broken leg, you will have to straighten things out somehow. If you cannot go to South Gumbo yourself, you will have to get in touch with Mr. Slanker and fix it up in any way you can, so that I can go down there and meet him under favorable conditions. We must get his order.

I shall expect, by return mail, a full account of the steps you are taking to remedy your blunders.

Very truly yours,
GILBERT HENDERSON.

ALEXANDER BOTTS
SALES PROMOTION REPRESENTATIVE
EARTHWORM TRACTOR COMPANY

METHODIST EPISCOPAL HOSPITAL,
VICKSBURG, MISSISSIPPI,
Monday, September 5, 1932.

MR. GILBERT HENDERSON,
CARE MR. EDWIN REGINALD FITZ WILLIAM,
MEMPHIS, TENNESSEE.

DEAR HENDERSON: Your letter, telling about the grand finale of your romance with little Miss Flora Higgins, is here. And it is a masterly effort. The other letter, telling about the beginning of the affair, was good too. But nowhere near as interesting and exciting as this last one.

I am sorry, however, that you have permitted yourself to get into such a worried state of mind about this tractor deal and everything. You take these things so seriously, and you seem to get all wrought up about them.

What you ought to do is try to act more like me. Here I have been flat on my back in a hospital for more than a week, and all the time I have maintained my usual bright and optimistic attitude toward life. My cheery wise cracks have been, and still are, a joy and an inspiration to all the nurses. On the other hand, you have been lapping up the night life of the great city, frisking about under the white lights, flitting from party to party, and in general acting the part of the little playboy of Memphis. Anybody would think you would be overjoyed at your good luck. But no; all you do is growl and complain.

And you have worked yourself into such a state of mind that you are accusing me of a lot of mistakes which I never made. As a matter of fact, I haven't made any mistakes at all. Every bit of the information I gave you has been correct. And all my advice has been perfectly sound.

For instance, I told you that I believed there might be someone behind the scenes in Mr. Slanker's organization who would have great influence over him in the purchase of equipment. This turned out to be true. The power behind the throne is the mechanic who drove the tractor in the demonstration I started.

I never told you that Miss Flora Higgins had any drag with the old man. I merely advised you to stop off in Memphis and see her. And I stated the exact truth when, a little bit later, I wired you, "I have absolutely no doubts regarding Miss Higgins' influence on Slanker." Of course, I had no doubts. Mr. Slanker had told me himself that the office at Memphis was of no particular importance—being used only for the storing of records and the forwarding of mail—and that Miss Higgins was merely a girl whom he had hired cheap about a month before.

In advising you to call on this woman, I did not delude myself into thinking that you would accomplish anything constructive. I merely wanted to keep you pleasantly occupied in Memphis for a few days, and thus avoid the unfortunate consequences that would have resulted if you had persisted in going down to South Gumbo and inflicting your presence, white collar and all, on Mr. Jim Slanker and his operator. I will admit that my method of keeping you in Memphis was slightly disingenuous, but you must remember that you had already disregarded my previous direct warnings. I had to keep you out somehow. And it was lucky I did so.

I have just received a letter from Mr. Jim Slanker. He mentions his little trip up to Memphis, and then he says, "I just fired my stenographer. I find she had been neglecting her work to run around with some boob from the Earthworm Tractor Company by the name of Henderson. Apparently he is even more of a wet smack than that other guinea pig—Fitz William, or whatever his name was. It beats me how a company that makes such a swell tractor, and hires such a good man as you, could stand for any such washouts as these two."

So you see how it is, Henderson. If you could annoy and disgust old Jim to this extent without coming any farther than Memphis, it stands to reason that your presence at South Gumbo would have driven the old guy pretty near insane, and just naturally knocked all our chances on the head.

As it is, everything is working out swell. You had a taste of gay city life. Flora and her friends had a merry whirl with a guy that turned out to be a good spender. Old Jim and his operator had a chance to carry on the demonstration undisturbed, and my stay in the hospital was brightened up tremendously by those two charming letters of yours. In fact, the only trouble was that I laughed so hard while I was reading them that I almost fell out of bed and broke my leg all over again.

Mr. Slanker's letter, in addition to discussing his Memphis trip, states that he has completed the tractor demonstration, and that both he and his operator are completely satisfied. He has signed and mailed to me an order, which I had previously made out, for twenty-five sixty-horse-power tractors and ten elevating graders. He has added one condition to this order. He wants me to be there to take charge of the delivery of this machinery, and he specifies definitely that the Earthworm Tractor Company must agree, as part of the contract, to keep Messrs. Fitz William and Henderson out of his neighborhood from now on.

Very sincerely,
ALEXANDER BOTTS.

COÖPERATION

ALEXANDER BOTTS
SALES PROMOTION REPRESENTATIVE
EARTHWORM TRACTOR COMPANY

QUITTYQUINK HOTEL,
QUITTYQUINK COVE, MAINE.
Monday Evening, June 26, 1933.

MR. GILBERT HENDERSON,
SALES MANAGER,
EARTHWORM TRACTOR COMPANY,
EARTHWORM CITY, ILLINOIS.

DEAR HENDERSON: I arrived in this little seaport town this morning, and immediately ran into a situation which fills me with joy and hope. It looks to me, Henderson, as if the depression is definitely licked. And I want you to know that I am doing everything in my power to see that it stays licked. I believe that the best way to encourage and strengthen this new flood of prosperity is for all of us business men to work together, forgetting our old-time suspicion and distrust of each other, and putting our shoulders to the wheel like one great, happy family. I have been much disappointed to note that you boys at the home office have been very slow in getting together with the other tractor manufacturers and drawing up a code by which you can do business in a reasonable and public-spirited way. I trust that you will be inspired to move a little faster when I tell you of the wonderful venture in coöperation which I am initiating in this locality.

As soon as I arrived in town this morning, I followed my usual procedure of calling on the local Earthworm tractor dealer to find out how I could best assist him in pepping up his sales. Unfortunately, the dealer was sick in bed, so I decided to take entire charge of his business for a few days.

I started in by inspecting the office and showrooms, and was pleased to find that the dealer has in stock one of our latest seventy-five horse-power Diesel tractors equipped with our new power-driven logging winch. My next step was to buzz about town and pick up information. I discovered that the lumber business in this region is definitely improving; before long, it may be possible for us to sell a lot of tractors for logging operations. I also discovered that we may have a certain amount of competition from one of the natives here—a very energetic gentleman by the name of Ezra Litchfield, who has the local agency for the Emperor tractor.

And then, toward the end of the morning, I ran into some really exciting news. Just by accident, I happened to meet a man by the name of Russell Jones, who is staying here at the hotel, and who told me a most interesting story.

Mr. Jones is an inventor, a designer of airships, and the chief engineer of the Detroit All-Metal Dirigible Corporation. He is up here working on a deal by which his company expects to sell an airship.

The prospective purchaser is Mr. T. Henry Mott, a big millionaire from New York, who has an elaborate estate covering the whole of Quittyquink Island, which is four miles long, two miles wide, and lies just off the coast here. It seems that Mr. Mott, back in 1928, bought a small dirigible, or blimp, which he used for commuting back and forth from New York. In 1930, he lost a lot of money, and had to sell the blimp for reasons of economy. But he still has an adequate landing field on the island, and a large hangar.

During the last few months, his business has been improving so fast that he has decided to buy a new airship, and Mr. Jones' company has sent one on from Detroit to New York to give him a demonstration. The demonstration will be a trip from New York up here—leaving New York next Thursday morning, and arriving here sometime Thursday afternoon. Mr. Jones came on ahead to get enough men for a ground crew and make all arrangements so that the ship may be properly landed and put in the hangar. He is all in a dither about it, because this is the first chance they have had to sell an airship for years, and and Mr. Mott has already told them that if he decides to buy it he will pay cash—which will mean exactly two hundred thousand dollars in their treasury. You can imagine my excitement when I heard this.

"Good Lord!" I said. "If people are actually buying two-hundred-thousand-dollar airships for cash, it must be that we are entering upon real boom times."

"He hasn't bought it yet," said Mr. Jones.

"If he is even considering such a thing," I replied, "it shows that times have changed. I should think, though," I continued, "that he would be better off with an airplane —which would probably be a lot cheaper, and also a lot faster."

At this remark, Mr. Jones looked very scornful indeed. Apparently, he is a nut on the subject of dirigibles. "Airplanes are all right for cheap sports," he said. "But a man of Mr. Mott's wealth would naturally prefer to spend a little more and get something really worth while. If he buys our ship, he will have a luxurious yacht with a large cabin, four attractive staterooms with wide and luxurious beds, ample kitchen and dining accommodations, with all accessories. The ship has a maximum speed of eighty miles an hour. So he will be able to come up from New York in less than five hours. This is fast enough. He can spend the evening in New York, going to bed any time he feels like it, have a refreshing night's sleep, and awake in the morning up here. Or he can make the trip in a single morning or a single afternoon—cruising along in a pleasant and civilized manner, admiring the scenery, conversing with friends, reading books, enjoying the radio, dictating letters, or occupying his time in any way he wishes."

"Couldn't he do that in a plane?" I asked.

"Certainly not," said Mr. Jones. "In a plane he would be bumped and bounced along over the air pockets, deafened by the roar of the motors, and half shaken to pieces by the vibration. His limbs would be numb and cramped from sitting in a small and highly uncomfortable seat, and the nauseating motion would have his stomach in a state of open rebellion."

"Well, well, Mr. Jones," I said. "You seem to have a sales talk that is as good as anything we tractor salesmen can hand out. I have ridden in airplanes quite a bit, and I always thought I was having a good time. But now that you have given me the real dope on the subject, I'll never be satisfied with anything less than a real airship."

"Any airship—even an ordinary one—is better than an airplane," said Mr. Jones. "And our all-metal ships are the best of all. They are, in fact, the last word in aëronautic construction. Instead of covering the aluminum framework with a fabric envelope, which is subject to leaks and rips, and which rapidly rots away on exposure to the weather, we use an envelope made of a new aluminum alloy which is as light as a feather, as tough as steel, and can be rolled out into sheets of a paper-like thinness. Constructed of this splendid material, our ships are lighter and also stronger than the older fabric affairs; they are leakproof, fireproof, weatherproof, and practically indestructible. The cost of upkeep is practically nothing."

"You don't know how you interest me," I said. "Are there any of these all-metal airships in existence?"

"So far," said Mr. Jones, "there are only two in the entire world—the one which we are now trying to sell to Mr. Mott, and another somewhat smaller one which was bought some time ago by the United States Navy. But in ten years there will probably be as many of them in the air as there are now ships in the ocean."

"And don't they have any disadvantages at all, aside from the expense?" I asked. "Aren't they rather clumsy things to land?"

"Any large ship is clumsy in port," said Mr. Jones. "An ocean liner requires tugboats to bring it into the dock. And an airship needs a ground crew to haul it into the hangar. This is, of course, a certain disadvantage—especially up here, where I am having trouble in hiring enough people. To be perfectly safe, in case next Thursday is a windy day, I ought to have at least a hundred men. Quittyquink Cove is such a small town that I'm afraid I'll have to bring some in from outside, which will mean a lot of expense at a time when our company is trying to economize. Also, I may have some trouble in getting a hastily gathered gang of men to work together."

At this point, it suddenly came over me that Old Man Opportunity himself had arrived at the door and was knocking loudly. I did not keep him waiting. "I should think," I said, "that instead of a lot of puny human beings, you could use a large tractor to haul this airship into its dock."

"Of course, I could," said Mr. Jones. "But I would need a pretty big one, and I couldn't afford to buy it just for one landing. Besides, the ship is arriving Thursday; it is too late now to send off and get a machine."

"Listen, Mr. Jones," I said, "I represent the Earthworm Tractor Company. I have a splendid, brand-new, seventy-five horse-power Diesel Earthworm tractor right here in town. It is equipped with our latest three-speed reversible power winch. This is the finest tractor ever built in this or any other country. If you say so, I will take it over to the landing field and operate it as a tugboat to pull your big ship into its dock. I won't charge you a cent, and I will guarantee satisfaction. This tractor weighs more than a hundred men, and can pull harder than five hundred. By running a line through the winch, we can pull in or slack off at will. Our control will be perfect. What do you think of the idea?"

"It sounds fine," said Mr. Jones, "and it's most generous of you to do it for nothing."

"It is not generosity," I said. "It is coöperation. I assist you in making a good landing, and this will help you in selling your airship. You give me a chance to show Mr. Mott what my tractor can do, and this will help me sell him the tractor as a part of the necessary equipment for his landing field. By working together and helping each other, we each gain greater advantages than if we worked alone. Isn't it beautiful?"

"It sounds all right to me," said Mr. Jones. "We really ought to have two tractors, though—one for the bow and one for the stern."

"I am sorry," I said, "but I have only one machine available. I'm afraid you'll have to get along with that."

"Very well," he replied. "I accept your proposition, and I thank you."

We shook hands. Then I asked him to keep the matter a secret, and took my departure.

I did not tell Mr. Jones why I desired secrecy. The idea, of course, is that Mr. Ezra Litchfield, the local Emperor tractor dealer, has one large machine in stock, and I don't want him horning in on this party—especially as Mr. Jones had indicated that he would welcome the help of a second tractor.

In closing, I wish to emphasize the importance of this new coöperative movement which I am starting. By working hand in hand with the airship industry, I am opening up an entirely new market for Earthworm tractors. If Mr. Jones ever succeeds in his plan of putting as many airships into the air as there are now steamships in the ocean, we shall be able to sell a truly fantastic number of tractors to tow them in and out of their houses when they come to earth.

I will keep you informed as to my progress.

Most sincerely,
ALEXANDER BOTTS.

ALEXANDER BOTTS
SALES PROMOTION REPRESENTATIVE
EARTHWORM TRACTOR COMPANY

QUITTYQUINK HOTEL,
QUITTYQUINK COVE, MAINE.
Tuesday Evening, June 27, 1933.

MR. GILBERT HENDERSON,
SALES MANAGER,
EARTHWORM TRACTOR COMPANY,
EARTHWORM CITY, ILLINOIS.

DEAR HENDERSON: You will be delighted to learn that I am extending the scope of my coöperative efforts over a field much greater than that described in my letter of yesterday. I am now coöperating, not only with the airship industry, but also—believe it or not—with Mr. Ezra Litchfield, the local selling agent of the Emperor Tractor Company. The idea of one tractor salesman actually coöperating with a rival tractor salesman is so novel, so unheard of, and so incredible, that I will have to explain the circumstances in some detail in order that you may understand why I embarked upon this remarkable enterprise, and so that you may appreciate the advantages which it will bring us. The whole thing came about because of an unforeseen difficulty which I ran into this morning.

Right after breakfast I began making inquiries as to the best way to take my tractor over to Mr. Mott's island. And you can imagine my shocked surprise when I discovered that there did not seem to be any practicable way to do this. There is no boat in this small fishing port capable of transporting a twelve-ton, seventy-five horse-power Earthworm tractor. And even if we brought in such a boat from somewhere else, there is no adequate pier or dock from which we could load the tractor onto the boat. The local seafaring men seem to think that I would have to drive the tractor half-way around Penobscot Bay to Belfast, and ship it from there. Besides being expensive, this might take three or four days—which would never do at all, as the airship is expected day after tomorrow.

In the hope of finding some way out of this dilemma, I went over and inspected the channel which separates Quittyquink Island from the mainland. At its narrowest point, it is almost a quarter of a mile wide. The bottom is nice, smooth gravel. But the water, even at low tide, is twenty feet deep, so it would be impossible to drive the tractor across.

As all of the more obvious methods for getting the tractor to the island were useless, I got the old bean working, and finally cooked up a plan of action which is somewhat unusual, but which seems to be the only way in which I can successfully overcome the difficulties of this somewhat peculiar situation. To carry out my plan, I would need two tractors, and this presented a momentary difficulty, owing to the fact that I had only one. The only other tractor in town was the Emperor machine belonging to Mr. Ezra Litchfield. I had hoped to keep this gentleman out of the affair entirely. But I absolutely had to have his tractor, so I went around to his office and generously offered to let him coöperate with me.

Mr. Litchfield, I am happy to say, turns out to be a very high-grade individual. I have had a great deal of experience in sizing up men, and I could tell from the virile way in which he shook hands, and from the frank and steady way he looked me in the eye, that he is a man of rugged honesty and great strength of character. Besides being the local Emperor tractor dealer, he holds the office of county sheriff, which shows that he is well regarded in the community. And he is a worthy son of illustrious forbears, being descended from a long line of New England sea captains—sturdy souls who, in days gone by, carried the Stars and Stripes to every seaport in the world and made the name "American" synonymous with courage, skill and enterprise.

As soon as I had introduced myself to Mr. Litchfield, I began a carefully prepared inspirational talk. "Mr. Litchfield," I said, "I represent the Earthworm Tractor Company, and I have just discovered a hot prospect for a tractor. Under the old cutthroat methods of doing business, I would have kept this information to myself. But under the New Deal, I feel that we should all work together as a band of brothers. And I am, therefore, inviting you to come along with me."

I then explained all about the airship and the wonderful opportunity it offered for a tractor sale. Mr. Litchfield was very much interested, and he thanked me most cordially for my remarkable generosity in sharing this great opportunity. After acknowledging his thanks in a graceful manner, I explained the difficulties of transporting ʒ tractor to Mr. Mott's island, and outlined my plans for overcoming these difficulties.

"I have made arrangements," I said, "with one of the local hardware and ship-chandler establishments to rent me a half a mile of two-inch rope and a large pulley. Tomorrow morning we will drive our two machines down to the shore at the narrowest point of the channel which separates Mr. Mott's island from the mainland. We will take the pulley and one end of the rope in a dory, and row across to the island. We will fasten the pulley to a tree at the edge of the beach. We will pass the end of the rope through the pulley and bring it back to the mainland in the dory. Do you follow me, Mr. Litchfield?"

"I think so," he replied. "You mean you are going to run this rope from the mainland across the channel to Mr. Mott's island, through a pulley, and then back to the mainland. Is that it?"

"Exactly," I said. "We will then remove from your tractor the magneto, the tools, the seat cushions, and all accessories which might be damaged by salt water. We will plug up the intake and exhaust pipes, the crank-case breather pipe, and all openings which might permit water to enter the machine. We will hook one end of the rope to the front of your tractor. The other end of the rope we will fasten to the rear of my machine. I will then drive straight inland, pulling your tractor under water along the bottom of the channel, and over to the island. As soon as this is accomplished, we will row across in the dory, install the magneto and other accessories on your machine, clean out any water which, in spite of our precautions, may have worked into the mechanism, and crank up the motor. Then you will pull my machine over to the island. What do you think of the idea?"

"It is most remarkable," said Mr. Litchfield. "Did you think this up all yourself?"

"No, indeed," I said. "It is an old trick in the tractor business. It is tested and tried. Mr. Luke Torkle, one of our oldest and most experienced service mechanics, once told me that he used this method as long ago as 1912 to get two Earthworm tractors across the Congo River in Africa. The same method has been used on various occasions in this country by both tractors and motor trucks. And I have been told that in 1918 a whole fleet of tanks were taken in this way across the Meuse River near Sedan. Of course, it is a rather unusual procedure. But I am sure, Mr. Litchfield, that a man like yourself, who is descended from a long line of venturesome sea captains, would not permit himself to be scared out of an undertaking merely because it is a little unusual."

"It is all right with me," he said. "If you are willing to risk your tractor, I am willing to risk mine."

"Mr. Litchfield," I said, "you are a man after my own heart. I can see that we are destined to get along together fine. It is going to be a real pleasure to coöperate with you. I will now wish you good-by until tomorrow morning."

With these words, I took my departure and came back to the hotel, where I informed Mr. Jones, the airship man, that I had arranged, for his especial benefit, to have two tractors instead of one. He was, naturally, very much pleased.

In case you have not grasped all of the finer and more subtle points in the arrangements which I am making, I wish to point out that my method of coöperation is so designed as to give us as many advantages as possible. In outlining my plans to Mr. Litchfield, I was careful to state that his tractor would be pulled across the strait first. As he made no objection to this at the time, I am reasonably certain that he will let me proceed in this manner. Although I am confident that my scheme for towing tractors under water will work, I feel that it will be much better to experiment a bit with Mr. Litchfield's machine before trusting our beautiful Earthworm beneath the salt sea waves.

If everything works out all right, and we are successful in our demonstration with the airship, the sale, of course, will be right in the bag for the Earthworm.

Mr. Litchfield's Emperor tractor is a fairly good machine—almost as good as the Earthworm of five years ago. But now that we have our splendid new Diesel model with its remarkable peformance and low fuel cost, there just is no comparison at all. Mr. Litchfield won't have one chance in a thousand of selling his machine. Thus, I have worked out a scheme of coöperation that is practically perfect— Mr. Litchfield will do half the work, and I will make the sale.

Yours for more and better coöperation,

ALEXANDER BOTTS.

ALEXANDER BOTTS
SALES PROMOTION REPRESENTATIVE
EARTHWORM TRACTOR COMPANY

QUITTYQUINK COUNTY JAIL,
CELL NUMBER 2,
QUITTYQUINK COVE, MAINE.
Wednesday Afternoon, June 28, 1933.

MR. GILBERT HENDERSON,
SALES MANAGER,
EARTHWORM TRACTOR COMPANY,
EARTHWORM CITY, ILLINOIS.

DEAR HENDERSON: My plans have had a terrific setback, and for the moment I am helpless. But I have not given up hope. Tomorrow morning I expect to be out of jail again, and we shall then see who is to come out on top in this deal.

The unfortunate situation in which I now find myself is due entirely to the fact that my generous and honorable efforts in coöperation were shamelessly taken advantage of by a man whom I considered my friend, but who has turned out to be an unscrupulous and crafty enemy. It is all very distressing, especially in view of the fact that everything seemed so promising this morning when I started my great experiment in the submarine transportation of tractors.

Mr. Litchfield and I arrived with our machines on the shore opposite Mr. Mott's island at about eight A.M., along with several dozen sight-seers from the town who had come out on foot and in boats.

The work of running the rope over to the island, passing it through the pulley, bringing it back, and then preparing Mr. Litchfield's machine for its underwater journey, took a little more than an hour. And at exactly a quarter past nine, I hooked onto one end of the rope, opened up the motor, and slowly but steadily drew the Emperor tractor into the water. Everything worked beautifully, and at twenty-five minutes after nine a spontaneous cheer arose as the machine emerged from the waters and rolled up onto the gravel beach on the other side of the strait.

Mr. Litchfield and I then rowed across to the island and worked for about an hour cleaning the salt water out of every last crack and crevice in the tractor, and installing the magneto and other accessories. At half-past ten we cranked the motor, and it started up with a roar. After Mr. Litchfield and I had congratulated each other on this happy result, I rowed myself back to the mainland, leaving Mr. Litchfield and his tractor on the island. I spent about half an hour in making the Earthworm shipshape for its voyage. I then tied the big rope to the front cross member of the frame and signaled to Mr. Litchfield to go ahead.

I saw him fasten his end of the rope to the drawbar of the Emperor tractor, and then put the machine in motion. The rope tightened, the Earthworm went rolling out into the water, and I hopped into the dory and rowed along right ahead of it.

For a while, everything seemed to go all right. But when the Earthworm reached the middle of the channel— where the water was about twenty feet deep—its forward motion abruptly ceased. The water was so deep that I could not see whether or not it had met some obstacle. In fact, all I could see of the tractor itself was a dim and quivering shadow far down in the watery depths. Looking over toward the island, I noticed that Mr. Litchfield had stopped his machine and got down out of the seat. After waiting for five minutes—during which time nothing happened—I rowed on over to the island, beached the dory, and walked up the shore to the point where Mr. Litchfield was standing beside his tractor. About a dozen of the sightseers from town were gathered around him.

"What's the matter?" I asked. "Has your tractor quit on you?"

"Oh, no," Mr. Litchfield replied. "The old baby is working fine."

"It doesn't seem to be accomplishing much," I said. "I hope my Earthworm hasn't run into a hole, or got so tangled up in the seaweed that you can't pull it."

"No, indeed," he said.

"Then what's the trouble?" I asked. "Why did you stop?"

At this point Mr. Litchfield smiled at me. But it was not a pleasant smile; it was more in the nature of an evil leer.

"There is no trouble at all," he said. "The only thing that has happened is that I have changed my mind about this demonstration."

"What do you mean, you have changed your mind?"

"It has just occurred to me," he said, "that one tractor ought to be enough to pull Mr. Mott's airship into the hangar. If we try to use two, we'll just be getting in each other's way and spoiling the whole demonstration. So, as long as we won't need your Earthworm machine, there is no reason for bringing it over here. It will be much better to leave it in its present location—where it is perfectly safe —until after the airship has landed. As soon as the demonstration is over, we will start figuring on how to tow it back to the mainland."

As he spoke these words, Mr. Litchfield smiled even more broadly than before. And never in my life have I seen a more obnoxious and repulsive smirk.

Now, I am not by nature a violent man. As well you know, Henderson, I have always been noted for my sweetness of disposition and my magnificent self-control in the face of all the usual annoyances which form a part of the life of a tractor salesman. But the fiendish ingenuity and monumental effrontery of this poisonous reptile were a little too much even for me. For the moment, I fear I lost control of my temper. But this did not in any way interfere with my sense of timing, or with my muscular coördination. After a brief wind-up, I made a long and graceful swing and landed my right fist, with the entire weight of my body behind it, just below Mr. Litchfield's left eye.

A theoretical moralist might argue that I should not have acted in this hasty and brutal manner. But, on the whole, I am glad that I did so. Even now—several hours after the event—when I recall the dull but magnificent thud with which my knuckles came in contact with that evil visage, I am filled with a feeling of indescribable satisfaction.

However, there have been certain other consequences of my act which are not so pleasing. In the excitement, it had momentarily slipped my mind that Mr. Litchfield was the county sheriff. He was not long in reminding me of this fact however. After staggering about for a moment or two, he began yelling for help. A half a dozen of the bystanders grabbed me before I could get in a second blow, and Mr. Litchfield informed me that I was under arrest for assault and battery, attempted murder and resisting a peace officer.

Two of the men who were holding me turned out to be deputy sheriffs. Acting under Mr. Litchfield's orders, they marched me down to the shore, loaded me into a motorboat, brought me back here to town and locked me in the jail—where I am still languishing, and where, they tell me, I will have to continue to languish until I am taken before the justice of the peace at nine o'clock tomorrow morning.

The jail is modern and sanitary, and from my window I have a very pleasing view, looking out over the ocean and Mr. Mott's island. I am comfortable enough, but it is, naturally, most annoying to have to sit around doing nothing when I ought to be working hard on the difficult problem of getting that tractor out of the ocean and preparing it for tomorrow's demonstration.

I am not licked yet however. As soon as I explain the situation to the justice of the peace tomorrow, he will see that my affair with Mr. Litchfield comes under the classification of justifiable, and even praiseworthy, assault. He will discharge me, probably with the thanks of the court. I will then start rushing around to see if I can work out some scheme for getting my tractor the rest of the way to the island. If I cannot accomplish this before the airship arrives, I will be on hand myself anyway, and I will be prepared to give Mr. Mott a description of the advantages of our Diesel Earthworm tractor that will just naturally compel him to start reaching for his fountain pen and looking for the dotted line.

I can produce a sales talk that will be better than anybody else's sales talk and demonstration combined. It will be especially easy this time, because I am always more eloquent when I am mad. And right now I am just about as mad as I ever get.

This whole affair just goes to show that you cannot trust anybody who is descended from a long line of New England sea captains. It is a matter of common knowledge that these Yankee skippers used to sail all over the world, swindling each and every man with whom they did business, and giving to the name "American" an unsavory reputation in every land which they visited. With such ancestry, it is no wonder that Mr. Litchfield is about as low as they make them. As a matter of fact, I was suspicious of him from the first. Whenever you meet a man who shakes hands in an unnecessarily hearty and virile manner, and who goes out of his way to look you straight in the eye, you can be sure he is doing it to cover up a very ripe state of inward corruption. A final touch is added by the fact that Mr. Litchfield is county sheriff—a sure indication that, in addition to his other vices, he goes in for dirty politics.

In the past he has apparently been successful in his nefarious schemes. But in locking horns with me, he will find that he has picked up a bigger cat than he can swing. Just wait until I get out tomorrow.

Later. Next morning. Thursday.
10 A.M. June 29, 1933.

What a world this is! When a man is down, everybody starts to kick him. As I wrote you yesterday afternoon, I confidently expected to get out of jail this morning. A little while ago, however, one of the deputies came in and said the justice of the peace had decided to postpone my hearing until tomorrow. The old duffer was so afraid that he might miss the thrilling spectacle of the landing of the dirigible—scheduled for this afternoon—that he went over to the island at about five A.M. He is going to camp over there until the airship appears. This, at least, is the explanation given me by the deputy. But the whole thing smacks of the Machiavellian hand of Mr. Ezra Litchfield, the dirty skunk. He has probably brought his slimy influence to bear upon this justice of the peace in order to keep me out of the way and give him a clear field for his own demonstration and sales talk.

The whole thing is an outrage, but I have not been able, so far, to do anything about it. Last night I talked on the telephone with Mr. Jones, the airship man, and begged him to help me. But he claimed he could do nothing, and seemed to take very little interest in my case. All he cares about is getting his airship landed properly. He is going to use Mr. Litchfield's tractor, and he forgets entirely that I am the guy that thought of the whole idea in the first place. As I could get nothing out of him, I called our local Earthworm dealer, but all I could get out of him was a request to stop bothering him while he was sick, and a statement that he intended to sue me for losing his tractor in the bottom of the ocean.

This is a bad business. It is bad for me, but it is even worse for Mr. Mott. He will see the Emperor tractor pulling the dirigible into the shed, and after listening to Mr. Litchfield's guileful and misleading sales talk, he will probably buy it. Naturally, I feel the deepest sympathy for poor Mr. Mott. If I could help him, I would do so. But just at the moment I seem to be pretty well blocked.

Later. 3 P.M.

I have just been watching, from the window of this admirably located jail, the landing of the great all-metal airship. The old baby came gliding in out of the mists of the Atlantic, circled once over the island, and then settled gracefully down onto the landing field, its aluminum sides gleaming in the afternoon sunshine. It was a truly inspiring and magnificent sight, but I was in no proper state of mind to appreciate it.

I borrowed some field glasses from the deputy in charge of the jail—I am the kind of guy that even when I am in jail, I make friends with the jailer—and with these glasses I was able to see the details of the landing very clearly. I could see a line thrown down from the bow of the airship and fastened to the Emperor tractor. Another line was thrown down from the stern of the ship, and this should have been fastened to my tractor. But, as my tractor was not there, it was grabbed by a crowd of bystanders. Probably Mr. Jones had hired them for this purpose. I saw the tractor and the people start across the field, with the great ship floating along above them. There was practically no wind. Slowly and majestically the ship moved to the open doors of the hangar, and then disappeared inside. The landing was perfect.

I don't know whether Mr. Mott has decided to buy the airship. If he has, it is very probable that he is, at the very moment, arranging with the nefarious Mr. Litchfield for the purchase of one or more of those unspeakable Emperor tractors. And here I am, with my tractor at the bottom of the ocean, and myself locked up in jail.

The situation is enough to drive a man insane. If I ever have to go through another afternoon like this, they will have to put me in an asylum rather than a jail.

But there will be no more such afternoons in my life.

From now on I am through with coöperation. Never again, at any time, at any place, will I ever, for any reason, coöperate, or even attempt to coöperate, in any way, with any person, in any manner whatsoever. I have learned my lesson.

> The next day. Friday Noon.
> QUITTYQUINK HOTEL,
> QUITTYQUINK COVE, MAINE.

Well, I am out of jail again—having been turned loose about nine o'clock last evening.

The circumstances surrounding my release were, on the whole, rather remarkable. I had just about made up my mind that I would have to spend another night in the lock-up, and I was just starting to get undressed preparatory to going to bed. As I was untying my shoes, humming gently the melancholy strains of The Prisoner's Song, two visitors arrived—Mr. Jones, of the airship company, and Mr. Mott, the big millionaire.

Mr. Jones was all in a twitter, announcing loudly that Mr. Mott had decided to buy the airship, and wasn't it wonderful? He seemed to be highly enthusiastic—as well he might. Mr. Mott, who was a very intelligent and forceful-looking person, seemed to be calm and unconcerned. My own condition might be described as morose.

Mr. Jones explained that Mr. Mott, having observed the beautiful black eye which, it appears, is now a most conspicuous feature of Mr. Ezra Litchfield's face, had expressed a desire to see the man who was responsible for it.

"So that's it," I said. "He comes to peer at me through the bars of my cage as if I were some strange animal at the zoo."

"Don't get insulted," said Mr. Jones. "He also wants to talk business with you."

"Yes," said Mr. Mott. "I will need two tractors to handle my dirigible here. And, after thinking over the interesting demonstration which you and Mr. Litchfield put on, I have decided that I want Earthworm machines."

"Say, that's swell!" I said. "But I don't understand about the demonstration. I wasn't there, and the Earthworm tractor wasn't there. You haven't even seen my machine, unless you caught a glimpse of it down under twenty feet of water as you came over from the island."

"I'm not talking about the machines," said Mr. Mott. "I'm talking about you and Mr. Litchfield personally."

"But what have we got to do with it personally?"

"Everything," said Mr. Mott. "Mr. Jones here has seen both your tractors, and he tells me that either make is good enough to handle the airship. As far as the machines themselves are concerned, one would be as satisfactory to me as the other."

"Oh, no, it wouldn't," I said. "If you had seen the Earthworm in action ——"

"It wouldn't have made any difference," Mr. Mott interrupted. "You see, Mr. Jones has told me all about the way you got Mr. Litchfield's tractor to the island, and what happened afterward. And that, to me, is the most important part of the demonstration."

"You mean you like to deal with a company that has bright men working for it, and you were impressed by the clever way I got that big tractor across the channel?"

"No," said Mr. Mott. "I was impressed by the clever way in which Mr. Litchfield stole the demonstration away from you and showed you up for a sucker by leaving your tractor way out there under water."

"You mean you are going to buy my machine because you are sorry for me?"

"Oh, no. If I buy a couple of tractors, it is probable that I will have to have a certain amount of service on them —repair work, new parts, and so on. That's right, isn't it?"

"Yes," I said.

"In other words," he went on, "as long as I own these

machines, I will have to have business relations with the man that represents the company which made them. If I bought the Emperor machine, I would have to deal with Mr. Litchfield. And he is far too clever for me. I much prefer to deal with a man like yourself, who is credulous, helpful, always ready to coöperate with the other fellow, and more or less gullible. You would not be smart enough to slip anything over on me. In fact, I could probably slip quite a bit over on you. And that is why I am buying the Earthworm, instead of the Emperor."

"Mr. Mott," I said, "your reasoning may be cockeyed, but your conclusion is sound. Your words fill me with joy. Now, as soon as I can get out of this filthy jail and figure out some method of rescuing my tractor from the ocean ———"

"That has been all arranged," said Mr. Mott, "through the coöperation of Mr. Litchfield."

"You don't mean that Mr. Litchfield is actually going in for real coöperation?"

"He has to," said Mr. Mott. "He has to get that tractor of his back to the mainland. I told him that if he would haul your tractor the rest of the way to the island, and also drop the charges against you and release you from jail, I was sure you would be willing to pull his tractor across the channel. Incidentally, I agreed to pay him a fair amount for his time and trouble in helping me land my dirigible. At first, he was pretty sore because I would not buy an Emperor tractor, but in the end he agreed to my entire proposition. Before we left the island he pulled your machine out of the water. It seems to be in perfctly good condition, so I will accept it as one of the machines which I am buying from you. On the whole, Mr. Litchfield is showing a very commendable spirit in this thing. He seems to be a good sport and a good loser."

"He ought to be," I said. "He is descended from a long line of New England sea captains—sturdy men, who had to learn how to accept success or failure, all as part of the day's work. It is natural that a descendant of such people should possess the same courage."

"Apparently, then," said Mr. Mott, "you hold no grudge against this gentleman. I take it you will be perfectly willing to pull his machine across the channel for him?"

"I should be delighted," I said. "I am always glad, at any time, to coöperate with anyone in any manner whatsoever."

"Splendid," said Mr. Mott. He then called in Mr. Litchfield, who had been waiting downstairs, and I was promptly let out of jail.

This morning I cleaned up the tractor and pulled Mr. Litchfield's machine back to the mainland. You will be glad to know that during all the time I was working with Mr. Litchfield I treated him with the most effusive politeness and consideration. This showed him what a kind and Christian disposition I have, and also had the happy result of making him madder than almost anything else I could have done.

I am now back on the mainland at the hotel. An order for one additional Earthworm is going forward through the office of the local agency. When this machine arrives, it will be taken to the island by my highly successful method of underwater transportation.

In the meantime, I will stick around here and see if I can stir up a few prospective tractor buyers in the lumber business. It is even possible that I may be able to entice Mr. Litchfield into some new coöperative scheme.

Very sincerely,
ALEXANDER BOTTS.

THE GREAT HIGHWAY CONTROVERSY

EARTHWORM TRACTOR COMPANY
EARTHWORM CITY, ILLINOIS
OFFICE OF THE SALES MANAGER

Saturday, July 8, 1933.

MR. ALEXANDER BOTTS,
BAXTER HOTEL,
BAXTER HARBOR, MAINE.

DEAR BOTTS: You will proceed at once to Belfair, Maine—where, at the moment, we have no dealer—and you will get in touch with the Belcher Lumber Company. The president of this concern has just written us that he expects, in the near future, to purchase five large tractors for logging operations.

If you hurry, you ought to be able to land this business for the Earthworm Tractor Company.

Very sincerely,
GILBERT HENDERSON, Sales Manager.

ALEXANDER BOTTS
SALES PROMOTION REPRESENTATIVE
EARTHWORM TRACTOR COMPANY

BAXTER HOTEL,
BAXTER HARBOR, MAINE.

Tuesday Evening, July 11, 1933.

MR. GILBERT HENDERSON,
SALES MANAGER,
EARTHWORM TRACTOR COMPANY,
EARTHWORM CITY, ILLINOIS.

DEAR HENDERSON: Your letter of July eighth has come, but I am so busy I have hardly had time to even read it.

I am still at Baxter Harbor. As the local dealer is sick, I am running his business for him. And you will be delighted to hear that I have just sold—or practically sold—ten of our new-model, seventy-five horse-power, Diesel tractors. The whole thing is as sudden and unexpected as it is delightful. This morning the local paper published a statement by the state highway department, saying that they are planning to build a magnificent new highway—or motor parkway, as they call it—from Baxter Harbor here to the town of Indian Bluffs, about twenty-five miles up the coast. The new road will be cut straight through what is known as the Baxter Forest—a tract of rough and densely wooded land about five miles wide, and extending along the seashore all the way from Baxter Harbor to Indian Bluffs.

As soon as I had read about this splendid project— which means lots of dirt moving and grading, and hence lots of work for tractors—I went around and called on one of the state-highway engineers, a man by the name of Dudley, who is here in town to boss the job. Mr. Dudley is rather quiet and studious-looking, but I feel that he is a good egg. Although he did not definitely commit himself, he hinted very strongly that when they started work they would need no less than ten large tractors. He also said that he considered the Earthworm the best machine for this work. So you see, the sale is practically in the bag.

Yours,
ALEXANDER BOTTS.

P.S.: I forgot to say that there is one minor feature in the situation which may interfere with our selling these tractors. The state highway commission, although it has worked out plans for this new road, has not, as yet, definitely decided to build it. It seems that state and Federal funds are available to meet the cost of construction, but before they go ahead they want to be sure that the people of the region here really want this improvement. The announcement in the paper this morning contained a complete description of the proposed highway, and stated that a public hearing is to be held on Tuesday evening, July twenty-fifth. If popular opinion is favorable, the construction will start at once. If it is unfavorable, the matter will be dropped. But I have no fears. This is a swell project, and everybody will be for it.

Very truly,
ALEXANDER BOTTS.

P.S.: Another possible obstacle to our selling these tractors is the fact that Mr. Abner Smith, the local dealer for the Emperor tractor, is making strenuous efforts to capture this business. When I arrived at Mr. Dudley's office this morning, I met Mr. Smith coming out. I was pleased to observe, however, that he looked pretty worried and discouraged. I shouldn't wonder if Mr. Dudley had told him perfectly frankly that his wretchedly constructed Emperor machine had no chance at all on this magnificent highway project. Of course, Mr. Smith will buzz around and do everything he can to make a sale. But I am not worried. With me here to present the advantages of the Earthworm, he is licked before he starts.

Yours,
ALEXANDER BOTTS.

TELEGRAM

EARTHWORM CITY ILL
JULY 14 1933

ALEXANDER BOTTS
BAXTER HOTEL
BAXTER HARBOR ME

YOUR LETTER SAYS NOTHING ABOUT GOING TO BELFAIR STOP IF YOU HAVE NOT ALREADY DONE SO YOU WILL GO AT ONCE STOP OTHERWISE WE MAY LOSE IMPORTANT ORDER

FROM BELCHER LUMBER COMPANY STOP IF YOU THINK
ADVISABLE YOU MAY ARRANGE TO RETURN TO BAXTER HAR-
BOR TO COMPLETE DEAL WITH STATE HIGHWAY DEPART-
MENT

                                        HENDERSON

                ALEXANDER BOTTS
        SALES PROMOTION REPRESENTATIVE
          EARTHWORM TRACTOR COMPANY

                BAXTER HOTEL,
                BAXTER HARBOR, MAINE.
                Friday Evening, July 14, 1933.

MR. GILBERT HENDERSON,
SALES MANAGER,
EARTHWORM TRACTOR COMPANY,
EARTHWORM CITY, ILLINOIS.

DEAR HENDERSON: Your telegram is received,
and I will get down to Belfair just as soon as I can. At the
moment, however, my presence is urgently needed here to
combat an unusually lousy trick which has just been pulled
on me by Mr. Abner Smith, the local dealer for the Emperor tractor.

Last Tuesday, as I related in my letter of that date,
this guy was making strenuous efforts to horn in on my
prospective sale to the State Highway Department. On
Wednesday, owing to the fact that he was away somewhere
on a business trip, he was forced to interrupt his activities.
But on Thursday—yesterday—he got back, and immediately started to act like a spoiled child. Having finally
recognized the fact—which he should have known from
the beginning—that he had absolutely no chance to sell
his pathetically inefficient Emperor tractors in competition
with our Earthworms, he allowed his entire mind to become permeated with envy and sullen hatred. He decided
that if he could not get this business, nobody else could

either. And as a result of his dog-in-the-manger attitude, he has initiated a malicious, but very plausible, attack on this whole highway project.

In the furtherance of his nefarious scheme, he spent most of yesterday in contacting various members of a local organization known as The Baxter Trail Club. This club is composed of nature lovers who are interested in the Baxter Forest. And although it does not own the land, it has, in a very public-spirited manner, constructed a trail from one end of this woodland to the other, and built small overnight cabins every few miles for the accommodation of anyone who wants to get out into the wilderness.

Mr. Abner Smith, by working upon the natural pride which the club members have in their trail, has succeeded in convincing them that a motor highway through the forest would completely ruin the usefulness of this dinky little footpath. In fact, he has been so successful with his falsehoods, misrepresentations and distortions of truth that he has succeeded in getting these good people worked up into a state of almost frenzied excitement and indignation. Not only are they opposing the highway by word of mouth among their friends but they have started bursting into print.

When I opened the paper this morning, the first thing I noticed was a rather plaintive letter from the president of the Baxter Trail Club, who, it appears, is a well-meaning but doddering old gentleman by the name of Quackenbush. Mr. Quackenbush, after dwelling at great length on the unspoiled beauty of the Baxter Forest, the "cool dark shade of the giant trees," and "the spiritual peace which comes only through close communion with nature," expressed the pious hope that this "primeval sanctuary" might be spared from the desecration of a motor road.

Mr. Quackenbush's remarks were pretty weak and sentimental, but they made me nervous. When a man has a sale of ten tractors hanging in the balance, it doesn't take much to upset him. As I read on through no less than six similar letters from other members of the club, my nervousness increased. And when I finally came to a communication from the arch conspirator, Mr. Abner Smith, himself, I was seriously alarmed. In order that you may understand my feelings, I will quote the letter in full.

"I have just been informed," wrote Mr. Smith, "that some demented engineer is actually proposing to build a vile motor highway through the very heart of the Baxter Forest. This vast wilderness—this peaceful refuge from all the nerve-racking noise and hurry of our modern machine-made civilization—this holy temple of Mother Nature—is to be 'improved' by a vast strip of concrete pavement so that speed-maddened motorists may drive their roaring machines through glades which once knew no sound but the delicate footfall of the deer and the sweet piping of the wood thrush. The very air of the forest, now heavy with the scent of pines, is to be befouled with the noisome stench of thousands of exhaust pipes, while the peace of the ages will be rent by the incessant honking of motor horns. And, worst of all, every hillside will blossom forth with unspeakable billboards and advertising signs. Every valley will sprout a poisonous, mushroom growth of miserable tourist cabins. And the entire landscape will be dotted with sordid hot-dog stands and mephitic filling stations.

"The colossal effrontery of this ghoulish scheme is enough to make one's blood boil. It is a nightmare of commercial sordidness. And every right-thinking man and woman in the entire state of Maine should rise up in active opposition to the barbarous marauders whose one purpose is the destruction of all that is fair and beautiful."

When I had finished reading the above letter, I was —as I have already stated—considerably alarmed. My nervousness in regard to the ten tractors I am hoping to sell became so pronounced as to be almost painful. Mr. Abner Smith's arguments, of course, were completely cockeyed, but they were expressed so strongly that I was afraid a certain number of people might take them seriously. In

order to check up on the state of public opinion, I made
a tour of the local garages and filling stations, which in
recent years have largely taken the place of the old general stores as forums for the discussion by the natives of
all matters of general interest.

The results of this tour—which occupied most of
the day—were not reassuring. Almost everybody seemed
to sympathize with Mr. Quackenbush, who apparently is
a rather nice old duffer and is highly regarded in the community. In addition, I heard many expressions of admiration for the snappy way in which Mr. Abner Smith handles
the English language. There seemed to be a very definite
trend of public opinion opposing the new road.

Having ascertained this fact, I called late this afternoon on Mr. Dudley, the state engineer who is in charge
of the proposed highway project. He seemed surprised
and distressed at the sudden hostility to his plans. But
when I asked him if he was making any effort to rally
public sentiment in our favor he replied, rather weakly,
that he had not yet decided what action he ought to take.

"The public doesn't seem to understand what we are
trying to do," he said, "in spite of the fact that we have
already published a complete explanation of our plans.
The only thing I can think of would be to explain the
whole thing over again. But if they didn't understand it
the first time, they probably wouldn't the second time."

"Mr. Dudley," I replied, "you may be a good engineer.
But as a molder of public opinion, you are rotten. Something, however, must be done. And as you are doing nothing, I will have to appoint myself director of publicity for
your splendid project. I will now sally forth and start a
counter-attack against our enemies. Good day."

And before he could even thank me, I rushed away
and came back to the inn here, where I have been planning
out a vigorous and powerful publicity campaign. Tomorrow
morning I will go into action with all the energy I possess,

and by the time I get through with my opponents they will
be just laying about in heaps.

Yours,
ALEXANDER BOTTS.

TELEGRAM

EARTHWORM   CITY   ILL
July 17 1933

ALEXANDER BOTTS
BAXTER HOTEL
BAXTER HARBOR ME
HAVE YOU BEEN TO BELFAIR YET QUESTION MARK

HENDERSON

ALEXANDER BOTTS
SALES PROMOTION REPRESENTATIVE
EARTHWORM TRACTOR COMPANY

BAXTER HOTEL
BAXTER HARBOR, MAINE.
Monday Evening, July 17, 1933.

MR. GILBERT HENDERSON,
SALES MANAGER,
EARTHWORM TRACTOR COMPANY,
EARTHWORM CITY, ILLINOIS.

DEAR HENDERSON: In reply to your telegram,
which has just been received, I beg to advise that I have
been unable, as yet, to go to Belfair. But don't worry. I
will rush down as soon as I possibly can—probably about
the end of next week. In the meantime, I am working early
and late on my publicity campaign against the opponents
of the great new highway. This campaign is based on the
principle that the best defense is a vigorous attack.

In planning my offensive, I have entirely disregarded
the published letters of Mr. Quackenbush and the other

members of The Baxter Trail Club. The complaints of these gentlemen, being mere sentimental tripe, offer very little opportunity for brilliant rebuttal. I am, therefore, concentrating my artillery on a vulnerable point which my quick mind has discovered in the arguments presented in the letter which Mr. Abner Smith sent to the paper. In this letter Mr. Smith was incautious enough to speak sneeringly, not to say unpatriotically, about those sturdy and well-established American institutions, the billboard, the filling station, the hot-dog stand and the tourist cabin. And I am now capitalizing on this mistake of his in a big way.

I spent last Saturday morning on a whirlwind tour of all the local filling stations—seven in number. I carried with me a copy of the paper containing Mr. Smith's letter, and I also carried a copy of an unabridged dictionary. The dictionary was very heavy, but I was well repaid for my efforts in dragging it around. In interviewing each filling-station proprietor, I would first show him Mr. Smith's allusion to "mephitic" filling stations. I would then open the dictionary, and point to the definition of "mephitic"— "poisonous; pestilential; foul; noxious; skunklike." In every case this got a good reaction. And by noon I had organized all the filling-station proprietors into a protective trade association; I had written out and persuaded them to sign a statement for the paper which contained a violent denunciation of Mr. Smith's gratuitous insult to an honest and useful business, and expressed their enthusiastic approval of the new highway on the ground that it would increase local prosperity.

In the afternoon, I succeeded in organizing the owners of various tourist cabins and refreshment stands, and prevailed upon them to sign additional statements in favor of the proposed road.

All of these statements, owing to the fact that I wrote them myself, were remarkable for their vigor and aggressiveness.

Having completed my work with these business men, I spent all of Sunday in contacting representatives of the general public. By Sunday night, I had persuaded fourteen different people to send letters to the paper. All of them were published this morning—Monday—and some of them were swell. I found one old codger who is a connoisseur of hot dogs. Whenever he takes a trip his main enjoyment comes from sampling the different varieties which he finds at the stands along the road. He stated that he is heartily in favor of the new highway because it is sure to mean more and better hot-dog stands.

One of the waitresses at the hotel here, to whom I had given an unusually large tip, was obliging enough to send in a letter in praise of billboards and advertising signs. She says that the handsome and distinguished young ladies and gentlemen who are so attractively portrayed in the large-sized cigarette advertisements provide her with invaluable and up-to-the-minute ideas on chic sports attire, as well as more formal dress. She also says that she took a motor trip to California last year. She reports that the Yosemite Valley is nothing but rocks and silly waterfalls. The Yellowstone is incredibly dull, and the great plains are perfectly poisonous. The one redeeming feature of the trip was the intellectual pleasure she derived from the witty wise crack on the signs put up by the Balmy Shaving Cream Company. She is highly enthusiastic over the new highway. What this part of the country needs, according to her, is more good advertising signs.

An elderly couple who drive down to Florida every winter sent in a particularly good letter, explaining that they are too old to sleep outdoors, have insufficient funds to stay at city hotels, and would be deprived of their winter vacation if it were not for the cheap tourist shacks which they find along the way.

The snappiest idea of all was a letter I wrote myself, and signed with a fictitious name. As a matter of fact, the letter was fictitious, too, but the editor of the paper never got wise, and he published it along with the rest. It read as follows:

"I am nothing but a cripple—a poor old man with one leg—but I wish to add my humble plea to the discussion of the proposed highway. For years I have been hearing of the beauties of the Baxter Forest. For years my greatest desire has been to visit this wonderful primeval wilderness. I have particularly wanted to see the great hickory tree from which, long ago, my brother cut a limb to fashion into a wooden leg for me. But, even with this leg, I am too lame to walk out over the trail. My only hope for realizing my dearest wish lies in the construction of this proposed highway. If the opponents of the plan succeed in blocking it, I want them to know that they will also succeed in breaking the heart of a poor old cripple."

I am particularly pleased with this last letter, owing to the fact that it injects a tender sentimental note into a controversy which has, of neccesity, contained a good deal of bitterness and sarcasm.

As a result of my efforts, it begins to look as if the great tide of popular opinion against the highway has been definitely stemmed. But we have not yet won the day. So I am keeping on with the good work in my usual relentless fashion. In addition to thinking up more letters for the paper, I am conducting a vigorous word-of-mouth campaign.

This morning I asked the president of the Baxter Harbor Rotary Club for permission to address their weekly meeting this noon. He stated that they already had a speaker scheduled, but invited me to attend—which I did. You can imagine my disgust when I found that the speaker was Mr. Abner Smith, himself. It appears that he is quite an effective orator in a cheap sort of way. And he is also pretty good at reciting poetry—they say he is quite famous around these parts for his rendition of The Shooting of Dan McGrew, and Gunga Din. At the meeting this noon he delivered a very emotional address on the subject of the proposed highway, which he referred to as "an attempted rape of the virgin loveliness of the wilderness." He had a lot to say about protecting "our little feathered songsters"—meaning birds, I suppose—and the "wee, furry, wild things"—referring probably to muskrats, skunks and other small mammals. And as a grand finale he recited, in a voice choked with emotion, a poem called Trees. When he sat down he had all those hard-boiled business men pretty near in tears. And I will have to admit that as I observed the effect this guy was making, and as I meditated on those ten tractors which seemed to be getting farther and farther from an actual sale, I was almost ready to weep myself.

But don't get the idea that I am discouraged. I am keeping after this thing like a professional bird lover running down a new species of feathered songster. And I want you to know that I am going to stay here on the job right up until the public hearing next Tuesday evening.

Sincerely yours,
ALEXANDER BOTTS.

TELEGRAM

EARTHWORM   CITY   ILL
July 20 1933

ALEXANDER BOTTS
BAXTER HOTEL
BAXTER HARBOR ME

WE DISAPPROVE COMPLETELY OF YOUR RECENT PROPAGANDA ACTIVITIES STOP WE WOULD RATHER LOSE THE SALE OF TEN TRACTORS THAN COMPROMISE THE HIGH REPUTATION OF THIS COMPANY BY SUPPORTING A PROJECT WHICH AIMS TO DESTROY THE NATURAL BEAUTY OF THE COUNTRY STOP THE FACT THAT THE REPRESENTATIVE OF THE EMPEROR TRACTOR IS ACTING IN AN UNSELFISH AND PUBLIC SPIRITED MANNER MAKES IT DOUBLY IMPORTANT FOR US

TO AVOID ANTAGONIZING THE MORE THOUGHTFUL MEM-
BERS OF THE COMMUNITY STOP YOU WILL DISCONTINUE
YOUR CLOWNISH CAMPAIGN ON BEHALF OF HOT DOG STANDS
BILLBOARDS AND ALL THE EYESORES WHICH UNFORTU-
NATELY CLUTTER UP SO MANY OF OUR AMERICAN HIGH-
WAYS AND YOU WILL GO TO BELFAIR AT ONCE AND CALL ON
THE PRESIDENT OF THE BELCHER LUMBER COMPANY STOP
IT IS IMPERATIVE THAT YOU GO AT ONCE TO AVOID LOSING
IMPORTANT SALE

HENDERSON

ALEXANDER BOTTS
SALES PROMOTION REPRESENTATIVE
EARTHWORM TRACTOR COMPANY

BAXTER HOTEL
BAXTER HARBOR, MAINE.
Thursday Evening, July 20, 1933.

MR. GILBERT HENDERSON,
SALES MANAGER,
EARTHWORM TRACTOR COMPANY,
EARTHWORM CITY, ILLINOIS.

DEAR HENDERSON: Your splendid long telegram
has come. I have just been counting up, and I find that it
has one hundred and thirty-four words, not counting the
address and signature. It must have cost quite a bit to send
all those words from Illinois to Maine, but it is well worth
the expense. I feel that you have hit the nail right on the
head, and I want you to know that I agree with you absolutely. You are perfectly right in your feeling that my
campaign in favor of billboards and hot-dog stands was ill-
advised. As a matter of fact, I had already come to the
same conclusion all by myself.

This change of front on my part was brought about
yesterday morning at an interview with Mr. Dudley, the
engineer who is promoting the new highway. I had called

on him to explain that I was the instigator of the great flood of letters to the paper in favor of his plan, and to receive the thanks which I supposed he would give me for my efforts in his behalf. Much to my surprise, however, he seemed far more irritated than pleased.

"I wish," he said, "that you people who engage in public controversies would take the trouble to familiarize yourselves with the facts of the case. I do not believe you even read my public statement on this new highway project."

"Well, Mr. Dudley," I said, "it was pretty long and dull, so perhaps I did only skim through it. But I got the main points."

"It does not seem to me," he said, "that the main points have been grasped by any of the people who have been rushing into print, either for or against my plan. All the discussion of hot-dog stands and billboards is aside from the point. There will be no such things on my proposed highway."

"What?" I said. "A state road without hot-dog stands and billboards? I never heard of such a thing."

"You have never heard of the difference between a parkway and an ordinary highway?"

"No, I guess not."

"In my statement to the press," said Mr. Dudley, somewhat feelingly, "which you did not even take the trouble to read, I explained that in the case of an ordinary highway the land along the sides of the road is privately owned. But in the case of a parkway it is publicly owned."

"What difference does that make?" I asked.

"All the difference in the world. The more you improve an ordinary highway, the worse it gets. The more it becomes cluttered with roadside nuisances, the more it acquires traffic hazards—crossroads and private driveways from which cars come shooting out into the main stream of traffic. But the more you improve a parkway, the better it gets. It is permanently protected from all undesirable developments."

"It sounds like a good theory," I said. "I wonder if it could be worked out in practice."

"It has been worked out already," said Mr. Dudley, "in a few roads like the Bronx River Parkway north of New York City. But we do not have enough roads of this kind. What this country needs is a complete national system of parkways to handle all through traffic, leaving the present highways for local traffic."

"You're not thinking of building this whole system right away, are you?"

"No, but I had hoped to make a start here in Maine. Our plan for the Baxter highway calls for the purchase of the whole Baxter Forest—five miles wide—as a state park. This would give more than adequate protection to the roadsides. We would have a real parkway, and as soon as people saw how good it was, they would want more. If we can only put this project through, I am sure it would start a much-needed movement for more intelligently planned highways."

"Mr. Dudley," I said, "you don't know how you impress me. Your ideas are so much better than I had supposed that I am lost in admiration at your intelligence. And I am ashamed of myself for not reading with sufficient care your statement in the paper. It is most fortunate that I came in to see you. In any controversy the people who do the talking are, of course, the most important. But it is, nevertheless, highly desirable that there be someone in the background who knows the basic facts and understands what it is all about. As a result of this interview, I am going to change my whole plan of campaign. And the change will be advantageous."

"Almost any change in your campaign would probably be a good thing," said Mr. Dudley. "But are you sure that even now you understand what it is all about? Don't you think it would be best if you were just to drop out of the controversy entirely?"

"Absolutely not," I said.

"But exactly what are you planning to do next?" he asked.

"I don't know," I said. "I am so bewildered by all these new ideas which you have given me that I will have to go back to my room and collect my thoughts. But you may be sure that I will do something. Whatever it is, it will be both sensational and effective."

Without giving Mr. Dudley time for any more protests, I took my departure and returned here to the hotel. After a prolonged period of meditation yesterday afternoon, last night and this morning, I have finally worked out a plan for my future activities.

I have resolved, for the present, to do nothing toward removing the barnacles of misinformation which have incrusted this controversy. I will let these boobs continue their great hot-dog-stand argument—which has nothing to do with the case—until the latter part of the public hearing on Tuesday. By this Fabian policy I will put myself in a very strong position indeed. I will be the only speaker at the meeting who will know what he is talking about. Mr. Dudley, of course, doesn't count; he knows his stuff, but he is no speaker.

The meeting is sure to be a lallapaloosa. I will let one opposition speaker after another holler and roar about the hot-dog stands and the billboards. The more they deepen the fog of ignorance and misunderstanding, the more they will help set the stage for me. At the proper dramatic moment, I will arise and deliver an address so weighted down with cold facts and so lifted up with warm emotion that it will act as a great searchlight of truth cutting through the murky shadows of falsehood. The entire hot-dog-stand argument will fall flat. Our opponents will be shown up as the saps which they are, and the meeting will be stampeded into a great ovation in favor of Mr. Dudley's wonderful parkway.

I have already started to write up my big speech. As long as Mr. Dudley's plan will discourage roadside nuisances and protect the wilderness by buying up the forest as a public park, I will have much to say about the wee, furry, forest folk and our little feathered songsters. And the scathing remarks which I will make about hot-dog stands and billboards will practically burn the paint off the inside of the building. This, of course, will be an exact reversal of my previous position in reference to hot-dog stands. But that doesn't bother me at all, because I am completely convinced that this time I am right. As a matter of fact, I have always disliked billboards and roadside shacks. But my point of view was temporarily distorted by the fact that I dislike even more to lose the sale of ten tractors.

Between now and the meeting on Tuesday evening I will stay right here, working on my address and keeping my ear to the ground in such a way as to be in constant touch with all phases of public sentiment.

Very truly,
ALEXANDER BOTTS.

TELEGRAM

EARTHWORM CITY ILL
JULY 24 1933

ALEXANDER BOTTS
BAXTER HOTEL
BAXTER HARBOR ME

YOUR LETTER RECEIVED STOP YOU WILL TAKE YOUR EAR OFF THE GROUND AND GET DOWN TO BELFAIR AT ONCE STOP FAILURE TO OBEY THIS ORDER WILL RESULT IN YOUR IMMEDIATE DISMISSAL

GILBERT HENDERSON

ALEXANDER BOTTS
SALES PROMOTION REPRESENTATIVE
EARTHWORM TRACTOR COMPANY

BAXTER HOTEL,
BAXTER HARBOR, MAINE.
Wednesday Evening, July 26, 1933.

MR. GILBERT HENDERSON,
SALES MANAGER,
EARTHWORM TRACTOR COMPANY,
EARTHWORM CITY, ILLINOIS.

DEAR HENDERSON: Many thanks for your telegram, which arrived day before yesterday—Monday—afternoon. From the wording of your message, I gathered that you were getting quite nervous over my delay in going to Belfair. And as I had finished writing my big speech, and had nothing really pressing until the Tuesday-night meeting, I decided I might as well follow your suggestion. Accordingly, I caught the night train to Belfair, and bright and early the next morning—yesterday—I called on the president of the Belcher Lumber Company.

As it turns out, it was a very good idea of yours to have me go to Belfair. I only wish you had been more definite in your instructions in the first place, instead of merely requesting me to go in such a half-hearted manner. Fortunately, however, you braced up and got me down there before it was too late.

My interview with the president of the lumber company was very satisfactory, and ended with his having me ejected from the office. Before he did so, however, he lost his temper a bit, and blatted out a few remarks that he now probably wishes he had left unsaid.

The whole affair was most interesting and delightful. As soon as I had introduced myself to this lumber king, I started in on a description of the advantages of Earthworm tractors. He interrupted to say that on July twelfth

he had been interviewed by Mr. Abner Smith, of Baxter
Harbor, and had promised him that if he bought any tractors they would be Emperors. This statement, of course,
only stimulated me to a greater flow of sales talk—which
seemed to irritate the big lumber man more and more.

Finally he got pretty sore. "Mr. Botts," he said, "I
have heard all about you in a recent letter from Mr. Smith.
Apparently you thought you could sell a lot of tractors to
the state highway commission by working directly against
me and in favor of that Baxter Forest park-and-highway
project, And now, when the project looks as if it would
fall through, you have the nerve to come around here
and try to sell your tractors to me. I tell you, Mr. Botts,
you can't play both ends of this thing and expect to get by
with it. I don't care to discuss the matter any more with
you."

With these words he called in the janitor—a very large
man—and had him escort me out of the building.

When I reached the sidewalk I was in a very thoughtful mood, turning over and over in my mind the somewhat
cryptic remarks of the president of the Belcher Lumber
Company. An ordinary man would probably have been
completely baffled, but I have a considerable gift for spot-
ting the ulterior motives of my fellow human beings, and
before long I began to see a faint glimmer of light. It
occurred to me that I ought to find out a little more about
the business activities of this Belcher outfit.

Accordingly, I called on the cashier of what seemed
to be the most important bank in town. I told him I was
thinking of selling the lumber company a number of tractors, and I asked if he could tell me something of their
credit rating and business standing. The cashier assured
me that their credit was very high, and he very kindly gave
me a copy of their annual report for stockholders, published about a month ago. Most of the stockholders reside
in the city of Belfair. So it is probable that no one in Bax-

ter Harbor—with the possible exception of Mr. Abner Smith—had seen or heard of this report.

As soon as I had read it, I decided that I had better be getting back here. I hurried down to the railroad station and caught a train which got me to Baxter Harbor last night just in time for the big public hearing on the highway project.

At the beginning of the meeting the chairman announced that all speakers would be limited to five minutes. This handed me a pretty heavy jolt, as the address which I had so carefully written out was designed to take up about an hour and three-quarters, not counting a long postscript which I had written on the train, and which discussed the Belcher Lumber Company.

For some time after the chairman had announced his outrageous gag rule, I was unable to collect my thoughts. All I could do was to sit there in more or less of a daze and contemplate with sorrowful eyes the voluminous manuscript which I had prepared with so much loving care. I heard very little of the first few speeches, which was probably just as well, as they were made by a lot of incredible nitwits—including Mr. Quackenbush and Mr. Abner Smith—and consisting almost entirely of ignorant and irrelevant remarks about hot-dog stands and billboards. Finally Mr. Dudley, the engineer, arose, and by that time I was able to concentrate sufficiently so that I could pay attention to his remarks.

Much to my surprise, he spoke very well—stating clearly and simply all the facts which he had given me in our interview some days ago. Most of the audience seemed very favorably impressed.

After Mr. Dudley finished speaking I decided it was up to me to do something. I arose, secured the recognition of the chairman, regretfully tossed my monumental manuscript out of a near-by window, and stated that I would first read a very interesting paragraph from the annual report of the president of the Belcher Lumber Company, and that I would then explain to them exactly why Mr. Abner Smith had been so active in his opposition to the Baxter Forest highway-and-park project. The paragraph from the lumber company's report was as follows:

"Last year, when prices were at rock bottom, your directors quietly secured options on various tracts of timber land, amounting to approximately forty thousand acres, and comprising about half of what is known as the Baxter Forest, situated just north of the town of Baxter Harbor. There is now a proposal that the state of Maine condemn for park purposes the entire Baxter Forest, including the land on which we have options. A decision in this matter is expected within a few weeks. If the proposal goes through, our options will be void. If not, we will immediately take up this land and start lumbering operations. As the timber is mature and very high grade, we expect to utilize more than 90 per cent of the trees. And as the purchase price will be very low, and as the price of the lumber is going up, we expect to realize a very handsome profit."

After I had finished reading this paragraph, there was an excited buzz of conversation. And, much to my surprise, Mr. Abner Smith leaped from his seat, rushed over to where I was standing, and began whispering excitedly into my left ear.

"What are you going to tell them about me?" he asked.

"It was my intention," I said, "to inform them that if the highway project fell through, so that the lumber company could go ahead and destroy the Baxter Forest, you had the promise of a very fat and profitable order for the sale of five big Emperor tractors."

"But you can't tell them that!" he said. "They would misunderstand. They would think I was not sincere in opposing this highway. They would think I did it just to make a profit."

"Well, you did, didn't you?" I asked.

"Yes, but it would never do to tell these people about

it. They are my neighbors and friends. They would think I was a crook and a hypocrite. It would ruin my reputation forever. You wouldn't want to do that. Think of my wife and children."

"Well," I said, "what do you want me to do about it—just lay down and let this highway be defeated?"

"No," he replied. "If you'll just keep your mouth shut, I'll explain this thing in my own way, and I'll make a speech that will be better for your side than anything you could do."

"All right," I said with my characteristic magnanimity. "I am not a man who harbors grudges. I have no desire to ruin you. I will give you a chance to see what you can do. And your speech had better be good. If it is not, I will just naturally spill your beans all over town." Having said this, I sat down. And Mr. Abner Smith addressed the meeting.

The first part of his speech was pure fiction, but the latter part was fairly sensible. "In the matter of this parkway project," he said, "I have been actuated by the highest and most unselfish motives. My one desire has been to preserve the wild life and the natural beauty of this region. But I now realize that I was completely misinformed as to the facts. I did not know that this project would be free from all roadside nuisances. I did not know that the alternative to the proposed highway and park would be the complete destruction of our beautiful forest. But now that I have heard Mr. Dudley's clear explanation of his plans, and now that my very dear friend, Mr. Alexander Botts, has divulged the nefarious plans of the Belcher Lumber Company, I must reverse my position. I realize that the only way to save the forest is to make it a state park. And I recognize the fact that if all the people are taxed to create this park, it will be only fair to have a road so that all the people can use it; without a road, it would be limited to those who have the time and physical strength to walk over the trail.

"We nature lovers who use the trail must remember that there are other sincere nature lovers who cannot use it on account of age, infirmity, or other reasons. We must not be so selfish as to deny the enjoyment of the wilderness to such people as the unfortunate one-legged man whose letter you have no doubt read in the paper. Furthermore, a road of the kind Mr. Dudley proposes would be no more of a desecration of the wilderness than the trail which is already there. Accordingly, Mr. Chairman, I move that this meeting pass a resolution in favor of the proposed Baxter Forest highway and park."

After Mr. Smith sat down, the resolution was promptly seconded by Mr. Quackenbush, the senile president of the Baxter Trail Club. Before a vote could be taken, there were several irate protests from a number of my friends in the filling station and hot-dog business, who were completely disgusted when they found out that they had been supporting a highway which would offer no opportunities for their respective businesses. But they were a hopeless minority, and the resolution was passed overwhelmingly.

That was last night. This morning the state-highway people at Augusta gave their final approval to the highway project. And this afternoon Mr. Dudley signed the inclosed order for ten seventy-five-horse-power, Diesel Earthworm tractors.

Yours,
ALEXANDER BOTTS.

GOOD NEWS

EARTHWORM TRACTOR COMPANY
EARTHWORM CITY, ILLINOIS

Interoffice Communication

Date: Wednesday, September 5, 1934.
To: GILBERT HENDERSON, PRESIDENT.
From: ALEXANDER BOTTS, SALES MANAGER.
Subject: Good news.

This is just a brief note to let you know that I am planning to be out of town for a while, and that I want you to look after my office work while I am away.

The cause of my sudden departure is a telegram just received from Mr. Sam Blatz, studio manager of Zadok Pictures, Inc., Hollywood, California. Mr. Blatz states that he is about to produce a motion picture called The Tractor Man Comes Through, with that well-known star, Buster Connolly, in the title role. The picture calls for twelve large tractors and twelve elevating graders. Mr. Blatz would like to use Earthworm machines. But they must be delivered in Hollywood within a week; otherwise he will have to employ equipment furnished by the Behemoth Tractor Company.

Naturally, I am getting after this business with all the energy I possess. It means not only a big sale but also a chance for us to get a truly stupendous amount of swell publicity. Imagine having our tractors and graders appearing in a motion picture which will be seen by millions of people all over the country, and throughout the world as well!

I am having shipped, this afternoon, twelve eighty-horse-power Earthworm tractors and twelve elevating graders on a special through-freight train which should reach California by next Monday. And, as this deal is too important to trust to our Los Angeles dealer, I am starting for the Coast tonight by plane.

You may rest assured that I am embarking on this venture with the greatest enthusiasm. After more than a month of dull office routine, I find myself with an irresistible yearning for action and excitement. And there ought to be plenty of both in Hollywood.

Don't forget to look after my job while I am gone. As it is only a little more than a month since I took your place as sales manager, on the occasion of your elevation to the presidency, you ought to remember enough about the sales work to get by all right.

As ever,

ALEXANDER BOTTS.

P. S.: I wanted to tell you personally about this great opportunity. But when I called at your office a few minutes ago, your secretary informed me that, in spite of the fact that this is Wednesday, not Saturday, you had departed for an afternoon on the golf links. So I am forced to give you the glad news in this written communication, which you will probably read sometime tomorrow—provided you should happen to drift into the office.

A. BOTTS.

EARTHWORM TRACTOR COMPANY
EARTHWORM CITY, ILLINOIS

Office of Gilbert Henderson, President

Air mail. Thursday, September 6, 1934.

MR. ALEXANDER BOTTS,
Care ZADOK PICTURES, INC.,
HOLLYWOOD, CALIFORNIA.

DEAR BOTTS: On my arrival at the office this morning, I found your communication of yesterday awaiting me. I wish you the best of luck in your attempts to make this important sale. And I will look after your work during your absence.

However, I wish to point out, for your guidance in future, that your place, as sales manager, is here. Actual selling work in the field should be left to our dealers and salesmen. Furthermore, I wish to remind you that it is not the policy of this company to go to the heavy expense of shipping large orders way across the country until a sale has actually gone through. And unless you have previously consulted me, I do not want you ever again to rush off this way on the assumption that I will handle your office work for you.

Please hurry back as soon as possible.

Very sincerely,
GILBERT HENDERSON.

HOLLYWOOD-PLAZA HOTEL
HOLLYWOOD, CALIFORNIA

Air Mail.   Saturday afternoon,
September 8, 1934.

MR. GILBERT HENDERSON, PRESIDENT,
EARTHWORM TRACTOR COMPANY,
EARTHWORM CITY, ILLINOIS.

DEAR HENDERSON: Your letter is received. I want you to know that I appreciate your doubts as to the wisdom of my procedure in shipping the tractors and graders ahead of time and in coming out here myself. Also, I can understand your reluctance to take over the work of my office in addition to your own heavy duties as president of the Earthworm Tractor Company. But when I explain what I have already accomplished out here, and what I am planning to accomplish in the future, you will see that my course has been entirely justified, and you will be very glad to do your part by carrying on my work during my absence —even though it may interfere to some extent with your afternoons on the golf links.

I arrived at the Glendale Airport on Thursday morning, and at once took a taxi to the studio of Zadok Pictures, Inc., which is several miles southwest of Hollywood. My first reaction, quite naturally, was a tremendous thrill of excitement at finding myself suddenly set down right in the midst of the glamorous activities of the motion-picture business. The Zadok Studio is truly amazing—an enormous lot, half a mile square, covered with tremendous sound stages, elaborate outdoor sets, huge administrative buildings and other structures, and swarming with carpenters, electricians, various miscellaneous helpers, actors, and actresses—the latter being, in some ways, the most intersting. The whole place is possessed of a quality which I can only describe as enthralling.

Even the surroundings of the studio are full of interest. The adjoining boulevard is lined with handsome filling stations, gay and colorful signboards, and a lot of refreshment stands that are truly astounding—one of them, for instance, being in the form of an old mill, and another built to represent a gigantic ice-cream freezer. A short distance away is a huge alligator farm, where—for some reason which I have not as yet discovered—they are engaged in raising literally hundreds of these curious reptiles. At one side of the studio is a low hill with a complete oil field— scores of big derricks and dozens of storage tanks. And scattered all over the landscape are countless thriving real-estate developments with clusters of little plastered bungalows sprouting up like mushrooms.

When I called at the office of Mr. Sam Blatz, the studio manager, his secretary informed me he was so busy that he could not see me until the following afternoon. This caused a certain amount of delay. But, as it turned out, it was all for the best, because it gave me a chance to roam about the studio and pick up a whole lot of firsthand information about the motion-picture business.

And when I finally saw Mr. Blatz, yesterday afternoon, I was able to speak to him in his own language, and put over a sales talk that was a real wow. Even so, I had a hard time. Mr. Blatz had already seen the Behemoth tractor people, and they had offered him unusually generous terms. However, when I explained that our machines were vastly superior, that we would agree to terms just as generous as the Behemoth, and that we could make delivery early next week, his resistance broke down completely, and in less than ten minutes he closed the deal for twelve Earthworm tractors and twelve graders.

And this is not all. After thanking me most effusively for everything I had done for him, Mr. Blatz gave me a cordial invitation to remain at the studio as long as I desired. He pointed out that I could be a great help in handling the unloading of the tractors, in teaching the mechanics to operate them, and, later on, in acting as technical expert on tractors during the filming of the picture. He said that he would put a studio car at my disposal, and that I would be considered a guest of the company for as long a period as I cared to remain.

This hospitable offer I promptly accepted—not, as you might suppose, because of the selfish pleasure I would derive from hanging around this fascinating studio, but rather because of the very real service I can render the Earthworm Tractor Company by remaining on the job out here a little longer. How important this service is you will realize as soon as I describe the interesting project on which I am now engaged.

After thanking Mr. Blatz, and congratulating him for his good judgment in inviting me to remain at the studio, I asked him to give me a copy of the screen play, The Tractor Man Comes Through. As soon as this was in my hands, I wished Mr. Blatz a very cordial good afternoon and hurried back to the hotel in my luxurious studio car.

Last night I read the play, and as soon as I had finished it, I decided that it was all wrong. Not only was it weak in a dramatic sense but it did not have anywhere near enough tractor stuff in it. What it needed was a complete revision by a real tractor expert.

Accordingly, bright and early this morning, I set to work. And I am getting along so well that I expect to have an entirely new version all ready to present to Mr. Blatz on Monday morning. The changes I am making will improve the quality of the picture so much that Mr. Blatz is almost certain to adopt all of them. And the wealth of tractor stuff which I am introducing will provide publicity of incalculable value to the Earthworm Tractor Company. A brief résumé of what I am doing will make this clear.

The original play is a rather uninspiring drama of love and hate in the swamps along the lower Mississippi River. The hero—played by Buster Connolly—is a more or less inconsequential young man in charge of a fleet of tractors which are being used in the construction of a levee. And the love interest is a girl who lives in the swamps. This is not a bad set-up, but the author has spoiled it by paying too much attention to the girl and not enough attention to the tractors.

I am changing this in two ways. In the first place, I am cutting out most of the silly love passages. And in the second place, I am improving the levee-building sequences by expanding them into an exhaustive pictorial study of tractor dirt-moving operations—including not only the work of the elevating graders but also a lot of activities with dump wagons, blade graders, sheep's-foot tampers, bulldozers, scarifiers, land levelers, fresnos, and a lot of miscellaneous scrapers, packers, rollers, winches, and other forms of equipment too numerous to mention.

In addition to this I am building up the character of the hero. Instead of having him a mere second-rate straw boss on the levee, I am presenting him as a person of real consequence in the community. Besides his levee work, he is a road contractor, which gives me a chance to introduce a lot of scenes of tractors working on the roads. Also, he owns a large cotton plantation and a lumber camp, which provides an excuse for showing Earthworm tractors engaged in plowing, harrowing, cultivating and skidding logs. And, before I get through, I may even give the hero a trip up north, so we can run in some snowplow work.

Another improvement which I am making is in the method of killing off the villain. Instead of letting him drown in a very uninteresting way in the Mississippi River, I am going to have all twelve tractors run over him, one after the other. This ought to be a scene that will cause a real shudder of horror to sweep through the audience.

But my greatest and most sensational contribution is the grand climax. In the original play, when a big flood comes down the river and breaks through the levee, the hero rescues the girl from her house in the lowlands and carries her off on horseback to the safety of the hills. In my version, all this horseback foolishness is cut out, and the hero arrives in a tractor. He finds that the rescue is apparently impossible, because the girl is suffering from pneumonia or pellagra or something, and cannot be moved from her bed. In this desperate extremity, the hero hitches his tractor to the house, and drags the whole thing, with the girl in it, through miles of deadly swamps, swarming with alligators—which they can rent from the alligator farm down the road—and, after many bloodcurdling adventures, he finally reaches the safety of the hills. The hero's followers, with other tractors, haul away the barn, with the cows in it, and the various corncribs, hen houses and pigpens, with their respective contents. Not only is the girl rescued but all her property is saved. And it is just in the nick of time, because, right on the heels of this spectacular and astounding moving operation, comes the awe-inspiring influx of the swirling waters of the flood.

As you see, my improvements are going to be the making of this play, both as an artistic production and as a colossal advertisement for Earthworm tractors. So it is very fortunate that I came out here.

I must now get back to my literary labors. Good luck to you, and don't work too hard.

As ever,
ALEXANDER BOTTS.

TELEGRAM
EARTHWORM CITY ILL SEP 10 1934

ALEXANDER BOTTS
HOLLYWOOD PLAZA HOTEL
HOLLYWOOD CALIF

DELIGHTED THAT YOU PUT OVER SALE BUT I AM WOR-RIED BY YOUR STATEMENT THAT YOU AGREED TO VERY GEN-EROUS TERMS STOP PLEASE WRITE ME FULL DETAILS AT ONCE AND INCLOSE COPY OF SALES ORDER STOP I DO NOT FEEL THAT THE PUBLICITY VALUE OF THIS PICTURE WILL BE SUFFICIENT TO WARRANT YOUR WASTING ANY MORE TIME ON IT STOP THE IMPORTANT THING IS THE SALE OF THE TWELVE TRACTORS AND THE TWELVE GRADERS STOP THIS HAS NOW BEEN ACCOMPLISHED SO THERE IS NO REA-SON FOR YOUR REMAINING IN CALIFORNIA STOP I AM TOO BUSY TO LOOK AFTER YOUR JOB MUCH LONGER STOP YOU WILL RETURN TO EARTHWORM CITY AS SOON AS POSSIBLE

EARTHWORM TRACTOR COMPANY
GILBERT HENDERSON PRESIDENT

HOLLYWOOD-PLAZA HOTEL
HOLLYWOOD, CALIFORNIA

Air Mail.   Monday evening,
                                   September 10, 1934.

MR. GILBERT HENDERSON, PRESIDENT,
EARTHWORM TRACTOR COMPANY,
EARTHWORM CITY, ILLINOIS.

DEAR HENDERSON: Your telegram is here, and I am somewhat disappointed in it.

I believe you are making a mistake in feeling that the publicity this picture is going to give us is only one of the minor advantages of the deal which I have put through. I regret that you are placing undue importance on the mere selling of the twelve tractors and the twelve graders. Also, it is a bit unfortunate that you are in such a hurry to know the exact nature of the somewhat generous terms which I granted Mr. Blatz. And it is kind of too bad that you want me to send you a copy of the sales order.

As a matter of fact, the publicity is not only the most important, it is the only advantage we get out of this deal. The sale is of no consequence at all, because the terms of my agreement with Mr. Blatz provide that we lend him the tractors and graders free of charge. Hence, there has been no sale, and I can't send you a copy of the sales order because there is no sales order.

I fear that this news may be somewhat of a shock to you, because the wording of your telegram seems to indicate that you read my former letter so carelessly that you jumped to the totally unwarranted conclusion that I had actually sold something out here. I never said anything of the kind. If you will read over my letter, you will see that I merely said I had closed a deal with Mr. Blatz. So it is not my fault if there was any misunderstanding.

However, there is nothing to worry about, because my arrangement with Mr. Blatz is perfectly fair to everyone concerned, and the terms are the best that we could get, under the circumstances. Naturally, I would have enjoyed selling all this stuff, but before I arrived, the Behemoth Tractor Company had already offered to supply, absolutely free of charge, twelve of their tractors and twelve of their elevating graders. And Mr. Blatz, although he preferred Earthworms, did not want them badly enough to actually pay any money for them. So there was only one thing to do. As a sale was clearly impossible, I abandoned all thought of making it, and concentrated my efforts on this wonderful opportunity for motion-picture publicity. And I have succeeded admirably. All I had to do, in addition to lending

them a mere hundred thousand dollars' worth of tractors
and graders, was to sign a simple agreement releasing the
motion-picture company from liability in case there is any
damage to this property while it is in their possession. And
in return for this, we get a chance to put over at least a
million dollars' worth of splendid publicity. So, you see, the
advantages are all on our side.

However, if we are going to exploit this magnificent
opportunity to the fullest possible extent, it will be necessary for me to stay out here long enough to make sure that
the picture is loaded with as much Earthworm-tractor propaganda as it can possibly hold. In a former letter I explained
how I was revising the screen play so that the picture will
do right by our tractors. The revision was completed yesterday, and the next step is to submit it to Mr. Blatz. But
I cannot do this right away, because the guy is out of town.
He left unexpectedly last night by airplane for New York,
where he is to confer with Colonel Zadok, the head of the
company, and with various bankers who seem to have acquired, in some mysterious and insidious manner, a considerable influence in the business. Mr. Blatz expects to be
back on Wednesday, and he left word that he hoped I
would be able to attend a story conference which he will
hold on that day for the purpose of discussing the tractor
picture. Obviously, there is only one course for me to pursue. I will have to stick around here until Wednesday, at
least.

In the meantime, I am finding plenty to occupy me.
This morning with the help of a large force of expert
mechanics from the production department, I unloaded the
tractors and graders, which had arrived on a nearby siding,
and brought them over to the lot.

This afternoon I visited a number of people who are
to be connected with the forthcoming tractor picture, and
tried to sell them my ideas for revising the script. I wanted
to get them on my side, so that they would back me up when
I present my plans to Mr. Sam Blatz at the story confer-

ence on Wednesday. My efforts, however, were not very successful.

The first person I interviewed was Mr. Buster Connolly, the star of the picture. I found him a short distance outside the lot, looking at a large and elaborate bungalow which belongs to him and which was in the process of being moved to the Zadok studio from another studio where he had previously worked. It appears that every motion-picture star that amounts to anything has to have a bungalow where he can loll around at such times as he is not actually working. When I arrived upon the scene, Mr. Connolly's bungalow was coming past the oil derricks on the shoulder of the hill at one side of the Zadok lot. It was being dragged along very slowly and painfully by means of an antique and clumsy arrangement of cables, pulleys and winches.

This gave me a wonderful opening. After explaining the changes I wanted to make in the forthcoming picture, I offered to bring up my tractors and put on a real demonstration. I told Mr. Connolly that I would move his bungalow down to the lot so fast that it would make his hair stand on end, and would also give him an idea of the sensational effect we would produce with the spectacular house-moving climax which I had decided to put into the picture. But Mr. Connolly was not impressed.

"I won't let you touch my bungalow," he said. "And, furthermore, I don't like your machines. When Sam Blatz gets back I'm going to see him and have practically all the tractor scenes taken out of the picture."

"But, Mr. Connolly," I said, "the tractors will be the making of the picture. They'll be the most interesting thing in it."

"That's just the trouble," he retorted angrily. "The audience will be looking at the tractors all the time, and they won't pay any attention to my acting. Thus, the picture will be ruined."

"Oh, I see," I said. And, indeed, I began to see only

too well what was on his mind. He knew the tractors would be splendid picture material. He was afraid they would steal the show from him. And he was so stubborn that I found it impossible to argue with him. Consequently, after a very disappointing interview, I left him and went around to see the director of the picture.

The director sprung an idea that was exactly the opposite of Mr. Connolly's, but just as bad from my point of view. He said he was in favor of cutting out practically all the scenes involving tractors, because tractors, in his opinion, are "slow-moving props," without any picture value whatever. I offered to disprove this assertion by giving him a demonstration. He refused. Then I tried to describe the thrilling effects which could be obtained by showing our Earthworms plowing majestically across horrible swamps, through dense forests and over rugged mountains. But he would not listen. He had seen the tractors coming into the lot that morning. They moved slowly. Hence, they were slow-moving props, entirely devoid of interest. And nothing I could say had any effect. So, finally, I had to abandon my efforts, and leave him in the same state of besotted ignorance in which I had found him.

My next, and final, call was on the production manager, who has charge of the studio equipment. This guy promptly announced that he was going to advise Mr. Blatz to cut out all the tractor scenes, on the ground that they would necessitate very expensive sets, or even more expensive trips to outside locations. And he was just as opinionated as Mr. Connolly and the director, so I soon gave up all thought of reasoning with him, and walked away in disgust.

But don't get the idea that I am discouraged. Mr. Sam Blatz is the boss around here. He has already shown his intelligence, and his appreciation of tractors, by arranging with me for the use of our machines. Consequently, I am able to contemplate the future with the greatest of confidence. When I see Mr. Blatz at the story conference on

Wednesday, I will be prepared to present my ideas in such a clear, forceful and convincing manner that he is almost certain to follow my advice. Hence, the ignorant opposition of such unimportant underlings as the star, the director and the production manager will count for nothing at all. And the picture will be produced in such a way that it will be not only a credit to Zadok Pictures, Inc., but also an invaluable piece of propaganda for the Earthworm Tractor Company.

Yours enthusiastically,
ALEXANDER BOTTS.

TELEGRAM

EARTHWORM CITY ILL SEP 13 1934

ALEXANDER BOTTS
HOLLYWOOD PLAZA HOTEL
HOLLYWOOD CALIF

OUR ATTORNEY BELIEVES THAT YOUR LENDING TRACTORS TO MOTION PICTURE COMPANY IS VIOLATION OF NRA CODE ALTHOUGH AS USUAL HE IS NOT QUITE SURE STOP IN ANY EVENT IT IS ABSOLUTELY CONTRARY TO OUR POLICY STOP YOU WILL NOTIFY MR. BLATZ THAT HE MUST BUY THE TRACTORS AND GRADERS AND PAY FOR THEM STOP IF HE REFUSES YOU WILL REMOVE ALL OF THIS MACHINERY AND TURN IT OVER ON CONSIGNMENT TO OUR LOS ANGELES DEALER IN HOPES OF FUTURE SALE ELSEWHERE STOP YOU WILL RETURN TO EARTHWORM CITY AS SOON AS POSSIBLE AS WORK IN YOUR OFFICE HERE IS PILING UP

EARTHWORM TRACTOR COMPANY
GILBERT HENDERSON PRESIDENT

HOLLYWOOD RECEIVING HOSPITAL
HOLLYWOOD, CALIFORNIA

Air mail.   Thursday evening,
                                       September 13, 1934.

MR. GILBERT HENDERSON, PRESIDENT,
EARTHWORM TRACTOR COMPANY,
EARTHWORM CITY, ILLINOIS.

DEAR HENDERSON: It is my painful duty to report to you that I have been suddenly overwhelmed by a
series of crushing and incredible disasters. Your telegram
has been forwarded to me here at my new address, but,
in the present situation, it does not mean anything at all to
me. I cannot do any of the things you want me to do. And
I cannot even do any of the things I want to do myself. I
cannot stay out here to help with the tractor picture, because there is not going to be any tractor picture. I cannot
hurry back to Earthworm City, because I am laid up in
the hospital with a broken ankle. And I cannot repossess
the tractors and graders, because there are no tractors and
graders any more. They have, in fact, ceased to exist as
such. So, about the only thing I can do is sit up in bed and
write you an account of the unbelievable combination of
catastrophes which have defeated all my best-laid plans.

The first blow descended upon me early yesterday
evening at the story conference held in Mr. Blatz's office
at the studio. All the people concerned in the tractor picture were there, and each one was prepared to present his
own ideas on the subject. But the wind was immediately
taken out of all our sails by Mr. Blatz himself, who had
just arrived from New York full of a whole set of new and
outlandish ideas.

Mr. Blatz told us that the financial powers had decided that what the company needs at the present time is
something that will ring the cash register in a big way.

And they had concluded that the best means of accomplishing this was to produce a picture which would cost more than any other picture heretofore produced in the entire history of the industry. The idea, if you can call it that, seems to be that, instead of making several ordinary pictures which would cost two or three hundred thousand dollars apiece and bring in perhaps a half a million apiece, they will concentrate all their efforts on one production which will cost over a million dollars, and will bring in— they hope—several millions at the box office.

In accordance with this plan, they are going to junk the tractor drama and three or four others that had been scheduled for early production, and put everything they have into a stupendous, monumental, sensational, magnificent, and overpowering epic superspectacle based on Milton's Paradise Lost.

Mr. Blatz admitted, quite frankly, that, from a picture point of view, Mr. Milton's stuff is not so hot, but he was fairly goggle-eyed with enthusiasm over the commercial possibilities. He pointed out that this man Milton has been built up and advertised so long and so extensively by all the college professors and all the high-school teachers of English throughout the entire country that his name has become a household word, synonymous with culture and the higher things of life. This situation is just naturally made to order for the publicity department, which will rush about the country organizing John Milton Booster Clubs in every city, town, hamlet and crossroads. Indorsements will be sought, and doubtless received, from women's clubs, parent-teacher associations, literary societies, and all the rest of the innumerable organizations which are interested in improving the mind and raising the standard of good taste and artistic appreciation in America. Fathers, mothers, clergymen, school teachers, college professors and civic leaders generally will be so thoroughly sold on the high value of the picture that they will urge every man, woman and child throughout the length and breadth of the land to see it.

As director of the picture, they are hiring a world-renowned Russian theatrical producer. This bird knows nothing about motion pictures, and he cannot even speak English, so he will be completely useless around the studio. But the real work can be done by an American assistant director who really knows his business, and the name of the famous Russian will tend to pull in that large and influential group of Americans who believe that nothing can be truly worth while in an artistic way unless it comes out of Europe.

And this is not all. It is realized that there exists in America a considerable substratum of ignorant dumbbells who have a deep suspicion of anything they think is high-brow. To attract this element, they will use, in the cast, a whole group of stars who have a known appeal to the lower classes. Besides Buster Connolly, who has a great following among lovers of thrills and Western melodrama, there will be four popular comedians, three lady stars of the hot-mamma type, and various handsome juvenile men, to say nothing of acrobats, adagio dancers, circus performers, stunt men, and an enormous corps de ballet. The sets and the costumes will be the most elaborate ever seen —they have already ordered one thousand harps and one thousand pairs of wings, with real feathers, for the angels —and the dance ensembles will be lavish beyond description. In fact, there is only one place where they will economize—they won't have to pay anything to the original author.

As soon as Mr. Blatz had completed a description of his ambitious plans, the entire group at the conference—with one notable exception—gave voice to their admiration and approval. The only sour note was sounded by myself, in the form of a plaintive protest at the way they were letting the Earthworm Tractor Company down with nothing to show for all the expense we had incurred in bringing the tractors to California at Mr. Blatz's express request. But my objections were completely drowned out in the great flood of enthusiasm for Mr. John Milton.

And then, while I was still reeling from the effects of this first blow, there descended upon my unfortunate head a second disaster of even greater magnitude. The building was suddenly shaken by the shock of a distant explosion, and soon after we began to hear cries of "Fire!" We all rushed outside, and followed a crowd of excited studio employees to the western boundary of the lot. And here a truly appalling sight met our eyes.

One of the oil-storage tanks up among the derricks on the near-by hill had caught fire. Apparently this tank was only partly filled with oil; it must have contained a certain amount of air mixed with oil vapor in deadly proportions. At any rate, it had exploded, and spread the fire all over the hill. The flames were roaring up from dozens of derricks and tanks. And, as we watched, another tank blew up with a tremendous report, and a great river of burning oil started down the hill toward the studio of Zadok Pictures.

Much to our relief, the flow of this fiery river was arrested, high up on the hill, by a long, low bank of earth, which had presumably been thrown up as a protection for the studio in case of just such an emergency as this. But our relief was short-lived, for it soon appeared that this embankment was not high enough. A small quantity of the burning oil came over the top, and it was evident that, if a few more tanks let loose, the blazing fluid would come pouring down the hill and engulf the studio. Fire engines were already on the way from Culver City, Los Angeles, Hollywood, Beverly Hills and Santa Monica. But it was obvious that they would be of little use.

There was only one thing to do. I rushed over to the shed where my tractors and graders were stored. And, as I went, I called loudly for my mechanics to man the machines. Fortunately, several companies were on the lot, taking night scenes. So most of my mechanics were present. And they—gallant and intelligent fellows that they are— had already conceived the same idea which had come to me.

In less than five minutes I had men on every tractor and every grader. And in less than ten minutes, we came charging out through the big side gate of the lot, and advanced up the hill toward the fire.

By this time, the electrical department had mounted hundreds of enormous kleig lights at various vantage points. And these, in conjunction with the light from the fire, made the entire scene as bright as day.

Directly in front of us on the slope of the hill stood Buster Connolly's expensive but silly-looking bungalow. We promptly hooked onto it with three tractors and hauled it down into the lot. Then I started running the twelve tractors, each one pulling a grader, back and forth across the face of the hill so as to throw up a really effective barrier about halfway between the studio and the small dam which was temporarily holding the burning oil in check.

It began to look as if the studio might be saved. The tractors were roaring on their way, and the elevating graders were plowing up the earth and casting it onto the new embankment so fast that victory would be assured in fifteen or twenty minutes.

At this juncture, however, my own participation in the fight was abruptly terminated. As I was rushing to and fro, and hither and yon, shouting orders and encouragement to my trusty followers, I inadvertently tripped over a large plant of the variety known as prickly pear. This unfortunate accident not only filled me up with a lot of spines, in a most annoying way, but also caused me to sustain, as I landed on the hard ground, a broken ankle. It was the same ankle which I injured once before down in Mississippi. A number of husky lads promptly picked me up and carried me down to the highway. And before I knew exactly what was happening to me, I had been loaded into an ambulance and dragged away to this hospital, where the doctors proceeded to give me ether, so they could properly set the broken bones.

When I finally regained the full use of my mental faculties, several hours later, I insisted that the nurse call up the studio and find out how things were going. The news that she brought me was partly good but mostly bad. When the inevitable break in the upper embankment occurred, the lower one, so hastily constructed by our tractors and graders, had reached a height sufficient to stem the tide of the burning oil. So the entire Zadok Studio had been saved. But at the time of the break, our tractors and graders were on the upper side of the new earthwork. The brave mechanics had time to leap to safety over the barrier, but the twelve tractors and the twelve graders were all left behind, and were completely destroyed.

Thus ends the magnificent enterprise upon which I embarked, last week, with so much hope and enthusiasm. At the moment, I am feeling too wretched and miserable to make any definite plans for the future. But, probably, as soon as I am well enough, I shall come creeping piteously back to Earthworm City, hoping and praying that my job has not been taken away from me.

Yours with deep sorrow,
ALEXANDER BOTTS.

HOLLYWOOD RECEIVING HOSPITAL
HOLLYWOOD, CALIFORNIA

Air Mail.   Friday afternoon,
September 14, 1934.

MR. GILBERT HENDERSON, PRESIDENT,
EARTHWORM TRACTOR COMPANY,
EARTHWORM CITY, ILLINOIS.

DEAR HENDERSON: I have a little news for you.
My ankle is getting along very well, and I am feeling quite
comfortable.

This morning I got in touch with the local adjuster
for the Illinois Eureka Fire Insurance Company, which,
as you know, handles our business. The adjuster has inspected the remains of our tractors and graders, and is reporting them as a total loss. So, under the terms of our
policy, we are to receive the full value, plus freight. This
means that the fire wasn't such a bad idea after all; we get
paid for these machines just the same as if we had actually
sold them.

And here is more news. Mr. Sam Blatz called on me
this morning to thank me for my part in saving the studio
and thus making it possible for them to go ahead, without
any delay, in the production of their great superspectacle.
When I asked if he was referring to the Paradise Lost
picture, he replied that he was, except that their plans had
been slightly changed and they were not going to use the
great Milton epic after all. It appears they had hired some
guy to read the book for them, so they could find out
what it is all about. And they had also consulted with the
Hays office. Most of the authorities had then agreed that
it would be pretty difficult to get Paradise Lost past the
censors and the various purity organizations. Apparently,
one of the main characters in the book is Satan himself,
and this puts entirely too much emphasis on sin. So they
have decided to do John Bunyan's Pilgrim's Progress in-

stead. This book—which apparently has nothing to do with
Paul Bunyan, owner of the famous blue ox—contains a
number of objectionable passages, but they can be elimi-
nated without much trouble.

Mr. Blatz pointed out that the switch to the Bunyan
opus was in reality only a minor change in their plans. The
really essential features—such as the elaborate production
and the publicity aimed at the culture groups—will go
through just the same. The only real difference would be
that, instead of forming Milton societies all over the country, the publicity department would bend its energies toward
the formation of bigger and better Bunyan clubs.

"And in this new setup," Mr. Blatz explained, "we
find we won't need Buster Connolly, so we are going to
have him make the tractor picture after all—only there will
be a lot of changes in that too."

"I suppose you're going to leave out all the tractors?"
I asked suspiciously.

"I'm afraid we can't," said Mr. Blatz. "You see, the
most spectacular part of the picture has been made already."

"I don't understand."

"It's like this, Mr. Botts. When that fire started, we
had four separate companies working on the lot. And the
entire production force was present, all ready to take advantage of this great opportunity. The electricians set up
their lights, and the directors and the cameramen went into
action. And the results are really extraordinary. Never before has a fire of this size been covered by so many expert
cameramen with such a wealth of high-grade equipment.
And never before have I seen such beautifully taken fire
pictures. We have the whole thing—blazing oil derricks,
exploding tanks, the moving of that bungalow from out
of the very jaws of death, the building of the embankment,
the escape of the tractor operators in front of the blazing
river of oil, and the final destruction of the tractors and the
graders. We even have a delightful bit of comedy relief—
where some jackass tripped and did a beautiful high-

gruesome into a prickly pear. It is all so astounding, so magnificent, so colossal, that we are going to use it as the climax of our tractor picture. To do this, we shall have to shift the scene of our story from the Mississippi swamps to California, and have the hero rescue the girl and her house from an oil fire. We want to make this a real tractor picture, with lots of tractor stuff all through it, so we are hoping that you will be able to lend us twelve more tractors and twelve more graders to be used in the earlier sequences."

"Nothing would please me more!" I said. And then my warm enthusiasm was suddenly chilled by the icy fingers of a cold doubt. "I am afraid, however," I said sadly, "that it can't be done. Look at this."

I handed him your telegram. He read it and glanced at me inquiringly.

"We must face the facts," I said. "You will have to buy these tractors and graders, and pay real money for them, or else you'll have to use Behemoth machines."

"We can't use Behemoths," said Mr. Blatz, "because the most important part of the picture has already been made with Earthworms." He pondered the matter for some time. "Oh, well," he said at length. "It's only a hundred thousand dollars—a mere drop in the bucket as compared to what we ought to take in on this picture. Do you want me to sign an order or something for these things?"

"As a matter of form, you might as well," I said nonchalantly. "And you might make me out a check also."

So he did, and I am enclosing the order and the check herewith. Please ship the stuff at once. And I'm afraid you'll have to handle my office work a little longer, because the state of my ankle makes it necessary for me to leave tomorrow for several weeks' vacation, as the guest of Mr. Sam Blatz at his luxurious ranch in Hidden Valley up in Ventura County.

Yours respectfully,
ALEXANDER BOTTS.

HOLLYWOOD IS WONDERFUL, BUT—

EARTHWORM TRACTOR COMPANY
EARTHWORM CITY, ILLINOIS
Office of Gilbert Henderson, President

Air Mail.

Monday, October 1, 1934.

MR. ALEXANDER BOTTS,

CARE MR. SAM BLATZ, STUDIO MANAGER,
ZADOC PICTURES, INC.,
HOLLYWOOD, CALIFORNIA.

DEAR BOTTS: Two weeks ago you wrote that you had completed your sale of tractors and graders to Zadoc Pictures, Inc., and that you were taking a short vacation to recuperate from an injured ankle. Since then we have had no news from you at all.

We are very anxious to have you return to Earthworm City at once. The Earthworm Tractor Company has just taken over the Crowder Shovel Corporation, of Chicago, and we are going to market their entire line of heavy excavating machinery under the name Earthworm. We want you here at the home office, so you can work out plans for pushing this new group of products.

Please advise when we may expect you.

Very sincerely,
GILBERT HENDERSON.

HOLLYWOOD PLAZA HOTEL
HOLLYWOOD, CALIFORNIA

Air Mail.

Wednesday, October 3, 1934.

MR. GILBERT HENDERSON, PRESIDENT,
EARTHWORM TRACTOR COMPANY,
EARTHWORM CITY, ILLINOIS.

DEAR HENDERSON: Your letter is received, and I hasten to report that I am getting along beautifully. My ankle, which was not hurt as badly as I had supposed, is now practically well. I have been spending the past few days at the Zadoc Studio, advising them on how they should handle their recently purchased Earthworm tractors in their forthcoming tractor picture. I want to be sure they get the greatest possible dramatic effect out of the machines and also—although I did not tell them so—I want to be sure they give us as much publicity and free advertising as possible. This advisory work is now completed, and I was just on the point of starting back to Earthworm City to take up once more my regular duties as sales manager.

But now that I have received your letter asking me to hurry home, I have decided that I really ought to stay a little longer. This does not mean that I am disregarding your instructions. It means, on the contrary, that I am planning to carry out your desires in a way that is far superior to anything you could have even thought of.

What you want is to launch the Earthworm Tractor Company into the power-shovel business with as large and sensational a splash as possible. For this we shall need lots of publicity. And I have decided that the best and cheapest way for us to achieve this publicity is for me to stay right on the job out here and devote all my energies to the task of putting our shovels into the movies, so that they may be shown, in all their glory, on the screens of all the motion-picture theaters of the country.

Now, it is obvious that I am better fitted than anyone else in our organization for carrying out this important project. In the few weeks that I have been in Hollywood I have acquired a thorough knowledge of the inside workings of the motion-picture business. I am personally acquainted with Mr. Sam Blatz, general manager of the great Zadoc Studio. And, having already succeeded in placing a group of our tractors in one motion picture, I know exactly how to go about placing a group of our shovels in another.

I am planning an attack that will be simple, direct and powerful. I will spend several days working out and writing up a fast-moving, red-hot, dramatic story dealing with the life of a power-shovel operator. As soon as it is completed, I will offer it, absolutely free of charge, to Mr. Sam Blatz. As he is a man of unusually high intelligence, he will at once recognize its possibilities, and seize upon it with the greatest eagerness. Then, when he starts producing the picture, he will find that the story calls for several shovels, and we shall make a nice little sale—which is not to be scorned, even though our main idea is the publicity.

In a very short time I hope to send you news of my complete success.

As ever,
ALEXANDER BOTTS.

TELEGRAM

EARTHWORM CITY ILL
OCT 5 1934

MR. ALEXANDER BOTTS
HOLLYWOOD PLAZA HOTEL
HOLLYWOOD CAL

I WISH TO REPEAT MOST EMPHATICALLY THAT A SALES MANAGER BELONGS AT THE HOME OFFICE JUST AS THE GENERAL OF AN ARMY BELONGS AT HEADQUARTERS AND

NOT IN THE FRONT LINE TRENCHES STOP PLEASE RETURN
TO EARTHWORM CITY AT ONCE STOP OUR LOS ANGELES
DEALER CAN HANDLE THE MOTION PICTURE SHOVEL
DEAL STOP IN VIEW OF THE FACT THAT WE DO NOT YET
KNOW WHETHER OR NOT MOTION PICTURE PUBLICITY WILL
BE OF ANY REAL VALUE TO US I DO NOT FEEL THAT YOU
SHOULD WASTE ANY MORE TIME ON THE MATTER

GILBERT HENDERSON

HOLLYWOOD PLAZA HOTEL
HOLLYWOOD, CALIFORNIA

Air Mail.
Friday evening, October 5, 1934.

MR. GILBERT HENDERSON, PRESIDENT,
EARTHWORM TRACTOR COMPANY,
EARTHWORM CITY, ILLINOIS.

DEAR HENDERSON: Your telegram arrived this
morning, and I was much flattered to learn how indispens-
able you consider my presence at Earthworm City. I was
also much pleased at the apt way in which you compare
my position as sales manager to that of a general in command of an army. I want to assure you that I agree with
you entirely in your estimate of my importance to the company. But I cannot help feeling that you are a little far-
fetched in your ideas on the subject of headquarters versus
front-line trenches. This is entirely a matter of tempera-
ment and circumstances. I will admit that it was entirely
correct, in the late war, for General Pershing to sit around
at Chaumont like a spider in the center of his far-flung web
of communications. Under the circumstances, it was doubtless the most effective procedure that he could have used.
And it succeeded. But there have been other wars, in which
other leaders have succeeded by using entirely different
methods. In my present campaign, I feel that it will be the

part of wisdom to employ the sort of tactics which are best adapted to my own personality. This means that I will not attempt to play any part so foreign to my nature as that of a spider sitting in the center of his web. It is far better that I should ride forth, like Joan of Arc, at the very front of the attack.

This procedure is especially desirable at the present moment because my campaign is not going as well as I had hoped, and it is, therefore, necessary that the commander in chief be present in person to direct the operations. Although my plans have received a temporary setback, I have no doubts regarding my ultimate success. And in order that you may understand the exact situation out here, I will give you a brief account of what I have done and what I am planning for the future. I hope you will read what I have to say with great care, because I want you to realize that my selling campaign here has been planned and executed with unusual efficiency and thoroughness, and my failure to accomplish any results so far has been due entirely to circumstances outside my control.

I spent three whole days—Monday, Tuesday and Wednesday—in creating, elaborating, embellishing and setting down what is probably one of the most remarkable motion-picture scenarios ever produced in the entire history of the industry. The hero of this opus, who is a steam-shovel operator, is one of nature's noblemen—a strong, courageous, red-blooded, 100 per cent American he-man. The heroine is young, good and beautiful, and I am making her just as fascinating and voluptuous as I can without getting into trouble with the censors. And the villain, who is probably the most striking character in the play, is a combination of the worst qualities of all the most objectionable people I have ever met in my entire career as a tractor man—which covers a lot of ground. He is so utterly and unspeakably low, vile and repulsive that—if he really existed—you could not even pass him on the street without wishing to put your foot in his face. He is sure to go over big—especially with those more discriminating people who like movies which are sophisticated, yet delicately handled.

The personalities of the three main characters are skillfully developed and presented in a series of colorful incidents, climaxes and super-climaxes which not only provide drama of the highest order but also give our power shovels an opportunity to show off in a way that will convince everyone of their superior quality. The play ends in a blaze of glory with the hero rescuing the heroine from almost certain death, and using his trusty machine to shovel the villain over the edge of a mighty precipice.

Taking it all in all, the scenario is a lollapaloosa. I presented it to Mr. Blatz at the Zadoc Studio yesterday morning, and, after skimming through it, he agreed absolutely with my opinion that I had produced something which might well be described as remarkable, not to say astounding. Unfortunately, he also told me, gently but with sickening firmness, that he did not feel justified in producing my picture at the present time. He stated that he was already making the tractor picture, and that he did not want to risk another machinery drama until he found out whether the first one would be successful. Naturally I disagreed with him with the greatest vehemence. But after arguing for about half an hour, I saw that he was—as we writers would say—adamant. I therefore withdrew as gracefully and politely as I could, and spent the rest of the day in futile assaults on two other major studios.

At neither of these other places was I able to reach the higher executives, so I had to waste my efforts on a couple of incredibly stupid, unimaginative fellows known as story editors.

These people used some of the same arguments which I had heard in my first attempts to introduce Earthworm tractors at the Zadoc Studio. They said that shovels are dull, uninteresting, slow-moving props, entirely lacking in entertainment value. They would not listen to me when I offered to prove, by an actual demonstration, that they were wrong. And they would not even read my scenario. So, when I returned to the hotel last night, I will have to admit that my heart was heavy with discouragement.

I did not, however, remain in this state of mind for long. A brief analysis of the situation convinced me that the only thing standing in the way of my complete success was my inability to persuade these motion-picture people to come to a shovel demonstration, so that I could overcome their abysmal ignorance regarding the pictorial possibilities of our splendid machines. And this diagnosis of the difficulty at once suggested a happy remedy. If the movie moguls would not come to me, I would take my demonstration to them. And I would present it in the medium of expression with which they are most familiar— in other words, I would make a short motion picture, showing one of our shovels performing the thrilling and spectacular maneuvers which are called for in the climax of my scenario, and I would then take the film around and run it off before the astonished and delighted eyes of the various studio executives, thus raising them to such a high pitch of enthusiasm that my only remaining task would be to decide which one of them should be the lucky man with whom I would consent to do business.

After deciding on the above promising plan of campaign, I turned in for a good night's rest. And this morning I began to put my ideas into action.

First of all, I visited the machinery house which has the Southern California agency for Crowder shovels—now Earthworm shovels. In answer to my requeest for the loan of a machine, they stated that they had none in stock, and that there was only one in the entire territory—a two-yard gasoline model owned by a local contractor named Joe Blake.

Note: Apparently this agency has not been pushing these shovels as hard as they should. I will get after them hot and heavy as soon as I have time. This morning, unfortunately, I had too many other things to do.

I at once proceeded to call on Mr. Joe Blake, the contractor. He informed me that his Crowder—now Earthworm—shovel is up in the mountains near Arrowhead Lake, where he is preparing to build a dam in the bottom of a rather inaccessible canyon. His description of the location indicates that it will be admirably suited to my purposes. The machine is on the upper rim of the canyon, getting ready to cut a zigzag road down the steep side wall into the trackless depths below—this road being a necessary preliminary, so that he can get his equipment and supplies to the site of the dam. When I asked Mr. Blake if he would permit me to take some motion pictures of his shovel, he replied that he would be delighted, and that he would drive me out next Monday.

Having accepted this kind offer, I rushed around to a small independent studio and arranged to hire a cameraman with a motion-picture camera and plenty of film, and also a reasonably competent actor and an actress. In addition, I have commissioned a painter to make a big "Earthworm" sign to put on the shovel. And I have purchased from a department store two clothing dummies, one male and one female.

I am using these dummies because I don't want to kill anybody. They will be substituted for the real flesh-and-blood players in the scenes where they are picked up and whisked around by the great shovel.

With any kind of luck at all, I ought to be able to complete my picture in one day—next Monday. But it will probably take a couple of days more to develop and exhibit the film. So the good news of my success, although it is inevitable, will probably not reach you till the latter part of the week.

As ever,
ALEXANDER BOTTS.

TELEGRAM

EARTHWORM CITY ILL

Oct 8 1934

MR ALEXANDER BOTTS
HOLLYWOOD PLAZA HOTEL
HOLLYWOOD CAL

I AM GETTING TIRED SENDING OUT MESSAGES TO WHICH
YOU PAY NO ATTENTION STOP I WISH TO REMIND YOU
THAT A COUPLE OF MONTHS AGO YOU SIGNED A ONE YEAR
CONTRACT TO WORK FOR THE EARTHWORM TRACTOR COM-
PANY AS SALES MANAGER STOP WE INSIST THAT YOU RETURN
TO EARTHWORM CITY AT ONCE AND FULFILL THE TERMS OF
THIS CONTRACT BY HANDLING THE WORK FOR WHICH YOU
WERE HIRED

GILBERT HENDERSON

HOLLYWOOD PLAZA HOTEL
HOLLYWOOD, CALIFORNIA

Monday evening, October 8, 1934.

MR. GILBERT HENDERSON, PRESIDENT,
EARTHWORM TRACTOR COMPANY,
EARTHWORM CITY, ILLINOIS.

DEAR HENDERSON: Your telegram is here, and
in some ways I am almost beginning to wish that I had
heeded your advice and come back to Earthworm City
before I even started in on this power-shovel-motion-
picture project. At the moment, nothing would please me
more than to follow your instructions by hopping on the
fastest airplane I could find and heading for Illinois. Such
a course of action, however, would, under the present circumstances, be distinctly cowardly and dishonorable. The
situation out here has suddenly become so involved and
so difficult that I feel it is my duty to remain a few days
longer for the purpose of attempting some adjustment in

the various lawsuits and claims for damages which seem to be coming in from all directions.

The unfortunate state of affairs in which I find myself this evening is rendered doubly distressing by the fact that it arrived so suddenly. When I awoke this morning, my mind was calm, serene and completely free from worry. And this happy condition continued for quite a while. My breakfast at the hotel was excellent. Soon afterward, Mr. Blake, the contractor, arrived with his car, and we started for the mountains near Arrowhead Lake, taking with us the big motion-picture camera, the cameraman, several cans of film, the actor and the actress, the male and female clothing dummies, and the big Earthworm sign.

Toward the end of the morning, after a delightful drive, we stopped for a bite to eat at a large vacation camp in a beautiful evergreen forest about half a mile distant from the point on the rim of the canyon where Mr. Blake's shovel was located. There were quite a number of people staying at this camp, having been attracted there by a series of important tennis matches. But as soon as the crowd discovered that we were about to take some exciting motion pictures, most of them deserted the tennis courts and followed our car over to the edge of the canyon. This crowd proved to be a good deal of a nuisance; we had to keep shooing them back out of the way all the time. But they were also a source of considerable gratification to me; for it was evident, from the eager way in which they pressed forward, and from the frequent bursts of applause and cheering, that we were putting on an act which had real audience appeal.

It did not take me long to get my performance under way. I located a medium-sized but very sturdy tree which grew on the rim of the canyon in such a way that one of its limbs extended far out over the edge. At this point the canyon wall sloped down, at an angle considerably steeper than forty-five degrees, to the stream several hundred feet below. My scenario called for an absolutely sheer cliff, but I was glad to modify this requirement slightly, especially in view of the fact that I was going to have the young actress climb the tree, and I did not want to run the risk of losing her entirely in case she made a slip. And it really made no great difference, as the cameraman assured me that, by skillful placing of the camera, he could create the illusion of a truly appalling precipice. As soon as these preliminaries had been decided, the actual taking of the picture got under way, the various scenes progressing in the following order:

The beautiful heroine—played by the young actress whom I had hired—comes tripping lightly through the forest on the way to meet her lover, who is supposed to be operating his big power shovel not far away. In her dainty hand she bears the map which shows where the treasure is buried. Suddenly she meets the villain—played by the actor whom I had brought along. His greedy eyes recognize the map. He attempts to seize it. The heroine flees shrieking through the forest; the villain pursues; and we have a really swell chase sequence.

Finally, the heroine reaches the edge of the canyon. She cannot go on. But she cannot go back, either, for the villain is right after her—so close that she can almost feel his hot breath on the back of her neck. She is, in short, in something of a dilemma. But all at once she spies the tree— the one which I had previously selected. She climbs the tree, and finally reaches the end of the branch which extends far out over the yawning chasm.

The villain gazes up at her, and a leering smile spreads over his repulsive face. He has not exactly caught the lady as yet, but he certainly has her out on a limb. And if he can only succeed in dashing her into the canyon, he can climb down later on and abstract the coveted map from her lifeless fingers. With a snarl of rage, he pulls a hatchet from his belt and starts chopping down the tree.

At this moment the excitement and suspense reach a very high point. Suddenly, in the distance, appears the handsome hero—played by myself—driving through the forest in the huge shovel which bears the recently attached sign, Earthworm. The hero sees that the heroine needs his help. He puts on full speed. The great machine fairly flies across the ground. The motor roars. But the villain is so absorbed in his chopping that he does not hear anything until the shovel is almost on top of him. At this point the grand climax is reached.

But before I relate exactly what happened, I wish to pause a moment to explain that right here I had intended to stop the camera and substitute the two clothing dummies for the two real people who were playing the parts of the heroine and the villain. This change seemed advisable because from here on—as I have previously indicated—the scenario called for some pretty rough action. Just as the villain raised his hatchet for the final blow which would sever the trunk of the tree and send the heroine to a cruel death on the rocks far below, I had planned to have the hero—played by myself—give a mighty lunge with the huge dipper, scoop up the villain and shovel him, like so much refuse, far out over the edge of the precipice. Then, with a skillful swing of the boom, I was going to bring the dipper up under the young lady just as her weary fingers were supposedly losing their grip on the branch, and pluck her from the tree like a ripe plum. I would then land her safe and sound on terra firma, and there would be a final close-up showing the two lovers locked in a fond embrace.

That, as I say, was my plan. And it is easy to see what a wonderful picture we would have had, provided everything had worked out as I had expected. But at the critical moment there occurred a small accident which ruined the whole thing.

As I sat in the driver's seat of the mighty shovel, steering it skillfully and accurately in its awe-inspiring progress along the rim of the canyon toward the tree in which the heroine was so precariously perched, I suddenly noticed that the machine was beginning to tilt at a very alarming angle. I looked around, and it was not long before I realized what was happening. I had driven so close to

the canyon wall that the tremendous weight of the shovel
had caused the earth to start crumbling away. Quick as a
flash, I swung the machine around and headed for solid
ground. But it was too late. Although the tracks were
whirling rapidly, they could not gain a foothold on the
rapidly disintegrating bank. Slowly the great machine slid
back until it tottered on the very brink. There was nothing
for me to do but leap from the cab. I did so.

And the next moment, while a cry of horror arose
from the crowd, the mighty mechanism went coasting back-
ward into the hideous abyss. Never have I seen a piece of
heavy excavating machinery travel so fast. Down it went,
like one of those boats on the chute-the-chutes at Coney
Island, and it ended with a sickening crash in the bed of
the stream far far below.

As you may imagine, I was somewhat appalled by
the magnitude of this catastrophe. And, to make matters
even worse, the motion-picture cameraman at once set up
an agonized wail, informing me that when I whirled the
shovel around, in my vain attempt to save it, I had run
over his precious camera. The man himself, being a nimble
fellow, had succeeded in leaping out of the way. But the
camera was completely smashed and all the film was ruined.
This made the disaster complete. There was no picture, and
there was no hope any more of making one. I might have
procured another camera, but the only available shovel
was lost in the abyss. It was almost more than I could bear,
especially when you consider that all the time I had to
listen to a continuous yapping from the cameraman.

I tried to explain that the accident had been unavoid-
able, but the fellow was most unreasonable, claiming that
it was all my fault, and that I would have to make good his
loss to the extent of something over five hundred dollars.
He said that he could show me receipted bills to prove that
his equipment cost that much. And he announced that if he
did not get full payment he would sue me.

At this point Mr. Blake, the owner of the shovel, entered the discussion, and put on a truly shocking display of

bad temper and worse manners. He informed me, in the most insulting way imaginable, that I would have to pay him fifteen thousand dollars for the destruction of his shovel. And when I pointed out that we did not yet know how badly the shovel was damaged, and that it might be possible to salvage it, he came back with a proposal that was even worse.

"All right," he said. "If you will put the shovel together again, and get it up out of that canyon, and pay me for the loss of time on this job, I will let it go at that. But you've got to make this thing right, or I'll sue you."

By this time I realized that I was not getting anywhere with all this talk, so I skillfully closed the discussion by simply turning my back and walking off in a calm and dignified manner. Without so much as turning my head to look back, I made my way to the vacation camp a half a mile distant, and hired a chauffeur and a car to transport the actor, the actress, the male and female clothing dummies, and myself back to Los Angeles. Before we left, I noticed Mr. Blake starting out in his car with the photographer, but I paid no attention to them at all.

The ride to Los Angeles was uneventful, but when we arrived at the hotel there occurred, as a climax to this day of unprecedented disaster, a final unfortunate episode. As I alighted from the car and thrust my hand into my pocket, I discovered that I did not have enough ready cash to pay either the chauffeur, or the actor and the actress. And at once all three of them began making nasty remarks about suing me. Fortunately, the hotel manager was kind enough to cash a check for me, so I was able to pay them off, and the matter was adjusted. But the whole thing was almost more than my bruised emotions could stand, and I retired to my room in a very low state of mind.

It is now evening, and I have been somewhat revived by a good supper. But I still don't feel any too good. I have abandoned all hope of making a shovel picture. And, as I said at the beginning of this letter, I would like nothing better than to follow your instructions and come hastening back to Illinois. But my high sense of honor tells me that it is my duty to remain here to fight this preposterous claim for fifteen thousand dollars in damages—to say nothing of the relatively unimportant five-hundred-dollar matter. At the moment, my nerves are so shattered that I am unable to plan out a course of action. I imagine that Mr. Blake and the cameraman will call on me very soon—possibly as early as tomorrow. If so, I can only hope and pray that by that time I may have sufficiently repaired my broken morale, so that I can successfully defend myself against what will probably be a very vigorous attack.

I will let you know what luck I have—if any.

Yours, in disconsolate sadness,
ALEXANDER BOTTS.

HOLLYWOOD PLAZA HOTEL
HOLLYWOOD, CALIFORNIA

Thursday evening, October 11, 1934.

Air Mail.

MR. GILBERT HENDERSON, PRESIDENT,
EARTHWORM TRACTOR COMPANY,
EARTHWORM CITY, ILLINOIS.

DEAR HENDERSON: It gives me the greatest pleasure to report that all of the fears and doubts which I expressed in my last letter to you have turned out to be absolutely without foundation. All my difficulties have been satisfactorily adjusted. And I find myself once more floating along on the crest of the wave. I am doing so well that I can hardly believe it myself.

This tremendous change in my fortunes began this morning when I received a call from Mr. Blake, the owner of the shovel. When he arrived, I will have to admit that I was prepared for the worst—in fact, for two days and three nights I had been skulking about the hotel in what I can only describe as an exceedingly apprehensive state of mind. You can imagine my surprise, therefore, when Mr. Blake greeted me with the greatest cordiality and started in to thank me for everything I had done for him.

"It seems incredible," he explained, "but that old shovel was hardly damaged at all. It stayed right side up all the way down; it had the good luck to miss all the rocks and big trees; and, although it must have taken a good healthy bump when it ended up in the stream, it is so strongly built that nothing of any importance got smashed. My operator has started it up and it is running great. So I have come to apologize for my hasty words the other day, and I want to thank you for sending the machine down there."

"But why should you thank me?" I asked, somewhat puzzled.

"Because you have saved me so much time in the construction of the dam. Now that the shovel is down at the dam site, I can start excavating at once. I don't have to wait a month or more to build a road into the canyon. Of course, I will need the road eventually, to transport my materials and equipment when I get ready to begin pouring the concrete. So I have just ordered, through your dealer, another shovel to use in building the road."

"Sir," I said, "you surprise and delight me."

"I am surprised and delighted, myself," he said, "at the way this thing is working out. You have no idea how much you have helped me by placing my shovel at the exact point where I wanted it."

I was so knocked into a heap by Mr. Blake's remarks that I could not utter a word. And, while I was still in a considerably dazed condition, the telephone rang.

It was my old friend Mr. Sam Blatz, of Zadoc Pictures, Inc. He said he wanted to see me. I pulled myself together as best I could, tottered out of the hotel, and took a taxi to the Zadoc lot.

Here I received another astonishing piece of news. It appears that the Zadoc people, in addition to their regular features, produce a newsreel. One of the news photographers had been sent out to take some movies of the tennis matches which were being held last Monday at the vacation camp near the scene of my shovel exploit. During a lull in the play, he had heard that some sort of excitement was going on at the canyon. He decided to go over, and arrived just in time to get a complete motion-picture record of the sensational descent of the shovel into the canyon. Of course, I knew nothing about this at the time—having been too excited to notice anything—and when I heard about it, it was all a glad happy surprise.

It appears that my flying leap out of the cab took place on the side away from the camera, so it did not show at all, and the picture created the impression that I had driven the machine down that awful slope, just as an ordinary part of the day's work. And to make the incident even more striking, the photographer had later climbed down into the canyon and taken a few shots of the shovel when it was started up and tested out by Mr. Blake's operator.

The whole thing made a very nice little newsreel bit. It had already been sent out all over the country. And most important of all, it had been seen by Mr. Blatz, and had converted him to the idea that power shovels might be motion-picture material.

All of this information was given me by Mr. Blatz himself, as a preliminary to a lot of questions about the cost of our shovels, the exact nature of the work which they could do, and their ability to perform other thrilling and spectacular stunts. Mr. Blatz was so interested, so enthusiastic and so absorbed in these technical questions that it was only with the greatest difficulty that I was able to direct his attention to my carefully written power-shovel scenario, which I had brought along, and which I kept thrusting continuously under his nose. At last, however, he took the manuscript and stuck it into a drawer in his desk. So, you see, he has probably accepted it, which naturally pleases me very much.

Taking it all in all, my visit with this great motion-picture magnate was delightfully satisfactory, though Mr.

Blatz did not place a definite order for the purchase of any shovels.

Naturally, I came away from the interview in a state of mind which can only be described as sheer ecstasy. And when I got back to the hotel, I felt so encouraged, so delighted, so pleased with myself, and so filled with enthusiasm, that I started in immediately to work out a plan of campaign by which I hope and expect to go on to future triumphs which will, I believe, eclipse the substantial successes which have already resulted from my efforts.

My new plans are simple, but magnificent. Now that I have succeeded in establishing tractors and power shovels as fit subjects for motion-picture exploitation, there is no reason in the world why I cannot do the same thing with all the other types of machinery which are manufactured and distributed by the Earthworm Tractor Company. I am, therefore, starting in at once to write up a whole flock of motion-picture scenarios, each one of which will present a highly dramatic story based upon the lives of the people who are engaged in handling these machines.

I have already worked out, in the short space of a few hours, the outlines for no less than three complete pictures along these lines. I have one stark and tragic drama dealing with life among the Eskimos, and featuring our entire line of snowplows—straight blade, locomotive type and rotary. I also have a charming pastoral comedy, full of whimsicalities and delightful lyrical passages, dealing with a country lad who wins the hand of his sweetheart by using one of our combined harvesters to cut the grain belonging to her father. In this particular drama I am depending more on atmosphere than on action, but I am using one very exciting incident at the end where the villain is fed through the threshing machine and comes out in the form of chaff which the wind driveth away. I also have a pile-driver story, which is a real humdinger, and which ends with the villain being pounded down into the mud of the river bottom just like a wooden pile. These, of course, are just a few of the ideas which I am going to use. I have many more. And before I get through, I may possibly put across as many as a dozen pictures; thus starting an entirely new cycle.

As you know, motion pictures are often developed in that way. Years ago we had a cycle of pictures dealing with the sheiks of the desert. More recently we have had costume-drama cycles, the gangster cycle, and at present we are in the midst of the Federal-detective cycle. My contribution will be the heavy-machinery cycle—pictures dealing with tractors, shovels, combined harvesters, snowplows, pile drivers, graders, dump wagons, and so on.

You see, I am really making the fur fly out here. And it is a great satisfaction to me to discover how well adapted I am to the motion-picture business. As a matter of fact, I have no doubt at all but that Mr. Blatz would be only too glad to offer me a permanent position in his organization at a truly princely salary. But as long as I am under contract to act as sales manager of the Earthworm Tractor Company, it would, of course, be unethical for me to leave you people in the lurch. I will, therefore, continue to work along on the same lines as I have in the past.

And I am laying my plans accordingly. As it will probably take me several months to complete work in promoting this new cycle of motion pictures, I am going to look around for a good apartment, and I shall probably send for my wife and the twins to come out and join me.

Yours, with the greatest enthusiasm,
ALEXANDER BOTTS.

TELEGRAM

EARTHWORM CITY ILL
Oct 15 1934

MR ALEXANDER BOTTS
HOLLYWOOD PLAZA HOTEL
HOLLYWOOD CAL

YOUR LETTER IS RECEIVED AND I AM FORCED TO ADMIT THAT I WAS ABSOLUTELY WRONG AND YOU WERE ABSO-

LUTELY RIGHT REGARDING PUBLICITY VALUE OF MOTION
PICTURES STOP APPARENTLY THE SHOVEL NEWSREEL HAS
BEEN RUSHED OUT ALL OVER THE COUNTRY AND WE HAVE
ALREADY RECEIVED TELEGRAMS FROM SIX DEALERS STAT-
ING THAT THIS IS WONDERFUL PUBLICITY AND THAT PROS-
PECTIVE PURCHASERS HAVE BEEN SO IMPRESSED WITH THE
STURDINESS OF OUR SHOVELS AS DEMONSTRATED BY THE
PICTURE THAT AT LEAST FOUR SALES HAVE BEEN PUT
OVER ON THIS ACCOUNT STOP IN VIEW OF THE FACT THAT
YOUR MOTION PICTURE ACTIVITIES ARE DOING US SO MUCH
GOOD AND AS LONG AS YOU WISH TO CONTINUE THIS WORK
WE WILL BE GLAD TO RELEASE YOU FROM YOUR CONTRACT
WITH US SO THAT YOU CAN ACCEPT THE MOTION PICTURE
JOB WITH THE PRINCELY SALARY WHICH YOU MENTION
IN YOUR LETTER STOP PLEASE WIRE CONFIRMATION SO THAT
WE MAY GO AHEAD AND APPOINT NEW SALES MANAGER
STOP CONGRATULATIONS AND MORE POWER TO YOU

GILBERT HENDERSON

TELEGRAM

HOLLYWOOD CAL
Oct 15 1934

MR GILBERT HENDERSON PRESIDENT
EARTHWORM TRACTOR COMPANY
EARTHWORM CITY ILL

HOLD EVERYTHING STOP YOU MUST BE CRAZY IF YOU THINK
YOU CAN GET BY WITH CANCELING MY CONTRACT STOP I
WONT STAND FOR IT STOP HOLLYWOOD IS WONDERFUL AND
THE MOTION PICTURE BUSINESS IS DELIGHTFUL BUT I AM
A NATURAL BORN TRACTOR MAN AND COULD NOT EVEN
CONSIDER A PERMANENT JOB IN ANY OTHER BUSINESS STOP
I AM ARRANGING MATTERS SO THAT I CAN CONDUCT ALL
MY FUTURE BUSINESS WITH THE MOVIES BY MAIL AND
TELEGRAM AND I AM LEAVING BY PLANE TONIGHT STOP
WILL BE AT MY OFFICE IN EARTHWORM CITY TOMORROW
AND IF I FIND YOU HAVE APPOINTED ANOTHER SALES
MANAGER I WILL SUE YOU   ALEXANDER BOTTS

SITUATION HAYWIRE

EARTHWORM BRANCH OFFICE
WASHINGTON, D. C.

May 1, 1944.

CAPT. ALEXANDER BOTTS,
EARTHWORM TRACTOR COMPANY,
EARTHWORM CITY, ILLINOIS.

DEAR BOTTS: My friend Gen. John H. Bessemer, Corps of Engineers, who is about to leave for the European theater of war, is in need of a technical expert on tractors. I feel that you, by reason of your long experience as our former sales manager, are admirably qualified. And, as I understand you are now back in Earthworm City on a routine inspection job for the Army, I have recommended you.

If the general takes you, I should be glad to hear from you as to how you make out.

Most sincerely,
GILBERT HENDERSON,
President, Earthworm Tractor Company.

ENGLAND, May 25, 1944.

DEAR HENDERSON: It pains me to inform you that your ill-advised and totally unsolicited recommendation has resulted in getting me into something so infinitely less important than my previous routine-inspection job that it is not even funny. It now looks as if I may spend the

213

next few weeks, months, or even years sitting in a dark cellar—merely this, and nothing more.

The only bright spot is the fact that General Bessemer has radioed Washington an urgent demand that you come over here to act as his tractor adviser during the period of my cellar sitting. As a patriotic American, you cannot, in wartime, refuse. So I am hoping that the trip will so thoroughly inconvenience you that you will take action strong enough to bring relief not only to yourself but to me also.

General Bessemer has agreed to give you this letter when you arrive in England, and I hope you will feel a fitting amount of remorse when you read of the trouble which has been caused by your unnecessary meddling in my affairs.

This trouble began a few days after our recent arrival in England, when General Bessemer and I happened to run across a certain Monsieur Georges Laffitte, whom you will doubtless remember as our former Earthworm tractor dealer at St. Pierre-en-Bessin, in the Department of Calvados, Normandy, France. We learned from Georges that back in June, 1940, he had in stock one sixteen-ton Earthworm Diesel tractor, equipped with bulldozer. On the approach of the Germans, he hid this in a secret wine cellar at a small hotel in St. Pierre run by his grandfather and grandmother.

Since then, Georges has been active in the French underground. He has equipped the cellar as a base of operations. He has a radio receiving set, and a printing press for turning out patriotic pamphlets. He has a microphone hidden in the hotel, which is now occupied by German officers connected with a near-by airfield. He has apparatus for making microfilm copies of letters and documents so they can be sent to England by homing pigeon. He has made secret trips to England by small boat, bringing valuable information. On his most recent getaway, he was shot in the leg by a German sentry, and is still too lame to make the difficult return trip.

"So far," said Georges, "the stupid Germans have failed to discover the hidden cellar. The tractor is still there—brand-new, in perfect condition, full of fuel and oil. It is at your service any time you can use it."

"Splendid!" said General Bessemer. "If we ever invade that part of France and capture that air field by advance parachute troops, we shall probably find the landing strip full of shell holes and bomb craters. This tractor —bigger than anything we could land by parachute—will be invaluable for putting the strip back in shape."

"What we should do," I suggested, "is smuggle a good operator over there just ahead of the invasion. Then he would be all set to go at an instant's notice—save time at the critical moment. When does this invasion take place?"

"It's a military secret," said the general. "All we can do is send a man over and let him wait. The invasion is sure to come sometime—if not this year, then next. But it's a dangerous job; it may be hard to find a suitable volunteer."

"Any good tractor man ought to be glad to volunteer," I said. And I added, in a burst of thoughtless enthusiasm, "If my time were not so valuable, and my services so needed here, I would go myself."

"Okay," said the general. "You are it."

"But listen——"

"You're not scared, are you?"

"Certainly not. But how can you get along without me here?"

"We'll just have to manage somehow," said the general.

And that was that. The only result of my protests was the general's decision to bring you, Henderson, over here, which, in turn, gives me a faint ray of hope. If you are anxious to return to America, you will have to use your influence with the general to make him bring me back to take over from you the job of tractor adviser. Furthermore, this whole unfortunate situation is your fault, because you are the guy that recommended me to a general who is so lacking in a sense of humor that he takes me literally when I jokingly pretend to volunteer for something I had no idea he would let me do. So it is up to you to help me out. Otherwise, instead of taking an active, important part in winning the war, I shall be condemned to an indeterminate period of subnormal inactivity in a subterranean French cellar.

Yours, with as much hopefulness as is possible under the circumstances,

ALEXANDER BOTTS.

ENGLAND, June 2, 1944.

DEAR BOTTS: General Bessemer handed me your letter when I arrived in London this morning. He says he will give you this note before your departure, which he says is set for tomorrow.

I am sorry that I shall not be able to see you off, and I want to assure you that I am most happy to be out of the madhouse that is Washington, and engaged on the interesting job of tractor adviser to General Bessemer. I would not think of interfering with the glorious mission for which you have so gallantly volunteered. I congratulate you on your courage and devotion to duty. And my only regret is that I am too old to embark on this wonderful adventure myself.

Yours, with admiration and respect,

GILBERT HENDERSON.

IN THE CELLAR,
Sunday evening,
June 4, 1944.

DEAR HENDERSON: This is to report that Alexander Botts has landed, and the situation is completely

haywire. Instead of too little, there is too much to do.
The Germans are all around us. The tractor won't run,
because all the fuel has leaked out. My attempts to get
more fuel have stirred up what amounts to a civil war
among the local French inhabitants. And if you don't help
me, I will be a blowed-up sucker.

This message—in cipher, and on microfilm—is being
sent, along with my report to General Bessemer, by homing pigeon. It is my earnest hope that you two can devise
some means of assisting me. And, in order that you may
appreciate the urgency of the situation, I will give you a
full account of what has happened so far.

My one-man invasion of France was effected early
last night. In total darkness, soaked by the rain, and chilled
by a raw wind, I waded up the dismal beach, still desper-
ately seasick from the long trip in the small boat. I was
wearing my Army uniform—which General Bessemer had
assured me would make the Germans "slightly less" apt
to shoot me as a spy in case they caught me. On my back
was a small coop containing a mournfully cooing pigeon
named Patsy, supplied by the Army Signal Corps, and in
my heart was the depressing memory of your congratula-
tory letter and all the sickening sentimentality with which
you prated of your regret that you were too old to embark
on this "wonderful adventure" yourself.

By the time I had climbed the bank, I was ready to
go back again, but the boat had already departed. And
almost at once I was met by a little old lady with an um-
brella.

"Ah!" she said. "It is mon Capitaine Botts, non?"

"Correct," I replied.

"Welcome to la belle France!" she said. "I am Maman Laffitte—the grandmother of Georges. We have received the radio code message that you come. It is Papa
who should meet you—Papa, he is my husband—but he
has himself what you call the bad cold in the head. So I
am here. Come with me."

With Patsy, the pigeon, still cooing away in his coop on my back, I followed, in the rain and the mud, along hedgerows, across brooks, and through forests. At several places we made detours to avoid German patrols. It was so dark I could hardly see anything. But Maman knew the country. Although she must have been seventy or eighty years old, she led the way with a sure tread. She was cheerful, confident and courageous. A very remarkable old lady, I decided—a regular old war horse, and a very fine person to have on our side in a war.

After many miles we came to a small stone house at the edge of a village on the side of a hill. This was St. Pierre-en-Bessin. A short distance up the slope a larger building loomed against the dull sky.

"Voila le Grand Hotel de l'Universe et de Saint Pierre-en-Bessin," said Maman. "It belongs to Papa and me. But the Boches have taken it. So Papa and I now live in this little house down here."

We cautiously approached, and she took me through the door and into a pantry, where we had some bread and cheese and water. She explained that an interesting little cask on the shelf contained only vinegar; alas, they had no more wine. Her next move was to hustle me, without any unnecessary modesty, out of my rain-soaked uniform and into a pair of pants and a shirt belonging to Papa. Then, still carrying my silly pigeon, I followed her into a sort of machinery shed that adjoined the house. At the rear was a huge wooden cupboard which swung back on ball-bearing hinges which she said had been constructed by her clever grandson, Georges, out of Earthworm tractor parts. Stepping around the cupboard, and closing it behind us, we entered the secret wine cellar.

It was a large, barrel-vaulted chamber extending back under the hill behind the shed, and lighted by a single candle. At one side was the big Earthworm tractor, apparently in perfect shape. On the other side stood an army cot, a printing press, photographic apparatus and radio equipment. As I deposited my pigeon coop in a corner, a frail and very distinguished-looking old gentleman rose from a chair beside a table, and laid down a pair of earphones. Maman introduced him as Papa Laffitte, her husband. Like Maman, and like most French hotelkeepers, he spoke English after a fashion.

"Mon capitaine!" he exclaimed, with a courtly bow. "Beloved ally! Courageous emissary of our great sister republic in America! With the most great pleasure, I salute you and beg you to be the welcome. We have prepared this couch"—he pointed to the cot—"because we think you must desire to sleep beside your tracteur. If you have other desires, you have but to command——"

"Et les Boches?" interrupted Maman.

"Rein," said Papa. He turned to me and explained: "My grandson, before departing, has installed a microphone under the floor of the taproom of the hotel—where the German officers meet. We listen down here. We learn important news, which we send to England. Very soon tonight we have here a conference of the underground, the Maquis, so I have listened with the hope of having news for them. But there is nothing. The Boche must be asleep."

Papa sat down and blew his nose long and loud—there could be no doubt that he had a bad cold—and I had a moment to size up these interesting characters. They were both splendid people, and they were very different. I decided that Maman was the practical executive who had probably run the business of the hotel, while Papa had acted as the gracious host, charming the guests with his delightful manner and distinguished personality.

But, at the moment, I was mainly interested in the tractor, As near as I could tell without actually running it, the machine was okay except for a loose connection in the fuel line, which, as I have previously indicated, had let all the fuel run out of the tank and soak away into the dirt floor of the cellar. Papa and Maman had no more fuel on hand. And, what was infinitely worse, they could suggest no method of getting any.

"At a pinch," I said, "our Earthworm Diesel motors can burn almost any combustible liquid—palm oil, cotton-seed oil, olive oil—even hard liquor."

"In other times we have had the oil of olive," said Maman. "But since the war all fat and oil has near disappeared. One would be at pains to find a single cupful. And the Germans have drunk up all our alcohol so that now even they have no more."

My eye lit on a small cask of perhaps ten gallons capacity, exactly like the one I had seen in the pantry. "What is that?" I asked.

"A cask of Calvados," said Maman.

"And what is Calvados?"

"It is a species of liqueur—a sort of eau-de-vie—fabricated from the apples of Normandie."

"What per cent alcohol?"

"Perhaps forty-five—perhaps fifty."

"Swell," I said. "It is not ideal fuel, but it will run the machine for a few hours until something better arrives."

"I do not understand," said Maman, apparently a bit startled.

"It's very simple," I assured her. "I am going to use your apple-jack as fuel for the motor of the tractor."

"Mon Dieu!" said Papa, rising up in a sudden frenzy of emotion. "You do not understand. This Calvados is the special Calvados of my great-grandfather. It has a hundred years of age. It is a veritable nectar of heaven. And you, barbarian from America, call it apple-jack, and announce the intention for employing it in this miserable tracteur——" There was a thud. Papa had fainted on the floor.

By the time Maman and I had got him revived, I was beginning to feel like Public Skunk No. 1. I was conscious of a decidedly hostile attitude on the part of Maman.

And my embarrassment was increased by Papa, who, as soon as his strength returned, insisted on delivering, with gestures, a scientific and historical address admirably contrived to put in their proper place any uncouth Americans who might happen to be present.

"The ignorant canaille," he said, "suppose that the best fruits for making the drinks is the grapes. This is wrong. The best, it is the apples, especially the apples of France. The best apples of France is Normandie. The best of Normandie is Calvados. The best of Calvados is the region of Bessin. And the best of Bessin is the orchard of my great-grandfather, where grow the most perfect apples, the famous pommes Ranettes, from which is made the most divine species of the celestial liquid we call Calvados—with an arome, a bouquet, a saveur, a parfum that is absolutely incomparable, magnifique, merveilleux——"

"All right," I said. "I give up. Let's forget the whole thing."

"My great-grandfather," continued Papa, "was le Colonel Charlemagne Laffitte, a man very important, officier of the Grande Armée of Napoleon, and a true artist in the preparation of this liquid ecstasy, this Calvados. In his old age, in the month of June in the year 1840, he created three small casks of Calvados, so refined, so delicate, so heavenly, that, by comparison, even the most noted of the Grande Champagne Cognac is nothing but a vain friperie, a contemptible gâchis, a thing to cause the mal-de-mer."

"If it's that good," I said, "I will just have to back down. As I said before——"

"I have not finished," said Papa. "You should know that two of the casks of my great-grandfather have, on occasions of importance in the past, been emptied. One is now in the house, filled with humble vinegar, and the second has been stolen by the Germans at the hotel. There remains only the third—which was directed in my great-grandfather's will to be guarded for one hundred years and consumed at a grande fête of his descendants to commemorate the solidarity of the Famille Laffitte. In June, 1940, the occasion was prepared, but the Boche arrived too soon. So the third, and last, cask is here before you, waiting until the liberation of France shall make possible a joyful reunion of our family."

During the course of these remarks, a half dozen members of the underground had drifted in for their meeting. All were residents of the village and relatives of Papa and Maman. And when they learned that a smart aleck from America had actually planned to use their ancestral nectar in a Diesel engine, there was an outburst that I feared would arouse the Germans in the hotel. They felt that anyone who could even think of such a sacrilege was not to be trusted. They regarded me, not as one who had come to help liberate la Belle France, but as a criminal more obnoxious than Hitler. They became so hostile Papa had to come to my defense.

He admitted that I was crazy, like most Americans, but he insisted that I meant well. He reminded his relatives that he was the head of the family and the official guardian of the cask. He said the tractor had to have fuel, and he threatened that if the time for action arrived, and there was nothing else available, he might be forced, in spite of everything, to sacrifice the Calvados.

This precipitated the condition verging on civil war that I mentioned earlier in this letter. There was angry muttering. There were dark threats. Even Maman seemed to be definitely against me. But Papa, with his air of quiet dignity, managed to quell the rebels, and they finally went resentfully home.

Papa then assured me, in a voice trembling with emotion, that he would stand by what he had said. He would if absolutely necessary, permit me to use the Calvados in the tractor.

"What about Maman?" I asked. "Will she allow it?"

"She will do as I command," said Papa. "In France, the wife always obeys the husband—he is the master."

To this Maman, at the moment, made no reply. Neither did I. But I wondered. And, before long, it being almost dawn, the old folks said good night, Papa politely, Maman curtly, and retired to the house to get some sleep.

Since then I have been sitting on my cot beside the tractor, writing this letter. And I hope that by the time you have read this far you will realize the incredible difficulties of my position. As previously noted, there is little chance of finding any fuel here. But I cannot run the tractor without it. And if I use the precious Calvados, even with the permission of Papa and the somewhat doubtful acquiescence of Maman, I am sure to inspire, in the local patriots, an undying hatred of America.

The only solution, therefore, is for you and General Bessemer to send me some fuel from England, either by parachute or boat. You can consult Georges about the best method, and then send a cipher radio message telling us where and when to pick the stuff up.

I will get Papa to put this letter into cipher and onto microfilm, and attach it to little Patsy's leg. Papa will take the noble bird to a near-by woods where it will be safe to release her. I can then only hope and pray that she may succeed in her perilous trip across the Channel, and that you and the general will have enough sense to send me that fuel, and send it quick.

Yours beseechingly,
ALEXANDER BOTTS.

RADIO MESSAGE

ENGLAND, JUNE 5, 1944. 6 P.M.

BOTTS: TOO LATE TO SEND FUEL. FILL TRACTOR TANK WITH ANYTHING YOU CAN GET AND STAND BY READY TO MOVE AT AN INSTANT'S NOTICE.

HENDERSON.

FRANCE, June 10, 1944.

DEAR HENDERSON: After sending you my pigeon message on the morning of June fifth, I went to bed and slept till early evening, awakening with a bad cold, brought on, no doubt, by my exposure to the elements on the previous night. I put on my uniform, now dried out, and joined Papa and Maman at the radio listening post on the opposite side of the cellar.

They reported that by means of their microphone they had heard the Germans in the taproom of the hotel say that they had just received about fifty litres of schnapps, which, to Maman's disgust, they had stored in the stolen ancestral cask under the bar. This schnapps, being a sort of highly potent white mule, distilled, I believe, from potatoes, was a possibility for the tractor, but it inspired us with little hope, because we agreed that any attempt to steal it from under the very noses of the Germans would be too risky.

So Papa and I spent the next few hours gloomily sympathizing with each other's miserable colds, while Maman went off to the other side of the village to spend the night with a niece who was ill.

It was late in the evening when your radio message, somewhat delayed, came through. Papa, between spells of sneezing and blowing his nose, deciphered it. Then he rose to the occasion in a way that was truly noble, but made me feel like a low reptile.

"Mon capitaine," he said, "this can mean but one thing—the great invasion—the liberation of la Belle France. Le jour de gloire is arrived. You must be ready with your great tractor. So we must consummate the great tragedy. We must sacrifice the divine Calvados."

"But how about Maman? Will she let us get by with this?"

"She will accept what I say. She is an obedient wife. Besides, she is at the far end of the village. That which she does not know will make for her no harm."

"Well——"

"But you will pardon me if I do not remain to assist at this dreadful sacrifice—it would be more than my failing strength could support. I must go. Bon soir, and I wish you the most great success."

Papa departed with tears running down his honest old face.

I did not feel so good myself. But I resolutely turned to the work in hand. I worked the wooden plug out of the bunghole of the cask. I sniffed, but the cold in my head had blocked my sense of smell. The supposedly divine aroma was lost to me. Perhaps, however, I could still taste. Cautiously I tilted the cask and poured a minute quantity into a clean beaker from the photographic laboratory. I took a sip. It was good. I poured myself a respectable drink. Possibly I had several—I cannot quite remember.

And then a strange thing occurred. Instead of befuddling the intellect, this remarkable liqueur seemed to have the property of inspiring a quality of thought so lucid and so logical that I was astonished.

Obviously, this Calvados was too heavenly to use in the tractor. How dumb I had been even to consider such an unspeakable crime! But I had to have fuel, and the only answer was the schnapps in the taproom of the hotel. At one time we had considered the theft of this schnapps too risky. But now that I was thinking more clearly, the risk did not seem to bother me.

All I had to do was sneak up and grab the stuff. I would be bold, but I would also be cunning. I would leave another cask in place of the one I removed, so the Germans would not notice their loss.

I sprang to action. I replaced the plug. Heaving the ten-gallon cask—which must have weighed almost a hundred pounds—to my shoulder, I made my way to the house. Leaving this cask of Calvados for safekeeping in the pantry, I shouldered the exactly similar cask of vinegar, and staggered outdoors and up the hill.

I found the back door of the hotel, and I found the

taproom. The Germans were all upstairs. I left the vinegar under the bar and I got back to the cellar with the cask of schnapps. The deed was done.

Before I had time to pour the schnapps into the tractor, I was startled by a sound like distant thunder. I slipped out to see what was going on. The night sky was full of planes, and for half an hour I watched great bombs bursting around the airport. Could it be that this was the prelude to the invasion?

I returned to the cellar, and ran right into Maman.

"Hello!" I said. "I didn't know you were coming back. Why didn't you tell us?"

"Because," said Maman, "if Papa had known all I was going to do, he would have forbidden it. So I did not tell him, because I did not wish to disobey. I am always the obedient wife."

"Oh," I said. "And what have you been doing?"

Maman smiled proudly. "I have just moved the vinegar from the pantry to the taproom. I have returned with the vile schnapps, which you can use for your motor. And I will now carry the good Calvados to the house of my niece, where I can guard it safe."

With these words the magnificent old war horse swung the heavy cask to her shoulder and departed.

It took me a full minute to figure out what had actually happened. The three casks looked exactly alike. And Maman had been fooled. Instead of taking the vinegar to the Germans in the hotel, she had made them a present of her beloved Calvados. She had left me the vinegar—which would be no good in the tractor. And she had walked off with the wretched schnapps.

As soon as I realized the full horror of the situation, I dashed after Maman. But it was too late—she had disappeared in the darkness. By this time the bombers had gone. Big shells, perhaps from battleships in the Channel, were forming a sort of box barrage around the airport. Suddenly the barrage stopped. More planes came over. The sky was filled with parachutes.

I could wait no longer. The time had almost come when the tractor would be needed, and needed bad. I rushed up the hill. A group of Germans coming down were too excited to pay any attention to me. I entered the hotel. I carried down the Calvados. I poured it into the tractor, and then looked outside again.

There was a brisk fight in the streets. Then silence. American soldiers appeared. The town was ours.

The rest was routine. I ran the tractor, coughing and sputtering, to the airport. By the time the Calvados was used up, a supply of regular fuel had arrived by parachute. And within a few hours I had filled all shell holes and bomb craters, and smoothed the runway so the transports could land with the troops and equipment that were needed to smash the German counterattack—all of which would have been impossible without the tractor.

But how can I take any satisfaction in this glorious victory? What is the good of liberating these splendid French people if, in so doing, we destroy their most cherished possessions? After depriving Papa and Maman of their treasured Calvados, I no longer have the courage to look them in the face. Since D day I have been hiding here at the Army camp at the far end of the airport, hoping for an order from General Bessemer that will take me far from the scene of my crime.

Perhaps, Henderson, you could influence the general to issue such an order. After all, you got me into this. So it is only fair that you should now lend a helping hand to

Your unfortunate former sales manager,
ALEXANDER BOTTS.

FRANCE, June 11, 1944.

DEAR HENDERSON: When I wrote you yesterday afternoon, I thought my fortunes had reached an absolute low. But last night the situation deteriorated even further. Maman suddenly appeared at the camp and dragged me over to the taproom of the hotel, where, to my unspeakable horror, I found a huge gathering of the Famille Laffitte, milling happily around a cask which they supposed contained their ancestral Calvados, and which they were preparing to open for the long-awaited celebration. Maman presented me as the guest of honor. I tried to tell them the cask contained nothing but vile schnapps, but my courage failed.

Then Papa made a remark that handed me a real jolt. "I do not know what you used in the tractor," he said, "but apparently it worked. So now I am glad I changed my mind and secretly moved the Calvados to a safe place."

"What!" I said. "Did you move some of those casks too?"

"I did."

This really knocked me for a row of cylinder heads. If all three of us had been monkeying with those casks, maybe none of us know what we were doing. I called Maman. We compared notes. And, after a general exchange of information, we were able to work out the true story of what actually happened that night—which can be explained, with the utmost simplicity, as follows:

After I had moved the Calvados from the cellar to the pantry, the vinegar from the pantry to the taproom, and the schnapps from the taproom to the cellar, Papa came along, full of good intentions but ignorant of what I had done, and moved what he thought was the vinegar from the pantry to the cellar, and what he thought was the Calvados from the cellar to the pantry, with the intention of later moving what he thought was the vinegar from the cellar to the taproom, and bringing back what he supposed would be the schnapps to the cellar so that I could use it in the tractor, but the falling bombs scared him out of making the latter two moves, and all he actually accomplished was to move the Calvados from the pantry to the cellar, and the schnapps from the cellar to the pantry, so when Maman arrived, knowing nothing of what Papa and I had done, and moved what she thought was the vinegar from the pantry to the taproom, what she thought was the schnapps from the taproom to the cellar, and what she thought was the Calvados from the cellar to her niece's house, she was actually moving the schnapps from the pantry to the taproom, the vinegar from the taproom to the cellar, and the Calvados from the cellar to her niece's house, and it was then natural for me to suppose, after I had heard Maman's story, but not Papa's, that what she had done was move the vinegar from the taproom to the cellar, the Calvados from the pantry to the taproom, and the schnapps from the cellar to her niece's house, so, later on, when I moved what I thought was the Calvados from the taproom to the cellar, I was really moving the schnapps, and it was therefore the schnapps that I actually used in the tractor, and the Calvados was safe all the time at the house of Maman's niece, from where it was brought to the party, all of which is easy to understand now that I have explained it so clearly.

The important part is that the Calvados was saved. It was there at the party. And when Papa opened it up, the entire room at once became suffused with an atmosphere like apple-blossom time in Normandy. It was an occasion absolument inoubliable. Everybody kissed each other on both cheeks. Georges, the grandson, arrived from England with the news that I had been promoted from captain to major. And everybody yelled "Vive la France!"—"Vive l'Amerique!"—"Vive Papa et Maman!"—"Vive le Commandant Botts!"—"Vive le General Aysen-ovair!"— "Vive le General de Gaulle!"—"Vive everybody and everything!"

So you ought to have a medal, Henderson, for getting me into this affair, because when a real American like me starts working with genuine French people like the Laffitte tribe, the whole project moves along just like this Calvados, with an arome, a bouquet, a saveur, a parfum, and a potency that is incomparable, incroyable, merveilleux, and pretty much all right.

Yours, with meilleures salutations,

MAJOR ALEXANDER BOTTS.

THE BOTTS PLAN FOR A
LASTING PEACE

SOMEWHERE IN GERMANY,
Monday, October 9, 1944.

MR. GILBERT HENDERSON,
PRESIDENT EARTHWORM TRACTOR COMPANY,
GRAND HOTEL DE L'EST, PARIS, FRANCE.

DEAR HENDERSON: This is to remind you that
I am no longer sales manager of the Earthworm Company. I am an officer in the Army of the United States.
Hence, you have no authority over me any more. And I
would be much obliged if you would keep your meddlesome
nose out of my business. The above remarks are inspired by
information I have received from a certain Lieutenant
West, just arrived from Paris, who reports that he saw
you there at the Grand Hotel de l'Est, and that you told
him you were trying to get the higher command to have me
transferred to a new job in some distant but undisclosed
locality.

Please lay off this stuff. At the moment, I am engaged
in building about a mile of road just inside the German
border—a job which has certain aspects of such vital and
world-shaking importance that I am planning to write a
book on the subject, under the title: The Botts Plan For a
Lasting Peace; or, What Shall We Do With the Germans
After the War?

As I am the only person with the insight and under-
standing to carry through this project, I naturally do not
want to be interrupted. So I hope that from now on you
will confine your activities to your own affairs.

Cordially yours,
ALEXANDER BOTTS,
Major, Corps of Engineers.

230

PARIS,
Wednesday, October 11, 1944.

DEAR BOTTS: After reading your recent letter, I wish to assure you that I do not consider I have done anything to which you can properly take exception.

When General Bessemer—whom I am accompanying as a civilian technical adviser—arrived in Paris last week, he learned that a good tractor man is urgently needed on a certain project whose nature and location I am not at present permitted to divulge. The general consulted me. Naturally, I recommended you. And as I do not understand how merely building a mile of road can have any world-shaking importance or contribute toward a lasting peace, I see no reason for withdrawing my recommendation.

Most sincerely,
GILBERT HENDERSON.

GERMANY,
Saturday, October 14, 1944.

DEAR HENDERSON: As long as you won't take my word for it, I suppose I shall have to give you a complete account of what I am doing, to the end that you may understand exactly why any interference with my present activities would be a tragic mistake. Lieutenant West, who is returning to Paris, has consented to take this letter, so I can write without any fear of possible censorship. As I do not want to strain your mind, I will begin with a simple statement of the facts in the case, working up gradually to the more abstruse international and intellectual angles.

One day last week, General McAndrews, who is the head man in this particular area of rain and mud, put me in charge of a small fleet of Earthworm tractors, bulldozers, wheel scrapers and graders, and directed me to build about a mile of road in a bridgehead which we have recently established just inside the German border on the far side of a river, which winds through a narrow valley, and which, as I am loath to divulge anything resembling a military secret, even in the absence of censorship, I will refer to as the Mosel, because maybe that is not it.

The road that I am building starts at the far end of a recently placed American pontoon bridge, angles up the steep side of the valley a half mile in one direction, and then doubles back to the rear of an ancient castle, where it connects with an existing highway leading directly to the front lines, several miles distant. The castle, which I will call Schloss Karlsburg, stands near the edge of the plateau at the top of a steep, vineyard-covered slope several hundred feet above the end of the bridge. The upper part of the old building, except for one small tower, has been knocked down by shellfire and bombs. Great piles of rubble have damned up water from the incessant rains, so that the moat has overflowed and flooded the lower portions of the castle. The whole place is thus an incredible mess, but it provides a splendid supply of broken stone for road building.

The road-building project itself is perfectly simple and straightforward. With my high-grade Earthworm equipment, I should, under normal conditions, have already completed at least half of the job. But war is seldom normal.

A few hours after he had assigned me the job, General McAndrews suddenly arrived in a jeep and took away all my men and most of my fuel for some urgent mission involving the quick repair and resupply of a tractor-drawn artillery outfit that had just taken a bit of a mauling from the enemy. The general, with easy nonchalance, remarked that he would expect me to proceed with the road regardless, and he then departed for his headquarters to the rear, leaving me standing mournfully in the rain, contemplating the problem, so to speak, of making bricks without straw, which, to a man of my resourcefulness, was in no way hopeless, because, after all, bricks can be—and usually are—made without straw.

While I was casting about for a good plan of action, my attention was attracted to a near-by barbed wire enclosure, in which several hundred German prisoners were sitting about in rude shacks, enjoying complete and luxurious idleness, while all the Americans in the neighborhood were out in the weather, badly overworked, and while I was confronted with a truly critical manpower shortage.

Something, I decided, should be done about this. I approached the stockade. I told the officer in charge that I was from G-2, and had been ordered to question the prisoners. This minor subterfuge worked very nicely. I was promptly admitted. And, after nosing about for a short time, I made one of the luckiest finds of my entire career—a very high-grade middle-aged German called Otto Krebs, who is a mechanic by trade, and who speaks very good English, having once spent a couple of years working for Henry Ford in Detroit.

When I asked him if he wanted a job driving an Earthworm tractor on a road-building project, his whole face lit up with joy.

"I love the Earthworm tractor!" he said. "And I understand the Earthworm tractor, because it has a Diesel motor, and when I was a young man I worked at the Diesel factory in Aachen. I was under the direct command of the great Herr Doktor Rudolf Diesel himself!"

"Splendid!" I said. "And have you any friends around here who can handle machinery?"

"I have many. Most of us here are not really soldiers. We are older men—mechanics and factory workers—who have just lately been taken into the army. We are happy to be prisoners. All we want now is to go home. Until that is possible, we are glad to work at any peaceful job."

"I want to be fair with you, Otto," I said. "If you take this job, you'll be working on a road that will carry supplies to our Army—which is fighting your army."

"It is not our army. It is Hitler's army."

"You birds were all in it, weren't you?"

"We were forced in, Major—uh——"

"Botts is the name," I said.

"I am so glad to meet you, Major Botts. And I hope you will believe me when I tell you that most of us Germans are good people. We are honest and hard-working. And we do not want to hurt anybody—especially our good friends, the Americans. We did not want this war any more than you did."

"Who did want it, then?"

"Not the common people like us. It is the people higher up that always make the wars. The other time it was the Kaiser and the generals. This time it is Hitler and the Nazis. When these people higher up—the ones that have the power—say there will be a war, how can we poor workmen stop them? When they order us into the army and tell us to fight, there is nothing we can do but obey."

"You might tell 'em where to go," I suggested.

"It would do no good," said Otto. "They would only shoot us."

"Well," I said, "I used to know a lot of Germans back in 1919, and they all seemed like honest, peaceful, solid citizens. That was after the other war, when I was in the American Army of Occupation a little way over the hills here near Cochem-an-der-Mosel."

"What! You have been to Cochem-an-der-Mosel, Major Botts? Why, my Uncle Heinrich was born in Cochem-an-der-Mosel!"

"Imagine that," I said. "This is getting to be like old-home week."

But Otto was very serious and earnest. He said, "If you have known the Germans at such places as Cochem-an-der-Mosel, Major Botts, you know that what I say is true. We Germans are a peaceful race, and we are victims of the Nazis even more than you are. We hate the Nazis. We love the Americans. Now that you have delivered us, we are ready to work with you for a better world. And we will prove it right now. We will work hard and faithfully under your orders to build this road that will help to make shorter the war and bring back the peace that we all desire so much."

"All right, Otto," I said. "It's a deal. You get together a couple of dozen of your pals, and we'll be on our way."

Note: I have given the above conversation at considerable length, so that you can see I am still very much the sophisticated man of the world. I did not accept this fellow's protestations of friendship until I had given him a rather severe questioning and satisfied myself that he was on the level.

While old Otto was splashing through the mud from shack to shack, rounding up his friends, I ran into a temporary setback—the officer in charge of the stockade refused to let me take out any prisoners without an order from higher authority. As the man was too dumb to listen intelligently to my arguments, I got into a jeep and drove back over the slippery roads to division headquarters, where I found General McAndrews on the point of leaving for an inspection of the rear supply lines. When I stated my errand, he merely said it was against the Geneva Convention —whatever that may be—to work prisoners so near the front lines, and he then hurried away, leaving me alone in his tent—and also in a quandary.

I now had two orders from the general—to build the road, and to leave the prisoners alone. I could see no way to carry out both. So I quite naturally decided to disregard the one which I felt the general would have considered the least important if he had listened to my explanations. Seating myself, therefore, at the general's typewriter, and using some of the general's official stationery, which he had carelessly left lying around, I wrote out an order authorizing myself to use such prisoners as I might need. After adding a reasonably good facsimile of the general's signature,

I hurried back to the stockade, and within an hour thereafter I had started road-building operations with the aid of good old Otto and twenty-four of his comrades.

From the very start it was evident that my plan was a success. The men turned out to be splendid mechanics and splendid workers. They obeyed orders promptly and willingly, and they handled the machinery skillfully and efficiently. Even the lousy weather did not seem to bother them; probably they are so used to it that they don't realize how bad it is.

With our bulldozers and graders we began carving out the road through the vineyards along the hillside. We shaped the greasy mud into a subgrade. With our big forty-yard wheeled scraper we hauled and spread the broken stone from the castle. The work went along with speed and precision.

I was pleased to find that I remembered enough of my 1919 Army of Occupation German to issue simple orders, and whenever I got into difficulties, old Otto was always there to act as interpreter. He also handled the job of master mechanic, and on top of this he provided me with information of incalculable value. At the very start of operations he told me the Germans had stored in the cellar of the castle several thousand cans of gasoline and Diesel fuel which they had been unable to remove because of the flooding of the place. He also warned me that German demolition squads had mined the river at the point where they thought we might put our pontoon bridge, and that they had run concealed wires up to the tower of the castle. It was Otto's opinion that his erstwhile Nazi comrades planned to explode the mines from the castle, but that they had retreated so fast they missed the opportunity. As we have had no time to drag the river, and as a careful search of the tower has uncovered nothing, it is possible Otto may be mistaken in this.

But his other report was magnificently correct. Using a couple of the bulldozers, we gouged out a ditch about four feet wide and six feet deep through the rubble piles and down the hill. This drained the moat and the cellar, and uncovered more fuel than we can use in a month, exactly where Otto said it would be. The stuff is all nicely packaged for us in these handy little German cans of about five-gallon capacity, which have much better spouts than our American fuel cans.

Each night my men go back into the stockade, where, as a reward for their good conduct, I have been able to supply them with better beds and blankets than they had before. At noon they get extra food, which I have contrived to steal from a near-by supply dump. I have also got them raincoats. The stockade commander insists on sending along one MP with a tommy gun when the prisoners are outside the stockade, but this is hardly necessary, as all the men are so docile and so loyal to me that they would not dream of making any trouble.

All in all, my plan is so successful that I have decided to expand the program. When this road job is finished— probably sometime next week—I will persuade General McAndrews, instead of sending my prisoners to the rear, to let me keep them, and to assign me more prisoners, which I will use in ever-increasing numbers on the various construction projects which are sure to come up as we continue our advance.

By giving these poor people the advantage of my enlightened leadership and providing a constructive outlet for their energies, I will build up their self-respect and win their complete coöperation. In this way we can get rid of our enemies by making them our friends. Instead of poisoning our minds with thoughts of hatred and revenge, and forcing the Germans into a mood of sullen resentment which would inevitably cause them to start another war in the next twenty years, I will steer them into the paths of righteousness by sheer kindness.

As previously stated, I am now writing up these ideas in what will eventually emerge as a very long and impressive book—to the end that my methods may become the basis of our entire policy for the postwar reconditioning of the German people, and the re-establishment of the German nation as an asset rather than a liability in the family of nations.

Now that I have explained the importance of what I am doing, I am sure, Henderson, you will agree that any interruption of my present activities would be as hideous a disaster as the Senate rejection, in 1919, of the League of Nations. So I will close with the firm conviction that you will promptly kill that order assigning me to another job.

Yours,

ALEXANDER BOTTS.

PARIS,
Tuesday, October 17, 1944.

DEAR BOTTS: Your letter is here, and I must confess that I am distinctly skeptical regarding your grandiose plan for remaking the world, and I am a bit worried for fear some of your more impulsive actions—such as copying a general's signature—may get you into difficulties.

However, that is your affair. As you so justly point out, I no longer have any authority over you. Nor do I wish to interfere unnecessarily in your activities. Consequently, as you will not be needed for at least two weeks in the new job we had in mind for you, I have persuaded General Bessemer to hold back your transfer, the order for which is already in his hands.

The general and I are leaving tomorrow for London, where you may address me at the Templeton Hotel. The general will take with him the order in question. If, within the next few days, you can get this General McAndrews to approve the continuation of your German-prisoner project, let me know, and I can probably get General Bessemer to cancel your transfer. If I do not hear from you in ten days, the transfer will go through.

I hope you will appreciate my fairness in this matter, and my desire to further your best interests.

Very sincerely yours,

GILBERT HENDERSON.

GERMANY,
Friday, October 20, 1944.

DEAR HENDERSON: Why did you let that general take my transfer order all the way to London? If, as you claim, you had really desired to further my best interests, you would have sent the order to me personally, so I could have used it when needed. Right now, I need it bad.

I have decided, for one reason and another, that I had better get out of this place before there is any more trouble. As your friend the general is holding back the order telling me where to go, I can obey only the first part of it by leaving here and going as far as Paris, where I will stop at that Hotel de l'Est, and where I want you to send me the order as quick as possible, so I can go on to wherever I am supposed to go. I hope it will be fairly far away. Considering the situation here, I should be perfectly happy to go to some place like the Central Pacific or even the South Pole.

In order that you may appreciate my reasons for this sudden change of plan, I will try to describe for you the sudden and totally unexpected reign of terror and violence which recently erupted into the peace and quiet of this section of the battle area, and which has created the situation which makes it seem wise for me to transfer my activities elsewhere.

When my prisoners reported for work this morning, everything seemed propitious. The weather, for a change, was fair. The sun was warm. Except for a few minor finishing touches, the road was finished—and a splendid job it was, if I do say so myself. The only remaining work of any consequence was the repair of a puncture in one of the tires of our biggest scraper—the forty-yard model. As you know, this is no bicycle tire; it is one of the largest pneumatic-rubber jobs in the world, being about nine feet in diameter and weighing pretty near two tons. Since the handling of such a monstrosity presents real difficulties, I put my entire force on this one job. After a few instructions from me, good old Otto took charge in his usual earnest and efficient way and directed his twenty-four willing comrades in the work of cribbing up under the pan, elevating the wheel, prying off the enormous casing, easing it down on its side, removing the voluminous inner tube, patching the hole, re-inserting the tube and partially inflating it, preparatory to wrestling it back on the rim.

By the time the work had reached this stage, I had ceased paying much attention to the details—which were being handled so competently by good old Otto. I was lean-ing idly against the far side of the scraper, which was parked at the brow of the hill between the one remaining tower of the castle and our big drainage ditch. I was en-joying the sunshine, gazing meditatively out over the beauti-ful Mosel Valley, and congratulating myself on the success of our enterprise. I noted the distant woods and fields and vineyards, and the villages across the river. I looked down at the bridge far beneath me, and at the intermittent traffic which came across and rolled off up the river road. My eye proudly followed the course of our beautiful new road, which would soon provide a shorter route to the front. I saw our one MP, whom I had posted at the foot of the hill to keep traffic from using the new road until we were ready for it. From far away I could hear the dull thunder of the artillery at the front. But in the immediate neigh-borhood everything was so calm and peaceful that I began to doubt whether such a condition could last. Well, it didn't.

There was a sudden commotion amongst the prisoners. I peered around the end of the scraper. From the door of the castle tower, in some recess of which he had doubtless been hiding for days, there emerged a very large and very tough-looking German officer. From his insignia I judged he was a colonel. With long military strides he advanced to the group of prisoners.

He jerked up his arm in a stiff Nazi salute, and then let go in a booming voice, "Heil Hitler!"

At once, with an automatic precision that astounded me, every one of those docile prisoners, including Otto, snapped to attention. They seemed to arrange themselves, almost unconsciously, in mathematically straight rows, like the pine trees in these planted German forests. Out shot their arms, "Heil Hitler!" they yelled. Down came their arms. Then, still standing rigidly at attention, they listened with respectful attention while the officer began sounding off with a long harangue.

By this time I had ducked back behind the scraper, where I was out of sight, but where I was in a position to hear what went on. And my 1919 German was still good enough for me to understand the gist of the officer's remarks. He told these men that there were very few *amerikanische Soldaten* in the immediate vicinity—which was true. He said he was going to blow up the bridge, thus preventing any interference from our forces across the river. Then they would bring gasoline from the cellar, pour it over our equipment and destroy it by fire. Next they would attempt to rescue the other prisoners in the stockade and make a break for their own lines.

After completing this interesting outline of his plans, the officer barked out a few sharp commands, and the entire group of Germans, with good old Otto right out in front, started moving obediently toward the door of the cellar where the gasoline was stored.

This was too much for me. I popped out from behind the scraper and let out a yell, "Hey, there, Otto! Pay no attention to this Nazi! You're not working for him any more! You're working for me!"

The German officer had an answer to this. He

promptly ordered those Germans to grab me and to do it *schnell*. They turned. They started after me.

Fortunately they had no firearms, and I had a head start. Furthermore, these jerries were a bit heavy and slow, while I have always been notably light on my feet. When faced with danger, I can move with all the speed of a young and graceful gazelle. On this occasion I outdid myself. Plunging straight down the slope through the bean-pole trellises of the vineyard, I soon left my pursuers far behind and, with Sir Isaac Newton to aid me, I reached the bottom in record time.

I leaped into a cute little twenty-horsepower Earthworm tractor, equipped with bulldozer blade, which was parked at the lower end of our new road. I picked up the lone MP with the tommy gun and started for the top of the slope. I didn't bother to follow the long loop of the new road. I took a short cut right up the big drainage ditch. The bottom of the ditch was slippery with mud. The slope, in places, was at least forty-five degrees. But the magnificent little Earthworm dug in its toenails and clawed its way upward in a way that filled my heart with joy and pride.

Looking ahead, I saw the prisoners had gathered near the top of the ditch. After returning from their futile attempt to catch me, they had apparently noted the beginning of my return trip, and had reported the news to the German officer. The officer had issued some sort of order. And the whole gang had started heaving and tugging at something on the ground.

I looked more intently. It was the big tire. They slid it sidewise and slowly eased it down until it stood upright in the ditch. Then I understood. The tire was a weapon—a two-ton juggernaut that stood nine feet high, all rubber and a yard wide. They were going to roll it down the ditch and squash me and the MP in the wreckage of our baby tractor.

By this time we were halfway up the ditch. It was too late to retreat. The ditch was at least six feet deep. The sides were wet, slippery and straight up and down. I couldn't climb the tractor out. I doubted if I could even climb out myself. Far ahead, I could see the mighty tire beginning to roll. It was just back of the brow of the hill. and moving very slowly. But it had almost reached the steep part of the ditch. When it once hit the forty-five-degree slope, it would come down on us like a dive bomber.

After analyzing the situation as thoroughly as I could in the short space of a fifth of a second, I decided we had only one hope—the bulldozer blade on the front of the tractor. I dropped the blade into the wet dirt in the bottom of the ditch. I opened the throttle. It was no good. The uphill slope was too great, and all I could do was spin the tracks. I coasted back a few rods to a point where a bulge in the hillside reduced the grade, for a short distance, to less than thirty degrees. I tried again. This time the grousers took hold. With two or three rapid passes I scooped out a hole for the tractor two feet deep and ten feet long, piling the dirt in a good-sized mound in front of the machine.

I took another look toward the top of the hill. The German officer was just disappearing into the door of the tower. The huge bulk of the tire, still turning slowly, was now poised at the very brink of the precipitous descent. With morbid fascination I watched the deliberate and ominous progress of that thing—until my attention was suddenly jerked away by a mighty boom behind me.

I turned. Great geysers of water were rising from the river about fifty feet upstream from the bridge. Apparently the Germans had made a slight error in guessing where we would place our bridge. However, a great wave of water swept over it, washing overboard a dozen soldiers who were crossing on foot. A little jeep barely escaped and arrived safely on our side under a deluge of spray—whereupon a sudden hideous yawp from the MP caused me to turn around just in time to see the tire come over the hump and start its awe-inspiring plunge directly toward us.

This, Henderson, was undoubtedly the low point of what had already been a rather trying morning. But probably you would not understand. After all, I don't suppose you have ever sat in a small tractor in the bottom of a steep ditch, waiting to be run over by a rubber doughnut weighing two tons and traveling at a speed apparently approaching that of light. It is something that just cannot be described.

So I will merely state that the MP and I crouched very low in the seat, and pretty soon there was the most incredible noise I ever heard—a whirring and a howling and a sort of long-drawn-out thud—as that mighty mass of rubber hit the sloping mound of earth in front of us and shot past over our heads with a rush of wind and a shower of dirt. A moment later we raised our heads and turned around just in time to see that thing as it rolled out of the ditch at the bottom of the hill, missed the little jeep apparently by inches and disappeared into the river.

At once I threw in the clutch, drove the tractor over the mound of earth, and proceeded rapidly up the ditch to the dry moat, climbed over a pile of rubble and reached the door of the castle cellar just in time to catch the entire gang of prisoners coming out with cans of gasoline. When they saw the tractor and the tommy gun, they rushed back inside.

Not wishing to take any chances with these babies while they were in charge of that Nazi officer, I promptly blocked the door by throwing up a pile of dirt with the bulldozer. We soon found, however, that the officer was not in the cellar. He suddenly came out of the tower— from which he had presumably been observing the results of his attempted bridge demolition. The MP covered him with the tommy gun. He put up his hands and surrendered, and I ordered the MP to march him over and deliver him to the stockade.

As I sat down to consider what to do next, I was interrupted by the arrival of a jeep—the same one that had been showered by water from the mine explosion and then almost hit by the rolling tire. This jeep had driven up my new road. As it stopped I rose to my feet, and General McAndrews got out, dripping wet and pretty mad.

"What goes on here?" he wanted to know.

I hesitated. Somehow I had a feeling that the events of the morning were something like Pearl Harbor—the less said about the whole thing the better for those concerned.

"Well," I began cautiously, "it looked to me as if somebody tried to blow up that bridge."

"There will be an investigation," said the general. "We can't have this kind of thing going on. Besides, it's the first day in two weeks without any natural rain, and somebody blows artificial rain all over me."

"Too bad," I said politely.

"And what was that outlandish doodlebug that came rolling down the hill and almost ran me down?"

Again I hestitated. I averted my eyes, and in so doing I happened to see something down on the river that gave me an idea.

"Sir," I said, "that thing you saw was a big tire off this scraper here. When I saw all those men washed off the bridge, I rolled it down to them to serve as a life raft."

The general looked down at the river. Sure enough, the makeshift liferaft was floating merrily downstream, and the twelve men who had been washed off the bridge were perched safely on top.

"Major Botts," said the general, "you certainly seem to be a man who can think fast in an emergency."

"Yes, sir. Sometimes I think very fast."

"You are to be commended for your quick action," he said, "and also for the fine job you have done on this road. Later on, you can tell me how you managed it—after I took away your men and refused to let you use prisoners. Right now, I'm in a hurry."

He got back in the jeep and whirled away toward the

front, leaving me to meditate on the problem of how I would answer all his questions when he had held his investigation and found out, as he inevitably would, a number of the more embarrassing facts connected with my recent activities.

Suppose he discovered that the wires that exploded those mines were connected to a castle where I was supposedly in charge? How would I explain that? Suppose he learned that my improvised life raft started rolling down the hill before, and not after, the men were washed into the water? I couldn't say it was just fast thinking if I got the answer before I could have legitimately known the problem. And if I explained my use of the prisoners by producing that signed order, how could I explain how that order got signed?

These problems were so tough that for a while I was pretty much nonplused. Then, suddenly, in a flash of inspiration, the answer came to me. I could solve everything, in an honest and straightforward manner, merely by doing my simple duty as a soldier. The chief duty of a soldier, admittedly, is to obey. So all I had to do was to obey that order which your friend General Bessemer has tucked away in London. As promptness is one of the cardinal military virtues, I would obey not only promptly but ahead of time. I would get out of here as fast as possible, and trust my good friend Henderson to send me the order in Paris.

By the time I had reached this decision, the MP had returned and reported the German officer safely incarcerated. I started up the bulldozer and pushed the dirt away from the cellar door. Timidly, the prisoners came out. Now that the hard-boiled officer was gone, they were as gentle and harmless as a flock of sheep.

As we marched them back to the stockade, poor old Otto almost dissolved into tears. "We did not want to do this!" he wailed. "But when one of these officers, who has all the power and authority, comes along, what can we do but obey?"

"You heard me when I yelled at you," I said. "Why didn't you obey me instead of that Nazi? Or do you like him better?"

"Oh, no. We love the Americans. We' hate the Nazis. But we are law-abiding people, so we had to obey this German officer because he is a colonel, while you are only a major. I hope you understand."

"Sure I understand," I said. "So, for your own protection, you are going to stay, from now on, inside a nice safe stockade, where you won't be bothered any more by orders from Nazi officers. I thank you all for the work you have done for me. Good-by and good luck."

As they filed into the stockade, I decided that my book on The Botts Plan for a Lasting Peace, or What Shall We Do With the Germans After the War? will be shorter than I had intended. It will consist of just three words: "Watch them guys."

Yours,

ALEXANDER BOTTS.

OUR GALLANT ALLIES

PALAWANG ISLAND, SOUTH PACIFIC,
Monday, February 5, 1945.

MR. GILBERT HENDERSON,
PRESIDENT EARTHWORM TRACTOR COMPANY,
EARTHWORM BRANCH OFFICE,
MELBOURNE, AUSTRALIA.

DEAR HENDERSON: This is an urgent air-mail appeal from your former sales manager, Alexander Botts, now a major in the Army of the United States. At the moment, I find myself in serious difficulties with an active volcano, and also with a hard-boiled Australian major general under whose command I have been assigned to take charge of a construction company of United States Army Engineers, for the purpose of building an air strip for the Royal Australian Air Force on Bongo Atoll, several hundred miles north of here.

Orders from my United States Army superiors state that I am to co-operate to the fullest possible extent, and do everything I can to promote friendly relations with our gallant Allies, the Australians. Naturally, I am trying to carry out these orders. But I have had bad luck. And if you do not help me, there just is not going to be any international friendship around here at all.

The trouble began yesterday. In the early morning I arrived here by seaplane, landing under a dense cloud of smoke from the Palawang volcano, which was in full eruption a couple of miles back of the port. I promptly reported at the headquarters of Maj. Gen. Reginald W. Griggs, of the Australian army, who commands this entire area.

The general was out, but a member of his staff gave me maps and complete specifications for the Bongo air strip, and told me I was to leave at once, as it was a rush job. It seems the air strip is needed right away as a base for an air patrol to cover a hitherto neglected area through which a certain amount of Japanese shipping has been sneaking.

Returning to the port, I found my new command already on shipboard. The personnel was excellent, but the equipment meager. There was only one tractor—a fifteen-ton Earthworm with bulldozer. But we had a scraper, a trailer, a complete machine shop with welding apparatus mounted on a truck, and plenty of tools. I decided we could get by.

The ship assigned to us was a very small and very old New Guinea river boat called the Wilhelmina, complete with a toy walking beam and cute little paddle wheels. When I expressed doubts about this quaint craft, the captain, a man called Van Horn, assured me the Wilhelmina was perfectly seaworthy—in calm weather. She had often been used between the islands. And, owing to the shipping shortage, she was the best we could get. So that was that.

By the time I had finished checking these details, the smoke had lifted somewhat. Looking toward the volcano, I observed a big stream of lava flowing slowly down the slope directly toward the big Australian army camp at the edge of the settlement. Here indeed was a real emergency, and a great opportunity for me.

Leaping into the big Earthworm tractor on the deck of the Wilhelmina, I started the motor, drove onto the pier, summoned one of the sergeants to come along as a helper, and headed for the volcano. As I passed the camp, an officious Australian officer stopped me.

"What are you planning to do?" he asked.

Even though it seemed none of his business, I answered with true international courtesy. "I am planning to promote good relations between America and Australia by saving the camp, the town and the port from yonder menacing lava stream."

"And just how are you going to do that?"

"By using this bulldozer to throw up a diagonal earth embankment in front of the lava—thus diverting it to one side."

"You will no no such thing," said the officer rudely. "The government vulcanologist from Melbourne has been studying the situation here for several days. He says the eruption has reached its peak. From now on, it will subside. He has assured us there is no danger from the lava. So you may take your bulldozer back where it belongs."

The officer turned, walked to the camp and disappeared into one of the tents.

"Well, I said to the sergeant, "a scientific government expert is probably more reliable than the crackpot economic variety. But even so, I don't see how anybody can be sure about a volcano. I think I shall go ahead."

"Against orders?"

"Certainly. Why should I take orders from that guy?"

"Do you know who he is?"

"No," I said. "And I don't care."

I opened the throttle, and further conversation was drowned in the roar of the motor. Driving through the smoke, which was once more settling down, I soon reached a point about fifty feet in front of the slowly advancing red-hot lava. Here I swung the big machine sidewise and started to throw up my diversionary dike.

Unfortunately, at this point, the motor stopped. I checked the fuel tank. It was empty. The sergeant and I leaped to the ground. We ran all the way to the pier. We grabbed a couple of cans of fuel. We ran all the way back. And we arrived just in time to see the lava engulf our beautiful machine in what I can only describe as an igneous deluge—or, to put it the other way around, a cataclysmic holocaust.

It took us some time to regain our breath. Then the sergeant said, "I don't think General Griggs is going to like this—especially after he told us not to come up here."

I thought this over. "You mean the officer we met back there was General Griggs?"

"Yes. I tried to tell you, but you wouldn't let me. I hope you won't blame me—"

"No," I said. "The important thing now is to plan for the future. And as long as you are so good at keeping your mouth shut, you can keep it shut about what has just happened. Fortunately, the smoke has hidden this disaster from everybody else, so we can keep it a secret until we figure out what to do next."

We returned to the port, and I spent the rest of yesterday and most of this morning making discreet inquiries. I was pained to learn that General Griggs is noted as a disciplinarian; the one thing he never forgives is disobedience. Fortunately, however, he has gone off to the other end of the island and will not return for several days. This would give me plenty of time to get hold of another tractor, except that there are no more tractors anywhere on Palawang. Thus, as you can see, I am in a quandary.

I absolutely must have another tractor to build that air strip. I would be justified, of course, in asking General Griggs to send for one, because, after all, the present mess is largely his fault. He never told me who he was. He disguised his rank by wearing Australian insignia which he must have known would be unintelligible to an American. And he distracted me by yelling at me at the very moment when I should otherwise undoubtedly have remembered to check the fuel tank.

But something tells me it would be useless to explain this to the general. He would only pass the buck on to me. He would claim he was right about the volcano, which, since yesterday, has quieted down so completely that all danger from the lava stream seems past. And he would raise such a stink about my alleged disobedience as would seriously impair that spirit of brotherly love between America and Australia which it is my high duty to promote.

Hence, for the sake of international friendship, I have decided to dismiss the general from my mind. I will start for Bongo Atoll this afternoon. And I want you, Henderson, to ship me, doublerush, to Bongo, one fifteen-ton Earthworm tractor with bulldozer. You will probably have to charter a special ship, but the expense will be well worth while. It will enable me to complete the air strip without stirring up the general—thus preserving that cordiality with our Allies which is a prerequisite to the future peace of the world.

Remember, Henderson, the fate of civilization is in your hands. Besides, if we get on the good side of these Australians now, we can sell them a lot of tractors after the war.

Yours expectantly,
ALEXANDER BOTTS.

EARTHWORM BRANCH OFFICE
MELBOURNE, AUSTRALIA

Thursday, February 8, 1945.

DEAR BOTTS: I once read of a man who mounted a horse and tilted with a windmill, but never before have I heard of anyone leaping into a tractor and going out to fight a volcano.

I admire your gallantry. But I cannot help you. The Army has taken all our tractors. And, even if I had a tractor, which I have not, I would have no means of chartering a ship to send it to you. So you will just have to work out the future of civilization in some other way.

Yours regretfully,
GILBERT HENDERSON.

BONGO ATOLL, Friday, February 16, 1945.

DEAR HENDERSON: Your letter has just been delivered by a small seaplane which—on account of the radio silence—has been assigned to keep us in touch with the so-called civilized world.

I am delighted to be able to inform you that the entire situation has changed. As a consequence, your failure to send me another tractor makes no difference at all.

What has happened is a veritable miracle. After an uneventful voyage over calm seas, the ancient Wilhelmina arrived last Monday at Bongo Atoll—an irregular ring of coral reefs and sand bars, perhaps twenty miles in diameter. Most of the reefs and bars are narrow and barren, but at one side they broaden out into a mile-wide island with a fringe of palm trees, and a central open space suitable for an airfield.

Guided by our map, we entered the one navigable pass through the reefs, and anchored in the lagoon near the wide island. A group of friendly natives came out in canoes. In outlandish pidgin English, they chattered out a strange tale. Several days before, they said, a large steamer had entered the lagoon. Some of the sailors threw over a couple of large life rafts, lashed them together, and then attempted to lower a big box on them. The box slipped off and sank. For some hours they vainly fished for the box with hooks and cables. Finally they gave up and the ship sailed away.

The natives pointed. Looking down through thirty feet of clear tropical water, we could see, resting on the sandy bottom almost under our stern, a wooden box similar to the export cases in which we send our tractors overseas. And that was not all. On the top of that box were stenciled words. And, so help me, Henderson, the words were as follows: "One Fifteen Ton Earthworm Tractor. One Earthworm Bulldozer. From Earthworm Tractor Company, Earthworm City, Illinois, U. S. A. To Maj. Gen. Reginald W. Griggs, Palawang Island."

Needless to say, I was for the moment dumfounded. And it was in a state of dizzy incredulity that I marshaled my forces to take advantage of this truly incomprehensible gift of the gods.

I induced the natives, with suitable gifts, to dive down, pry apart the box and attach cables to the machinery. Our entire force got busy with the ship's steam donkey engine, crane, winches, extra cables, chains, timbers, rollers and bars. After two days' hard work, the tractor and bulldozer were safely on deck.

In the course of two additional days my splendid mechanics have disassembled all critical parts, such as the motor and transmission, and cleaned and dried them out, and almost completed the job of reassembling them. The brief exposure to salt water has done no damage. Everything is in perfect order. We have plenty of fuel and lubricating oil. And tomorrow we will run the bow of our little shallow-draft side-wheeler up on the beach, unload the machinery and start grading the center of the island—

which is already so smooth and relatively unencumbered that the air strip should be ready in a few days.

The seaplane is almost ready to leave, so I will close by assuring you that I hold no resentment against you whatsoever because of your failure to co-operate. Now that success is assured, I even have a kindly feeling for the egregious Griggs, for it is a tractor originally consigned to him that was so providentially delivered to this island. Thus, the very man who almost wrecked my plans by hollering at the wrong time is now unwittingly coming to the rescue. Truly, this is poetic justice, as well as a miracle of the first water.

Yours happily and raring to go,
ALEXANDER BOTTS.

BONGO ATOLL,
Tuesday, February 20, 1945.

DEAR HENDERSON: Disregard my former letter. Everything is now worse than ever. You absolutely must find a tractor somewhere, and send it to me by some ultrarapid method such as knocking it down and loading it on one or more large seaplanes. Otherwise, I am sunk—as you will understand when I explain what has happened.

Last Saturday, the day after I last wrote you, and just when we had the tractor almost together again, an American merchant ship named the City of Ripton came sailing into the lagoon. The natives said it was the same ship that had lost the tractor. I called my men together and spoke as follows:

"Obviously," I said, "these people are after this tractor. If it were still on the bottom it is probable, considering their clumsy methods, that they could not get it up. Thus, unless we take measures to protect ourselves, it may well turn out that our salvage work will accomplish nothing beyond providing assistance to these pirates in robbing us of our booty. Unfortunately, they probably have the law on their side. Hence, if open defiance does not work, we may have to use cunning." I then explained what was to be done if worse came to worst.

A few minutes later, the captain of the City of Ripton, accompanied by several members of his crew, arrived in a small boat and climbed on the deck of the Wilhelmina. He started to explain, politely enough, that he had come to try to salvage the tractor, and that he was delighted to find the job already done. Before he got any further, I interrupted.

Realizing that a vigorous offensive is the best defense, I spoke as vigorously and offensively as possible. "You're crazy!" I yelled. "This is our tractor. You threw it away. We found it. By all the laws of marine salvage and flotsam and jetsam, it belongs to us. We are going to keep it. And you know where you can go."

"You're crazy yourself!" he yelled back. "This tractor is consigned to Major General Griggs, who commands this entire area. Do you want me to report you for deliberate disobedience of the orders of your commanding general?"

"Always this Griggs keeps getting in my way," I said bitterly. "But as long as you would be such a louse as to report me, I'll have to give in. If you want to take this machine to the general at Palawang, I can't stop you." I turned to my men. "Give him back his tractor!" I ordered.

With a concerted heave they sent the machine over the side. There was a mighty plop. It disappeared under the waters of the lagoon. "All right, captain," I said. "There is your tractor—right where you left it."

With these words, I struck a dramatic attitude, curled my lip in a derisive sneer and gazed with smug satisfaction at the expression of bewilderment and consternation which gradually spread over the captain's face. For me, it was a moment of real triumph. Unfortunately, it did not last.

"Tell me," said the captain, "are you Major Alexander Botts?"

"I am."

"And did you throw this machine overboard to keep me from taking it away to Palawang? Did you plan to fish it up again after I had left?"

"What do you think?" I asked.

"I think," he said, "I had better complete what I was starting to say when you so rudely interrupted me at the very beginning of our visit." He then related a tale which left me feeling as futile as a flat tire.

It seems that the previous week, on his way to Palawang, he had received a radio order—apparently originating with the Australian General Staff at the request of somebody by the name of Henderson—directing him to put ashore at Bongo for the use of a major called Alexander Botts a tractor which was consigned to General Griggs at Palawang. He had brought his ship as close to the Bongo shore as he could, attempted to float the tractor ashore on two large life rafts, lost the tractor overboard and tried unsuccessfully to recover it—all as previously related by the natives. After a quick trip to Palawang with urgently needed supplies, he had returned to see if he could fish up the tractor and put it ashore as ordered.

"So all you wanted was to give me the tractor?" I asked weakly.

"That's right."

"Why didn't you tell me?"

"You didn't give me a chance. However, I shall be delighted to make the presentation at once." He pointed down into the water. "There is your tractor," he said pleasantly, "right where you put it—and where I suppose you want it. I am sorry I cannot stay longer, but it has been nice meeting you, anyway."

When, after two days' work, we finally swung the ponderous machine in over the side the second time, something slipped. The big Diesel motor broke loose and crashed completely through the half-rotten planks in the bottom of the ancient Wilhelmina.

As the water came rushing in, Captain Van Horn started up his engine, raced for the beach, and almost made it. When we finally sank, we were in such shallow water that the deck, which held most of our equipment and supplies, was well above water. But this was small comfort. The tractor motor, which we managed to fish up, was beyond repair.

As a last forlorn hope, I asked Captain Van Horn if we might use the engine from the Wilhelmina. Since the ancient craft was now worth very little except as the basis for an insurance claim, he consented. But the mechanical difficulties of mounting a marine steam engine in a tractor are so tremendous that I can put little hope in this scheme.

And we absolutely must have a working tractor to fix the airfield, and fix it in a hurry, because the seaplane has just brought a message from General Griggs saying he will arrive here in about two weeks with a complete unit of the Royal Australian Air Force, and he expects the field to be in shape for immediate use.

The general's message indicates that he knows about the tractor on the City of Ripton, and that he thinks I have two tractors here, instead of none at all. As I cannot think of any good explanation to send the general, I am not sending him any explanation at all.

Instead, I am throwing myself on your mercy. After all, you sent me one tractor after claiming it was impossible. All you have to do now is send another—this time by plane, and within a week.

For the sake of international friendship and world peace, I demand your help. I know you will not fail.

Yours,

ALEXANDER BOTTS.

EARTHWORM BRANCH OFFICE
MELBOURNE, AUSTRALIA

Friday, February 23, 1945.

DEAR BOTTS: Your two most recent letters, the first somewhat delayed, both arrived today, and I hasten to assure you of my constant willingness to give you all the help I can in your earnest but curiously inept efforts to do the right thing by our Australian brothers in arms.

After my earlier letter, in which I told you I had no way of sending you a tractor, I happened to learn of the presence of the City of Ripton, with a tractor on deck, in your neighborhood. By pulling every wire I knew of, I was able to get the tractor diverted to you.

Unfortunately, now that you have contrived to ruin two tractors, I can see no possibility whatever of procuring a third for you. All available machines have been taken by the military, and they refuse to give them up.

The best advice I can give you is to devise some other method of smoothing down both the airfield and our Australian friends. How about picks and shovels for one, and courtesy and diplomacy for the other?

Yours,
GILBERT HENDERSON.

BONGO ATOLL
Wednesday, March 7, 1945.

DEAR HENDERSON: This is to let you know, in case you get hold of a tractor for me, that it is now too late to send it. Old General Griggs has arrived, and he and I have been involved in a highly sensational fight.

The excitement started at dawn yesterday when an Australian transport entered the lagoon, and General Griggs came ashore in a small boat. At once the general started yelling at me.

"Have you finished grading the airfield?" he demanded.

"Yes, sir," I said—"that is, not quite, sir. We're working on it now."

"With what?"

"A tractor."

"There was a rumor at Palawang," said the general, "that you lost your tractor under a lava flow on the volcano. If so, you were disobeying orders, and I shall probably have to prefer charges against you. But we can take that up later."

"There's no need to do that," I said, "because we got another tractor."

"The captain of the City of Ripton told me that this other tractor was at the bottom of the lagoon."

"Yes, sir," I said. "But we fished it up."

"After which," said the general, "according to a radio message from the City of Ripton, you deliberately threw it in the lagoon again."

"Honestly, general," I said, "you seem to find out about everything. But we fished it up a second time, and everything would have been all right, except we dropped the motor through the bottom of the boat, and the boat sank, and the motor was ruined——"

"And you still claim that you have almost finished the airfield?"

"Yes, sir—at least we are working on it."

"With what?"

"A tractor."

"Where is it? I want to see it."

"It's pretty far," I said doubtfully—"almost a mile away, at the other end of the island. I wouldn't want you to overtire yourself, sir."

"Let's go."

"All right, but I'm afraid you're not going to like it."

With considerable reluctance I conducted the general and his aides through the semidarkness—it being just be-

fore sunrise—toward the northern extremity of the island.
At this hour the entire area was overlaid by a thin layer
of mist, scarcely six feet deep, through which the palm trees
projected toward the brightening sky. Far ahead loomed
the upper part of a moving machine, emitting clouds of
smoke interspersed with flying sparks. We could hear a distant clanking and puffing noise.

"What kind of a tractor is that?" asked the general.

"Well," I said, "it's a kind of an Earthworm. A sort
of a new model."

The general grunted, and said no more until we finally
reached the machine—which the sergeant in charge had
stopped for some minor adjustment. After a long look,
the general asked, "And what in heaven's name is this
monstrosity?"

"I can explain the whole thing," I said. "When I
found that our tractor motor was beyond repair and our
chances of getting another were somewhat doubtful, I got
busy with my crew of mechanics and my truck-mounted
machine shop and welding outfit. By the application of
skill, ingenuity and plenty of sweat, we have succeeded in
the course of two weeks in mounting on our tractor the
engine from the little paddle ship, Wilhelmina—including
cylinder, piston, connecting rods and walking beam. You
will note that after removing the paddle wheels we have
shortened the ship's crankshaft and mounted thereon a
couple of gears from the tractor transmission which mesh
with the gears on the steering-clutch shafts, thus transmit-
ting the power to the final-drive assemblies—truly a triumph of mechanical improvisation."

"It looks to me like nothing but a pile of junk."

"At least," I said, "it is unusual. This is without doubt
the first time in the entire history of the world that there
has been a tractor with a walking beam. And see how the
boiler is mounted on a trailer behind, with a steam hose
connecting with the cylinder——"

"Never mind all that," the general interrupted. "Does the fool thing work?"

"Well," I said, "we didn't get it finished till late last night, so it has been running only about half an hour."

"Good Lord, and it's broken down already!"

"Oh, no! Look, the sergeant is starting up again."

With a tremendous hissing, wheezing, coughing and banging, the huge apparatus lurched forward at a speed of about one mile per hour. The bulldozer caught in a small hummock of grass and fell off. The machine stopped.

Just then an orderly ran up with a radio message stating that a Japanese destroyer had in some way slipped through our patrols, and had been spotted by a small scout plane less than thirty miles to the north and steaming rapidly in our direction.

The general and his staff held a somewhat frenzied conference. It was agreed that if the enemy destroyer came past the island it would be sure to spot the totally unprotected transport and sink it by shellfire long before help could possibly arrive. It was several hours' flying time from the nearest air base, and no surface warship could reach us until the next day. However, the general, more or less in desperation, ordered one of his officers to send out a radio call for bombers. And before he started back toward the transport, he fired a few parting shots at me.

"Major Botts," he said, "if we lose our transport and all the equipment for this air base, it will be due to your negligence. If you had obeyed orders and completed the grading of the field, we would have planes here to protect us. You are hereby relieved of your command. You will consider yourself under arrest. At the earliest possible moment I will see that charges are preferred against you before a general court."

As the general walked away, I got so mad that I gave him a piece of my mind. "You big bum!" I said. "You can't hang everything on me just because I had some bad luck and was a little slow about this grading job. The real

reason you are in trouble here is that you never dreamed
a Japanese destroyer would show up this far south. So
you took a chance and came out in a soft-skinned tub without any protection at all."

Note: Mindful of my duty to treat all Australians
with courteous consideration, I was careful to keep my
voice so low that the general could not hear what I was
saying. However, he must have sensed that I was saying
something. He turned and slowly and menacingly, walked
toward me.

Involuntarily I glanced about—possibly in a subcon-
scious effort to locate some avenue of escape. I saw that
the eastern sky was getting brighter. I noticed that the thin
and silvery layer of early-morning mist completely concealed all distant objects near the surface of the sea and
land, but, unfortunately, failed to provide any cover at all
for the superstructure of the transport, which loomed up
clear and distinct above the low-lying blanket. And then,
in the twinkling of an eye, as often happens to me in mo-
ments of stress, my mind conceived one of the most brilliant
ideas of my entire career.

I climbed into the tractor, motioned the sergeant to
one side and grasped the throttle. Glancing over my shoulder, I addressed the general. "In case you are interested,"
I said, "I am about to put into operation the only plan I
can think of which has any chance of saving us from that
Jap destroyer."

I backed the tractor out of the bulldozer frame, and
then drove the lumbering machine out along the narrow
barren sand bar which extended for eight or ten miles
straight north from the end of the wide airfield area. I
asked the sergeant on the seat beside me if he was willing
to take part in a dangerous mission. He said he was. The
corporal who was acting as fireman in the trailer gave me
the same answer. And then I noticed that danger was arriving much quicker than I had expected. Old General
Griggs was running after us, brandishing a tommy gun.

A moment later he leaped aboard. But he did not try to shoot me. Instead, he patted me on the back. "I think I can guess what you are planning to do," he said. "And it may work. I want to come along."

"Okay, general," I said. "Make yourself at home."

The machine clattered on. Without the bulldozer, it made about six miles an hour. Gazing over the low blanket of mist, we could see smoke off the port bow. After fifteen minutes we could make out masts and funnels. In half an hour we knew it was the Jap destroyer. In another fifteen minutes, just as the sun came over the lagoon on our right, the destroyer was opposite us on the left—several miles out to sea, and heading south.

I began to fear they would not see us. I ordered the fireman to pile on coal. Smoke poured from the stack. Then the lusty old general opened up with his tommy gun, sending a stream of tracers toward the enemy. And apparently this did it. The destroyer swung around and headed straight for us.

"Splendid!" said the general. "They see a walking beam above the mist. They think we are a boat. They think this is the open sea. Splendid!"

A shell came howling past overhead. Then another.

The next shell must have hit right beside us. There was a tremendous crash. The tractor swung around and stopped. And the next moment all four of us were running south along the beach. After several hundred yards we paused. None of us had been touched. There was another report. We turned just in time to see a direct hit. I saw the walking beam sailing through the air. Then the destroyer, racing through the mist, piled up on the sand bar, hopelessly stranded.

We got back to the main island in truly sensational time, and later in the day, after the mist lifted, a flock of bombers came over and finished the destroyer. Then the transport crew began unloading the air-base equipment, including a brand-new Earthworm and bulldozer, which the general had procured somewhere, and which will probably finish the airfield within a week—thus releasing me for another job.

And tonight General Griggs, having forgotten all about his court-martial threats, gave a dinner in my honor at which he proposed a toast to the commander of the only tractor in the history of the world that was equipped with a walking beam and that successfully outmaneuvered an enemy warship in a naval battle.

In my response, I told of my keen satisfaction at being permitted to serve with such a gallant gentleman as General Griggs, and I expressed the hope that the smooth and cordial relations I had always enjoyed in my contacts with our beloved Allies, the Australians, might continue and increase through the lives of ourselves and our descendants to the very end of time.

Yours for international friendship,
ALEXANDER BOTTS.

THE MÖBIUS STRIP

HOLLANDIA, NEW GUINEA,
Saturday, July 21, 1945.

MAJ. ALEXANDER BOTTS, AUS,
MUNGOMORI ISLAND.

DEAR BOTTS: My friend Gen. E. E. Smith, of the Australian Army, with whom I have been conferring here on various tractor problems, tells me you have gone with the Australian Air Force to Mungomori Island, to conduct experiments in dropping tractors by parachute.

I am glad to inform you that Lieutenants Dixon and Humbolt, of the American Army, formerly safety engineers with the Earthworm Tractor Company, are due to arrive at the harbor on Mungomori next Tuesday, July twenty-fourth. They are making a checkup of Earthworm equipment all over the Australian area and suggesting measures for cutting down accidents and operational casualties. For this work they have been assigned a small escort vessel, and for demonstration purposes they have a sixty-H.P. Earthworm tractor and bulldozer, equipped with all the latest safety devices.

As former sales manager of our company, you should be interested in their project. I trust you may have a chance to meet them at Mungomori. And any courtesies you may show them will be appreciated by,

Yours very sincerely,
GILBERT HENDERSON,
President, Earthworm Tractor Company.

FIELD HOSPITAL NO. 334,
MUNGOMORI ISLAND,
Monday, July 23, 1945.

DEAR HENDERSON: Your letter stating that a couple of guys are arriving tomorrow with a tractor brings a veritable burst of refulgent hope into a situation that has been fraught with nothing but black despair ever since day before yesterday.

On the morning of that day—Saturday—my Australian colleagues and I were over at our base on New Guinea preparing for the first test of our new and unprecedented mammoth parachute designed to drop a full-sized five-ton Earthworm tractor, complete with bulldozer, from a heavy bomber. Word reached us that a bulldozer was needed at once to make an air strip in a remote mountain valley twenty miles from the harbor on Mungomori, so that thirty Australian soldiers, severely wounded while cleaning the Japs from near-by caves, could be flown out. The men were in a poorly equipped field hospital. They had to be moved at once. Their condition was too critical to take them over the rough mountain trails. Air transport was the only answer.

We promptly decided to combine our parachute experiment with an errand of mercy. We made the long flight to Mungomori. We let go the tractor with its stupendous parachute over the valley. Two of my best tractor mechanics, Sergeants Venturi and Watkins, followed in standard chutes. I followed them, also in a standard chute.

The experiment was not a complete success. Venturi and Watkins landed safely. I escaped with nothing more serious than a sprained ankle and minor contusions sustained as I came down through the branches of a tree. But the big parachute, after breaking a few shrouds, sideslipped over into a swamp, where the tractor became so completely mired that it will take another tractor to get it out.

Since then I have been nursing my ankle in a bed in the field hospital here, and the two sergeants have done little more than run in circles. I have sent dozens of radio messages—with no results. There are no tractors available on this island. The New Guinea air base has no more giant parachutes to drop us another tractor. Any plane big enough to carry a tractor is too big to land at the little airfield down at the harbor. I was told it will take two weeks to get a tractor here by boat. Every other lead has fizzled out. And the doctor in charge of the field hospital and the head nurse have kept pleading so piteously with me to do something, I have almost gone crazy at my own helplessness.

Then, this evening, came your letter—by air mail to the harbor and by jeep over the mountains to our valley. And never before, Henderson, have you written anything which has brought such tidings of pure joy to a group of suffering humanity. In my happiness I actually burst into

song, and then announced the thrilling news that a beautiful Earthworm tractor would land at the harbor tomorrow.
The doctors, the nurses, my two sergeants and all the
patients who were well enough to be informed were at once
lifted from the valley of despondency to the heights of new
hope and felicity.

Tomorrow morning, with my ankle well bandaged
and with a pair of handsome crutches for emergencies, I
will drive down to the harbor in a jeep with Venturi and
Watkins. We will bring back the tractor, pull the other
machine out of the swamp and clear an adequate air strip
in two or three days.

With heartfelt thanks for sending me the good news,
I remain, yours, bathed in the sunshine of pure happiness,

ALEXANDER BOTTS.

MUNGOMORI HARBOR,
Tuesday evening, July 24, 1945.

DEAR HENDERSON: This is to inform you that
the sunshine of pure happiness mentioned in my letter of
yesterday evening has suddenly been blacked out by the
dark clouds of a new disaster so unexpected and so idiotic
that you will scarcely believe it possible. I arrived at the
harbor late this afternoon. I talked to Lieutenant Dixon,
who is in charge of both Lieutenant Humbolt and the tractor. And, incredible though it may seem, and in spite of
all my most frantic arguments, this egregious shavetail
flatly refused to let me use his machine.

Unfortunately, I have no authority to take it away
from the noisome skunk. But I naturally have no intention
of taking his refusal lying down. I am therefore forced to
resort to low cunning. And, as this may result in trouble
later on, I want a little co-operation from you. Such being
the case, I will now give you a brief résumé of what is going
on, and what I want you to do.

It was early in the evening when I first discovered

this obnoxious Dixon, along with his apparently innocuous side-kick Humbolt, at one end of the camp here, in a pump house used to pump water from a spring to a tank on the hillside which supplies water to the camp. I was at once impressed by the man's revoltingly conceited personality. And when I learned what he was doing, I realized that his mind is as stunted as his self-importance is overgrown.

Paying no attention to my polite request for his tractor, he insisted on showing me a large poster which he had hung on the wall, and which expressed the theme song of his crusade. At the top were the words, ACCIDENT PREVENTION BRINGS VICTORY. In the middle were a lot of gruesome pictures showing an assorted group of morons getting their hands, hair and clothes caught in various gears, belts, presses and machine tools. Other careless imbeciles were getting in the way of trucks and tractors. Underneath was a poem:

> *Every accident such as these*
> *Impedes the war against the Japanese.*

"Very praiseworthy, I am sure," I said courteously. "But right now it happens that we have a group of badly wounded Australian soldiers——"

His only response was to drag me around to inspect the different units of the pump installation, while he expounded his safety ideas. He showed me an Earthworm Diesel motor in a small steel house, and a pump in another house about thirty feet distant, with a four-inch belt running between. Inside the motor house, the pulley and the belt are covered by a guard. This, according to Dixon, is good. Between the two buildings, the belt runs through a long wooden box. This also is good. But inside the pump house there is no protection for the pulley or for the belt—which comes in one hole in the wall and goes out another.

"This," said Lieutenant Dixon, "is very bad, especially when you consider how dim the light is in here. I have provided a guard for the belt and pulley. But the guard has to be removed to oil the pump. Somebody might leave it off. So do you know what I am going to do to provide additional safety?"

"If you are interested," I said, "in the safety and well-being of those wounded Australian sol———"

"Tomorrow morning," said Dixon, "I am going to paint the belt red."

At this, a corporal, who seemed to be in charge of the pump station, spoke up. "Won't that make the belt slip?"

"I will paint the outside, but not the inside. If I spill any on the inside, I promise you I will clean it off."

"Okay," said the corporal. "I won't be here myself. The tank at the other end of the line is full. We don't have to pump tomorrow. So I am getting the day off. But I'll leave you some paint remover in case of need."

"I will be careful," said Dixon, "and I hope you all realize how important this painting is. Industrial statistics have amply proved that painting dangerous moving parts in bright and contrasting color provides a very effective warning and substantially reduces the incidence of accidents."

"I have no doubt of it," I said. "And now I will tell you why I need your tractor."

I gave him the full story of the wounded Australians, substantially as I have set it forth to you. But the incredible dolt was so obsessed with the meticulous details of his safety campaign that all my arguments were completely lost on him.

"If I lent you the tractor," he said, "I should have to waste several more days here. As this pumping motor is the only piece of Earthworm equipment at this harbor, I have already spent too much time. I do not intend even to unload my demonstration tractor at this unimportant locality. I must pursue with all possible speed my vital mission of installing much-needed safety measures in connection with the many thousands of Earthworm units in other parts of this theater of operations."

At this, I opened up with everything I had—logic, pathos, drama, eloquence, sarcasm and even threats. He could see no point of view but his own. I tried to pull my rank. He knew I had no authority over him.

His final words were, "Lieutenant Humbolt and I will spend the night on the boat. We will paint this belt first thing tomorrow. And by the middle of the morning we will sail for our next port of call."

Taking Humbolt with him, he departed.

Having failed with this Dixon person, I promptly took all the other more obvious measures. I tried to appeal to the local Australian commander. He was away on a trip up the coast, and nobody else wanted to assume the authority of interfering with an American lieutenant traveling under independent orders. I tried to send messages to the higher command and to you. But the pitiful little local radio station had suffered a breakdown.

Temporarily baffled, I hobbled back on my crutches to the barracks where I had been assigned a bed. I sat down to meditate. In my usual keen manner, I analyzed the situation. The tractor was on the boat. Probably I could bluff the captain of this craft into letting me take it the next morning while the two lieutenants were at the other end of the camp painting the belt. But this painting job would hardly take long enough to give me time to get the machine far enough on its way to prevent the lieutenants from catching me.

Was there any way to prolong the painting job? I remembered that the belt ran through two holes in the pumphouse wall. It would be impossible to remove it without unlacing it—which would be too much trouble. The two lieutenants would probably paint it in place. One guy would probably crank the engine very slowly, causing the belt to travel past the other guy, who would apply the paint at the only place where the belt was accessible—in the pump house. I tried to picture all the details in my mind. Dixon had said they were going to paint one side of this belt, but not the other. I considered this point for some time. One side, but not the other——

And then, in a sudden brilliant flash of pure inspiration—Eureka!—I had the answer. I limped out and got hold of Sergeants Venturi and Watkins. I took them to the deserted pump house. We unlaced the belt, gave one end a half twist, and laced it together again—thus neatly converting it into that baffling mathematical paradox known as the Möbius Strip.

The effect this is going to have on the unsuspecting Dixon tomorrow morning will be something to see. When he tries to paint the outside without painting the inside, he will, of course, be attempting the impossible—because the belt now has only one side. If he persists in his ill-omened plan, he and his partner will be delayed indefinitely, and there will be plenty of time to get away with the tractor.

Having prepared my erudite little trap, I dismissed Venturi and Watkins, and returned to the barracks, where I have been writing this letter. It will go out by plane early tomorrow morning, and should reach you before noon. As soon as you receive it, I want you to bear down on your friend, General Smith, and make him send an order to Dixon directing him to let me have the tractor as long as I want. Make it retroactive, because I shall already have taken the machine, and the only need for the order is to prevent this mug from preferring charges against me or rushing over the mountains and trying to take back the tractor before we are through with it.

If you work fast, the order should be here tomorrow night, which ought to be in plenty of time. As my ankle still bothers me, I will stay here at the harbor and check up on the expected droll antics of Dixon and Humbolt, while Venturi and Watkins take the tractor over the mountains and clear the air strip.

Certainly, this peculiar belt-painting project has proved a rare piece of good luck for me. And, if my luck holds, I should be able, before the end of the week, to report complete success in the one mission which right now is uppermost in my mind and heart—the rescue of those gallant Australian soldiers.

Yours,

ALEXANDER BOTTS.

HOLLANDIA,
Wednesday, July 25, 1945.

DEAR BOTTS: Your letter is received, and I agree with you emphatically that the rescue of the Australian soldiers should take precedence over Lieutenant Dixon's plans. General Smith is of the same opinion, and orders have been sent Dixon to place the tractor at your disposal.

I am worried, however, at your wild and irresponsible action in stealing this machine—even though it is in a good cause. And I deplore your talk of your "rare good luck." Someday, if you keep relying on mere luck to get you out of trouble, you will be sadly disappointed.

Incidentally, your garbled remarks about this Möbius Strip—whatever that may be—are obviously unsound. After all, a belt running around two pulleys is a simple contrivance, and no amount of pseudo-mathematical jargon and hocuspocus can alter the fact that such a belt must have two sides. If a man wants to paint one side and not the other, there is no reason why he cannot do so.

Perhaps you are a little delirious from your parachute injury. Or maybe you have been overexerting yourself. In any case, I would strongly recommend that you take the earliest opportunity to get a complete and well-earned rest.

Yours very sincerely,

GILBERT HENDERSON.

MUNGOMORI HARBOR,
Saturday, July 28, 1945.

DEAR HENDERSON: Thank you for your letter, which has been delivered to me here at the little Mungomori Harbor hospital, where I was dragged in last Wednesday in an unconscious conditon brought on by the unexpected results of my Möbius Strip project, and where I am following your recommendation to take a well-earned rest. I also thank you for your promptness in getting through that order to Dixon.

But I must take exception to your erroneous belief that I get out of trouble by what you call "mere luck." Actually, there is nothing "mere" about it. I always earn my good luck.

In the present case, it just happened that this Dixon, whom I had to keep busy while I stole the tractor, was planning to paint one side, and one only, of a belt which just happened to be covered through most of its length. This was a lucky break, but only because I knew how to take advantage of it. An ordinary person like you would have been helpless; your letter, in fact, shows you are still all at sea, even after I wrote you my plans.

What I did was make use of the Möbius Strip, which I read about some years ago in a very fine book called Mathematics and the Imagination, by a couple of smart cookies named Kasner and Newman. As my previous description of this Möbius Strip failed to penetrate your somewhat obtuse mind, I would suggest that you try again with a model.

Get yourself a strip of paper about a yard long and an inch wide. Lay this flat on your desk, lift the two ends and bring them together. You now have an endless paper belt with two sides—an inside and an outside—similar to the ordinary belt I found at the pump house.

Next, separate the two ends, turn one of them over and bring the two ends together again. This time you might as well lap these ends and paste them. You have now done exactly what I did to that belt. You have created a Möbius Strip, whose outstanding feature is that, although any section of it obviously has two sides, it, nevertheless, possesses, in its entirety, only one side. Incidentally, it has only one edge. And you can get other interesting effects if you try to cut it into narrower strips lengthwise. But I do not wish to strain your intellect unduly.

The important thing, from my point of view, was that I had fixed that belt so that the outside was continuous with the inside, and so that Dixon, when he tried to paint the outside, but not the inside, would actually be attempting to paint—and at the same time not to paint—the same side. This, I hoped, might cause a certain delay in his operations.

As it turned out, my plans worked exactly as I had anticipated—for a while. Early on Wednesday morning, Venturi, Watkins and I repaired to the neighborhood of the pier and waited till Dixon and Humbolt had left the boat and were well on their way to the pump station a half mile away at the other end of the camp. Then we approached the officer in charge of the boat. With nonchalant assurance I explained that my men had orders to take the tractor. Having no reason to suspect dirty work from an American major, the officer acquiesced, and obligingly assigned some men to help unload the machine and place it on the pier. As this looked as if it would take at least an hour, I left Venturi and Watkins on their own, and ambled along on my crutches to the pump house.

As expected, I found Dixon standing next the pump pulley, applying a handsome coat of red paint to the upper surface of the belt. As soon as he finished as much as he could get at, he would let out a yell, and Humbolt, over in the motor house, would crank the belt along, so as to bring another section in reach.

"Good morning," I said.

"Good morning," he replied gruffly. "It won't do you any good to keep asking for that tractor—if that's what you came for."

"No," I replied. "I just stopped in because I am so deeply interested in your safety campaign. . . . Look out! You're going to spill paint on the inside of the belt."

"I certainly am not."

"If you do, I hope you remember you promised to clean it off."

"I remember."

I limped outside and took a look in the direction of the pier. Apparently the tractor had not yet got going. After a while I went back into the pump house. Dixon was going faster than I liked.

"Here is something funny," he said. "I thought I painted past the belt lacing awhile ago, and here it comes again."

This took a bit of quick thinking on my part. I realized that the belt lacing actually had been past once before, at which time the guy had painted the other side of it. If he started investigating, he might find out too much too soon.

"Probably," I said carelessly, "the belt is made up out of two or three pieces, so there are two or three lacings."

"Maybe so," he said, and went on wielding his brush.

More time went by. I went out and had another look toward the pier. There were no signs of the tractor. I thought of the desperate plight of the Australian soldiers. I began to be worried. I returned to the pump house.

The painting went on—interspersed with yells from Dixon, followed by short pauses while Humbolt, at the other end, cranked the belt along. Finally there emerged a section already painted red. Dixon covered the remaining surface, and stepped back to admire his work. The job was finished.

I moved forward on my crutches. "Too bad!" I exclaimed. "You got some paint on the inside."

"I did not! At least, I don't think I did."

"Look."

Dixon bent over in the dim light. He ran his finger along the inner belt surface. It came away dripping red. "I can't understand it," he said. "I took the greatest pains not to spill a single drop. But the inside is completely covered as far as I can see."

"You don't suppose," I asked incredulously, "that the inside is painted solid all the way around?"

"Hey, Humbolt!" yelled Dixon. "Crank this thing along! Keep going till I tell you to stop!"

Slowly the belt began moving. We watched. It went around several times. Sure enough, the entire inner surface was painted a rich and beautiful red.

"It's impossible!" said Dixon.

"You certainly must be absent-minded," I said cheerfully. "Imagine just painting along—here and there, on one side and the other—without paying any attention to what you are doing."

"You know I didn't do any such thing," he replied angrily. "Somebody has been slipping something over on me."

"Possibly gremlins."

"Don't be silly." He gave me a keen look. "Say," he said, "you didn't have anything to do with this, did you?"

"How could I? I haven't been near that belt since you started."

"Maybe this was done before I started."

"It's your own paint—same shade and still wet on both sides. If you're trying to blame it on somebody else just so you can crawl out of your promise to clean it off——"

"I'm not trying to crawl out of anything! But I tell you I didn't paint the inside of this belt!"

"You must have—unless maybe this Humbolt is a practical joker."

"What do you mean?"

"Well, he could have brought along a can of this paint himself, couldn't he? While you were painting the outside from this end, he could have been painting the inside from the other end—just for a little joke, perhaps."

"Why, the big bum!" said Dixon. He went rushing out the door and over to the other building. I followed as fast as I could, and arrived just in time for his opening blast.

"Come clean!" he snarled. "Why did you smear up this belt?"

Humbolt looked mildly astonished. Dixon advanced threateningly. "Did you or did you not paint the inside of this belt?"

"I did not," said Humbolt. "How could I, when it's all covered up by that guard? And I have no paint anyway."

Dixon inspected the guard. It was firmly fastened in place by at least a dozen bolts. None of the nuts looked as if they had been recently tampered with.

"If you would tell me what is the matter," said Humbolt, "maybe I could be of some help."

"Come with me," said Dixon grimly.

He led his assistant out the door and back to the pump house. As I straggled along in the rear, I reflected that never before had I heard a conversation so inane, and yet so happily contrived to use up a lot of time that needed so badly to be used up in just such a way as this.

Back in the pump house, the two lieutenants examined the belt in bewilderment.

"The paint remover," I said, "is right there in the corner."

"All right, all right," said Dixon wearily. . . . "You may go back to the motor house, Humbolt, and stand by to crank this thing when I give the word. And remember, no funny business."

Humbolt departed, and Dixon started the long job of scrubbing the paint from the inside of the belt. It soon appeared that the paint remover, which is designed to soften up old dried paint, was not much help here. It only made the wet paint wetter. Dixon wandered around the pump house and gathered in all the old rags and cotton waste he could find. He got a pail of Diesel fuel, and when this did not work too well, he brought another pail filled with gasoline from the small starting motor on the side of the Diesel. He finally sat himself on the floor beside the pulley, and settled down to rubbing, scrubbing and wiping his way along the inner surface of the belt, stopping only long enough for Humbolt to crank the thing along.

After the poor man had slaved for a good while, I wandered outside and almost ran into the mail orderly, who was heading for the near-by barracks where I had been assigned a bed. He handed me a letter. It was from the head nurse at the advance field hospital, begging me not to delay in getting back with the tractor. Several of the patients were worse. It was more than ever necessary to fly them out at once. They were counting on me to prepare the landing strip, so the planes could come in. I was their only hope.

Anxiously I gazed across the camp toward the pier. I strained my ears. From far away came the beautiful sound of an Earthworm-tractor motor. Then I saw the machine itself, just leaving the neighborhood of the pier and starting along the trail that led over the mountain. My heart beat fast with hope. But the tractor had taken a long time to get started. It was moving with maddening slowness. And it would probably take another half hour to reach the jungle, where it would be safely out of sight. If Dixon saw it before it disappeared, he might still have time to get together his men on the boat, organize a pursuit and bring the machine back.

I re-entered the pump house, where I was dismayed to find that Dixon was getting along entirely too fast. That portion of the belt's surface which he had first scrubbed clean on the inside had now been cranked all the way to the other end, then back again, and around the pump pulley —this time on the outside. The unsuspecting Dixon, seated on the floor with his head lower than the upper part of the belt, had not, as yet, observed this interesting phenomenon —which seemed to me just as well. The longer I could keep him working along quietly, the better it would suit me.

Unfortunately, however, the man was restless. Hearing my step behind him, he turned his head and began complaining that the job was taking too long. "Somewhere,"

he said, "I have heard that the quickest way to remove
paint is to burn it off with a blowtorch."

"That is sometimes done," I admitted.

"And isn't that a gasoline blowtorch over there on that
workbench?"

"Yes, but a blowtorch is used only to remove paint
from something solid, like structural-steel work, or sometimes, with proper precautions, from wood. You can't use
a blowtorch on that belt. You would burn the material."

"Not if I'm careful," he said. "I'm going to try it
anyway."

He rose—with never a glance at the top of the belt—
gathered up his rags, his cotton waste and his pails of fuel
oil and gasoline, and carried them over and set them down
beside his paint cans in the doorway of the building. He
then stepped to the workbench, pumped up a bit of pressure in the blowtorch, opened the valve and lighted it.

"You can't do that," I said, "that belt is soaked with
gasoline."

"You may outrank me, Major Botts," he said coldly,
"but I am not aware that you have any authority over me
in this matter."

He picked up the torch and walked toward the pump.
He stopped. He pointed.

"Look!" he said weakly.

"What's the matter now?" I asked cheerfully.

He spoke haltingly, "The paint . . . has disappeared
. . . from the outside of the belt."

"So it has, so it has!" I exclaimed, in tones designed
to express surprise. "How did that happen?"

"I don't know . . . yet," said Dixon. His voice was
getting ugly. "But I'm going to find out. And when I do,
somebody is going to be sorry." He began to shout, "Humbolt! Humbolt! Come here, right this minute!"

A half minute later, Lieutenant Humbolt joined us.
"Did you want something?" he asked.

"Yes, I want to know what sort of monkey business you think you are pulling off now."

"Monkey business?"

"Yes. Did you or did you not scrub the paint off the outside of this belt?"

"I thought I was just supposed to crank the engine over. Was I supposed to be scrubbing paint too?"

"You were not. But somebody has been taking the paint off the outside of this belt."

Humbolt took a look. "That's right," he said. "But what's the idea? I thought you were just going to take it off the inside. Why did you take it off the outside too?"

By this time Dixon was ready to blow up.

"I did not take it off the outside. But somebody did. And I am going to find out who it was."

"Well, I didn't."

"You deny it?"

"Of course I do. And, furthermore, I don't see why you keep accusing me of messing up your old paint job. First you claim I painted the inside. Now you claim I cleaned off the outside. Probably you did it yourself."

"That will do, Lieutenant Humbolt. If you don't want to co-operate in this matter, I am perfectly capable of taking care of it myself. Before we proceed any further, I am going down to the boat, and I will bring back an adequate guard to watch both ends of this job."

"Oh, I wouldn't do that," I said hastily.

"Why not?" he demanded.

For a moment I hesitated. The real reason why I did not want him going down to the boat was that I did not want him to discover the departure of the tractor until it had had time to get a safe distance away. Naturally, I could not tell him this. But I had to say something, if only to keep up the conversation and use up a little more time. I decided to speak softly.

"If you ask me," I said, "the explanation is very simple. It is nothing to get excited about—just a little innocent absent-mindedness on your part, Lieutenant Dixon. And what a droll performance it has been, to be sure! First, while painting the outside, you absentmindedly cover the inside. Then, while cleaning the inside, you absentmindedly scrub off the outside. The next you know, you'll be giving yourself a shampoo with the paint remover or possibly painting up the inside of your pants."

Unfortunately, this type of soft answer did not seem to turn away any wrath.

Lieutenant Dixon became what I can only describe as livid with rage.

"That's a lie, and you know it!" he yelled. He took a couple of steps toward me and swung back the blowtorch, preparing, apparently, to bean me with it. This was a mistake on his part. In his excitement, the torch slipped out of his fingers, sailed back across the room and landed in the pail of gasoline. There was a flash and a roar. The doorway —which was our only means of escape—was at once a mass of flames.

The three of us retreated to the other end of the building. Right away the whole place filled with thick oily smoke from the burning gasoline, fuel oil, rags and paint. We dropped to the floor, where the air was clearer. We crawled behind a pile of boxes. The smoke swirled down around us. We couldn't get away from it. I felt myself choking . . . choking . . . choking ——

When I came to, I was in the hospital. That was three days ago, and by this time I have learned what happened. Some Australians arrived and put out the fire in a hurry with some sort of fancy foam-extinguisher equipment. The building, the pump and even the belt were saved. Dixon, Humbolt and I were merely overcome by smoke. We are all right now, although I am staying in the hospital till my sprained ankle gets better.

Venturi and Watkins crossed the mountain, jerked the other tractor out of the swamp and cleared a primitive air strip—all in two days. Today, the Australian wounded were flown down here in small planes and sent on toward Australia in big seaplanes. Venturi and Watkins hauled the hospital equipment out over the trail and returned Lieutenant Dixon's tractor. And the head nurse from the field hospital has just been in and wept tears of gratitude on my shoulder.

You may also be interested to know that the stubborn Lieutenant Dixon was all for going back and finishing the impossible task of making that one-sided belt red on one side but not on the other. However, the Australian colonel in command of the port, who got back just in time to see the fire, has ordered both Dixon and Humbolt on their way. "These safety engineers," he says, "may be all right back home in peacetime, but over here where there is a war going on they are entirely too dangrous."

Yours,
ALEXANDER BOTTS.

I WANT OUT

TELEGRAM
FORT QUINAULT, WASH.
SEPT. 24, 1945.

TO GILBERT HENDERSON, PRESIDENT,
EARTHWORM TRACTOR COMPANY,
EARTHWORM CITY, ILLINOIS.

BIG EMERGENCY. JUST RETURNED FROM PACIFIC EXPECTING DISCHARGE. FIND MYSELF ASSIGNED HERE TO TRACTOR BATTALION APPARENTLY SLATED FOR EARLY SHIPMENT BACK TO HONOLULU. HAVE ADVISED COLONEL DAGGETT,

COMMANDING OFFICER, THAT THE EARTHWORM TRACTOR
COMPANY'S RECONVERSION PLANS ABSOLUTELY DEMAND
MY IMMEDIATE DISCHARGE SO I CAN RESUME MY OLD JOB AS
SALES MANAGER. DAGGETT, WHO SEEMS TO BE CRAZY, ABSO-
LUTELY REFUSES CO-OPERATION. NOTHING MORE I CAN DO
HERE. IF YOU HAVE ANY INFLUENCE WITH THE WAR DE-
PARTMENT, PLEASE PULL ALL POSSIBLE WIRES AS HARD AND
AS QUICK AS YOU CAN. THE WAR IS OVER. I DON'T WANT TO
STAY IN THE ARMY. I WANT TO GET OUT. HELP. HURRY.
URGENT. RUSH.

ALEXANDER BOTTS, MAJOR, AUS.

EARTHWORM BRANCH OFFICE
SEATTLE, WASHINGTON

Tuesday, September 25, 1945.

MAJ. ALEXANDER BOTTS,
FORT QUINAULT, WASHINGTON.

DEAR BOTTS: Your telegram has been forwarded
to me here, and I hasten to assure you that you have no
cause for worry. Your many friends in the Earthworm
Company have not forgotten you. We want you back. You
are perfectly right in assuming that our reconversion plans
absolutely demand your immediate discharge so you can
resume your old job as sales manager. We need you so
badly that we have been continuously hounding the authorities in Washington. And I am glad to report that they
have promised us you will be discharged at the earliest
possible moment.

I can also reassure you regarding the Fort Quinault
tractor battalion. As it is equipped with a hundred of our
Earthworm tractors, I have kept in close touch with it.
The order sending it to Honolulu was issued away back
on July fifteenth, but held up because of lack of shipping.
On August third the battalion was ordered to Manila, but
again there were no ships available.

After the Japanese surrender, it was decided that this tractor outfit would not be needed overseas, and I was able to negotiate an agreement, in connection with the cancellation of our war contracts, by which the hundred tractors in the Fort Quinault battalion—which are badly needed by our customers—are to revert to us.

The order of August third was therefore killed. And I have come to Seattle to investigate sales outlets for these very machines.

You can see, therefore, that you need not worry about your discharge—which will be along very soon. And you need not worry now—in September—about being sent overseas under an order of July fifteenth, which was superseded by an order of August third, which has since been canceled.

Most sincerely,
GILBERT HENDERSON.
President, Earthworm Tractor Company.

FORT QUINAULT, WASHINGTON.
Wednesday evening, September 26, 1945.

DEAR HENDERSON: Your incredibly complacent letter is here, and this is to let you know you are all wet, and if you really feel that you are going to need me as much as you claim in the coming reconversion program of the Earthworm Tractor Company, you will snap out of your dreams and do something. I would have telegraphed or telephoned you, only you are the kind of person who never seems to grasp an idea until it is explained at great length and in tedious detail, so I will give you the story in full, and send it by air mail, which should reach you sometime tomorrow.

To begin with, I want you to try to get through your head the following basic points: 1. I am still in the Army. 2. I want to get out. 3. I am assigned to an outfit that has orders to proceed to Honolulu on the next available ship.

4. Regardless of anything they tell you in Washington, nobody here has been informed of any change in these orders, so they still stand. 5. If I once get started for Honolulu, I may be in the Army for months to come. 6. I don't want to be in the Army for months to come. 7. I want to get out.

Maybe you are wondering why I don't handle this myself. The answer is that in the Army everything has to be taken up through channels—which, in this case, means that I have to work through my immediate superior, Colonel Daggett, who is not easy to work through—as you will understand when I explain the sort of mug he is.

My first contact with him was several days ago when I first arrived in this dump. The colonel was making a speech to a company of tractor drivers who had apparently just joined his outfit. They looked like a highly competent bunch, and most of them had many service ribbons and overseas stripes. The colonel had them lined up at attention, and he was sounding off like a bass horn.

"I'm going to give you men some plain talk straight from the shoulder," he said. "I will mince no words. Never in my life have I seen a more unmilitary group. Just because you have been overseas doesn't mean that you are soldiers. Far from it. In fact, the discipline in combat areas in this war has, in general, been so lax that the longer you have been overseas the sloppier you have become.

"But now that you are members of my command there is going to be a change. I'm going to make real soldiers out of you. From now on, you're going to stand up straight, shave every day, rub those grease spots off your pants. When you meet an officer, you're going to salute, and salute properly. When you get an order, you're going to obey, with no back talk or monkey business. Starting tomorrow, you're going to have four hours of close-order drill every day, and you're going to watch yourselves and behave like soldiers . . . or else. That is all. . . . Sergeant, you may dismiss the company."

After hearing this oration, I decided to get a little information before reporting to the colonel. I approached a lieutenant who looked reasonably civilized.

"What," I asked, "is the matter with this Colonel Daggett? Is he the guy that won the war or something?"

"Nerts," said the lieutenant, urbanely. "He has never even been out of the United States. And that, if you ask me, is the main trouble with him."

"What do you mean?"

"Colonel Daggett," said the lieutenant, "is an old-timer with a one-track mind. All his life he has been wrapped up in the Army. He never relaxes. He has no social life. He reads practically nothing but the Maxims of Napoleon and the works of Clausewitz. He never thinks of anything but discipline and military etiquette."

"And why wasn't he sent overseas?"

"How do I know? Maybe they thought he was too narrow-minded. Anyway, while many of his fellow old-timers were fighting the war and becoming generals, and while civilians like me were slapping the Japs, he was stuck with training-camp duty back home. And it has gradually soured his whole character."

"I'm glad there's some explanation," I said.

With vague misgivings, I reported to Colonel Daggett in his office, saluted as snappily as I could, and was immediately bawled out like a recruit. After the colonel had given me a lesson in the proper method of saluting, I got in a few remarks.

"Sir," I said, "there has been a mistake in my orders. Now the war is over, I'm supposed to be discharged, so I can return to a highly important civilian position as sales manager of the great Earthworm Tractor Company. I'm not supposed to be here. I'm not supposed to be sent back overseas."

A sergeant entered, saluted and said, "Sir, Lieutenant Brown is here."

Lieutenant Brown entered. "Sir," he said, "I wish to report on that tractor transmission you ordered replaced.

Since disassembling the machine, we think we can repair the old transmission all right ——"

"Your orders," said the colonel severely, "were to replace it."

"I know, but I thought ——"

"You're not supposed to think. You're supposed to do as you're told."

"Yes, sir." The lieutenant withdrew.

"As I was saying," I resumed, "there has been a mistake in my orders ——"

"It is not my habit," said Colonel Daggett, "to permit my subordinates to criticize military orders. You have been assigned to this organization. You will remain with this organization and accompany it overseas. The matter is closed. And I shall expect you, in your relations with the men under you, to inculcate in them the same habit of instant and unquestioning obedience that I require of you. That is all. You may go.

"Yes, sir," I said, and walked out.

Since then, my desire to get out of the Army has been even more acute than before. But the direct road of escape is hopelessly blocked in this Daggett bottleneck. That is why a detour is indicated through you, Henderson, and your Washington contacts. You may think you have got everything fixed. But you have not.

Inquiry among some of my fellow officers reveals that we still have our original orders to sail for Honolulu. All we are waiting for is word that a ship is available at the Army supply base and port at Cove Point on Puget Sound. This word may come at any moment. When it does, our plans are all prepared to drive the equipment over the twenty miles of forest roads between here and the port. It should take only one day to make this trip and load the stuff on the ship. And then we shall be on our way.

So I beg of you, Henderson, if you have any regard for me or for the Earthworm Tractor Company's postwar program—and if you want this batch of a hundred tractors

—please shake yourself out of your lethargy and get those orders changed before it is too late.

Yours, between hope and despair,
ALEXANDER BOTTS.

FORT QUINAULT, WASH.
SEPT. 27, 1945, 8 A.M.

TO GILBERT HENDERSON,
EARTHWORM BRANCH OFFICE,
SEATTLE, WASH.

FLASH! SHIP IS AT COVE POINT. WE HAVE OUR ORDERS TO LEAVE HERE TOMORROW MORNING; EMBARK TOMORROW NIGHT; SAIL THE NEXT MORNING, SATURDAY. PLEASE, PLEASE, QUICK, QUICK, HURRY, HURRY, DO SOMETHING ULTRA SUPER HYPER, URGENT, RUSH.

BOTTS.

SEATTLE, WASH.
SEPT 27, 1945, 11 A.M.

MAJ. ALEXANDER BOTTS,
FORT QUINAULT, WASH.

HAVE TELEPHONED WASHINGTON. FIND YOU ARE RIGHT. THROUGH SOME ERROR THE NEW ORDERS WERE NEVER ISSUED. HOPE TO GET THESE THROUGH BY SATURDAY NIGHT. CAN YOU DELAY SAILING TWENTY-FOUR HOURS?

HENDERSON.

FORT QUINAULT, WASHINGTON.
Thursday evening, September 27, 1945.

DEAR HENDERSON: Can I delay sailing twenty-four hours? Honestly, Henderson, sometimes you think of the damnedest things. I am not the captain of the ship, nor am I in command of this tractor battalion. So my first reaction, on receiving your wire this noon, was to reject this twenty-four-hour-delay business as an utter impossibility.

However, I am not one who easily gives up, even when things seem hopeless. In this case, I hated to see all these tractors, which are so urgently needed in the United States, being sent to Honolulu, where they are not needed at all. I hated to see all these overseas tractor drivers, who would presumably prefer to stay in this country, being shipped far away. And, finally, I was completely outraged at the thought that I might have to waste an indefinite period going to Honolulu and then trying to get back. At the moment, my main idea—as I may possibly have mentioned—is that I want to get out of the Army.

Stimulated by this desire, I resolved to concentrate all my powers of intellect and all my aptitude for low cunning on the one problem of finding some way to delay the embarkation of this tractor battalion. For a while, however, I was completely nonplused.

Early in the afternoon Colonel Daggett made a speech to his entire command. After explaining our orders for embarking, he pointed out that on our twenty-mile trip to the port we would follow rough, narrow, winding roads through dense forest. There would be many false turns. The weather prediction was for fog and rain, which meant poor visibility. Hence, there was danger of getting lost.

"Under these conditions," said the colonel, "it is highly essential that the most rigid march discipline be preserved. The tractors will proceed in column. The first machine will be under my direct command. The driver of each succeeding machine will maintain an interval of one hundred feet. And at all times and under all circumstances he will follow the machine ahead. There will be no exceptions or modifications to this rule. Any disobedience will subject the offender to trial by courtmartial. Let me repeat —each driver will follow the machine ahead."

The colonel ceased speaking, and I reflected sadly that

the old boy seemed to have worked out an absolutely iron-clad system for getting those tractors to the port on schedule. This follow-the-leader system was completely foolproof. Then I began to wonder. I had a vague feeling that somewhere I had heard of a system like this that had gone wrong in a big way. I meditated a long time. Finally, I decided that the idea I was trying to recall was something I had read in a book—but I couldn't remember what book.

As you know, Henderson, my success in getting out of difficulties is often due to the fact that I have piled up ahead of time a vast store of the sort of knowledge that is useful in emergencies. Most of this knowledge comes from actual experience. But at times, in my efforts to improve my mind, I have actually gone so far as to read a book. You will remember that my information in the curious case of the Möbius strip came from a book on mathematics.

In the present instance, I was certain that somewhere, sometime, I had read something about somebody who had used a very simple strategem to render completely haywire a system very similar to Colonel Daggett's projected tractor convoy. Unfortunately, I could not remember anything definite about what it was or where I had read about it. All my efforts to jog my memory only made me more bewildered.

Finally, I decided to dismiss the matter temporarily from my mind, and get a little firsthand knowledge of the country through which tomorrow's march will proceed. Accordingly, I got into a jeep and spent the rest of the afternoon making a thorough reconnaissance of the terrain between here and the port at Cove Point. I took along a map, and examined every road and intersection in the entire area. As I have a natural aptitude for topography, I came back with a complete and detailed mental picture of the whole theater of operations.

So far, I have produced nothing in the way of a definite plan. But I will sleep on the problem tonight. And tomorrow I have every confidence that something will occur to

me. If it is humanly possible to delay that column of tractors, I will do it. And I will let you know later how it
works out.

In the meantime, keep working on those birds in
Washington. I am depending on you.

Yours hopefully,
ALEXANDER BOTTS.

COVE POINT, WASHINGTON,
Friday evening, September 28, 1945.

DEAR HENDERSON: I have much to report. I
have evolved a plan. I have put it into operation. But it is
still too early to know whether it will succeed. The situation
is tense, but hopeful.

When I got up this morning I was still in a mental fog.
I was haunted by the feeling that the answer to this whole
business was somewhere in the back of my mind. But I
could not get it out. All I could do was go along and hope
for an inspiration later on.

Instead of riding in one of the command cars, I decided I would be in a more strategic position if I drove one
of the tractors. As soon as the machines had been formed
in column, I started walking along beside them. I noticed
that the driver of the fifth tractor from the front had a
bandage on his thumb. At once I ordered him to ride with
one of the other drivers, and climbed into the cab myself.

A moment later we started. It was six A.M. The trucks
and auxiliary vehicles had gone on ahead and were soon
out of sight. Colonel Daggett was in the lead tractor with
complete road maps and a competent guide. There was no
possibility of his losing his way. He was holding the speed
down to two miles per hour; it being his idea that this is
necessary to prevent the motors from overheating, although
there is, of course, no reason why these Earthworms cannot hit it up to five or six miles per hour. Even at our slow

speed, however, we would presumably reach the port according to schedule at four P.M. There was no chance of running out of fuel; each machine was carrying an extra supply.

The column rolled along. With our hundred-foot intervals, we were strung out for a distance of about two miles. It was foggy and it was raining. We entered the forest. The road became more winding, and so narrow that it would be impossible for the colonel to check our progress by sending anybody along the side of the column in a jeep or even a motorcycle. At sharp turns, the tractor ahead would be out of sight around the curve. When we reached a straight stretch, I would see it again, dimly visible through a hundred feet of mist and rain.

We passed a side road. I eyed it wistfully. It would be very easy for me to make a wrong turn. If, before doing so, I slowed down so as to let the tractors ahead get out of sight, it seemed reasonable to expect that the tractors behind would follow me without knowing they were leaving the column. I could then lead them far away. But this, I decided, would be too obvious. It would be impossible to conceal the fact that I was the leader of this unauthorized detour. And what the colonel would then do to me I did not like to contemplate.

I tried to think of something better. I thought and thought. The steady drone of the tractor motor began to make me drowsy. And then, with a sudden blinding flash of inspiration, I had the answer. I remembered that book.

It was "The Life of the Caterpillar," by a wise old Frenchman named J. Henri Fabre. In this excellent work the author tells of the Pine Processionaries—caterpillars which travel in a long line, like elephants in a circus parade, with each one hanging on to and following the one ahead. Apparently they do this automatically and without thought or reason. To find out just how automatically, Monsieur Fabre devised an experiment. He contrived to get the lead caterpillar turned around and hooked up to the rear of the procession—whereupon these witless creatures continued to travel around in a circle for seven days and seven nights, getting nowhere, until they finally collapsed from exhaustion.

The important point was that the Pine Processionaries' normal mode of travel was the same as Colonel Daggett's system for getting his tractors through the woods. And what Monsieur Fabre so aptly calls the "inconceivable imbecility" and "abysmal stupidity" of the Pine Processionaries is exactly comparable to what Colonel Daggett has described in such terms as "rigid march discipline," "unquestioning obedience," and "you aren't supposed to think; you're supposed to do as you're told."

"Eureka," I said to myself. "If Monsieur Fabre could cross up his Pine Processionaries for seven days and seven nights, I ought to be able to keep Colonel Daggett's Earthworm tractor processionaries similarly bewildered for a mere twenty-four hours."

At once I put my plan into operation. We were approaching an unusually sharp curve which I had noted on my previous day's reconnaissance. Beyond was a fork in the road, followed by more sharp curves. Just before reaching the first curve, I slowed down.

The machine behind me closed up to fifty feet and also reduced speed. The one behind that came into view. Cautiously I started around the curve. I noticed that the machine ahead had taken the correct turn—to the right—and was just disappearing around a bend farther on. As soon as it was out of sight, I speeded up. At the fork I turned left, into the side road. I kept on. The machine behind me followed. At a short straight stretch I caught sight of two more machines farther back. So far, so good. The colonel, with four tractors, was presumably rolling merrily on the way to the port. The rest of the pack was following me.

After three miles on the side road, I came to a place that I remembered from my reconnaissance of the day before. The woods were dense. And there was a pattern of intersecting roads exactly suited to my purpose.

By swinging two sharp corners and following dozens of twists and turns in the narrow road, I was able to bring my tractor, with its long trail of followers, around in an irregular two-mile loop, and head it back toward the side road I had been following.

As I approached this road, I slowed down. Ahead of me, dimly seen in the mist, a tractor went by. This machine, I decided, must be near the tail end of the procession which I was leading. I stopped. I looked over my shoulder. The machine behind me had stopped fifty feet away—too far for the driver to see what was going on ahead. Another tractor went past on the road in front of me. Then, for two minutes, all was quiet. The end of the parade had passed.

I started forward, swung the corner and drove rapidly after that last machine. In five minutes I came in sight of it. I settled down to the prescribed two miles an hour at the prescribed hundred-foot interval. The machines behind me followed in an orderly manner. The circle was complete, and only one more maneuver was needed.

At a blind hairpin curve near an intersecting road, I was out of sight, for almost thirty seconds, from both the tractor in front of me and the tractor behind me. With a quick, right-angle turn, I sent my tractor off the road and into the concealment of a dense thicket. I shut off the motor. I listened. The machine that had been following me came roaring around the curve. It passed. Then I heard the motor speed up. The driver had evidently noticed he was too far behind the machine in front of him. He was closing up the interval. A second machine came by. Then another. I felt pretty good. The circle was once more complete—this time with me out of it.

I started the motor. I drove cautiously through the thicket to the intersecting road. I followed this for several miles. I got back on the main road to the port. By speeding up to six miles per hour, I finally managed to overtake the rear end of the little four-tractor convoy that the colonel was so confidently leading along at two miles per hour.

At four P.M.—exactly according to schedule—we reached the port at Cove Point. The ship was there. The trucks and auxiliary vehicles were there, but they couldn't be loaded, because all the tractors had to go in first at the bottom of the hold. So far, of course, there were only five tractors.

The reactions of the colonel were interesting, and, to me, both entertaining and delightful. My only regret, Henderson, is that you were not present to share in my enjoyment of the affair.

As soon as we had driven the five tractors onto the pier and shut down the motors, Colonel Daggett came striding back along the column. Spying me in the cab of the fifth machine, he at once opened up.

"Why are you driving this tractor?" he demanded. "What has happened to the regular operator?"

"Just as we were starting, sir," I explained, "I found he had an injured hand. As there was no time to get another operator, I drove the machine myself."

"Most irregular," he growled. "But what I want to know is what has happened to the rest of this convoy. Where are the other tractors?"

"I don't know, sir."

"You don't know! Why don't you know?"

"Sir," I explained humbly, "the orders were for each driver to follow the machine ahead, with no exceptions or modifications."

"But you are an officer. You should have assumed some responsibility for the man behind you. You must have noticed he wasn't there."

"I did indeed, sir. But at the time, I was driving the tractor. If I was to follow your orders and follow the man ahead, I could not at the same time go back and look for the man behind."

"All right," he snapped. "I'm going to find out what happened." He called one of the lieutenants and ordered him to drive back in a jeep, locate the tractors and hurry them along.

As the lieutenant departed, the master of the ship arrived to find out what was the matter.

"Even with these new improved methods of loading," he said, "it's going to take a long time to get a hundred tractors and all that other stuff stowed away. If we're going to sail tomorrow morning, we've got to get busy right now."

"The tractors will be here at any moment," said the colonel.

"They had better be," said the master. He walked away.

The rest of us waited and waited, while the colonel got madder and madder. At the end of almost an hour, the lieutenant returned in the jeep.

"Sir," he reported, "I drove all the way to Fort Quinault and all the way back, and I couldn't find a single one of those tractors."

"What?" roared the colonel.

"Sir, I drove all the way to Fort Quinault and all the way back, and I couldn't find ——"

"You couldn't find even one out of ninety-five big tractors? Are you blind? Are you crazy?"

"Well ——" began the lieutenant doubtfully.

"Move over," snapped the colonel. He climbed in behind the wheel. And by this time he was so mad he couldn't think straight any more. Apparently it never occurred to him that there could be any real difficulty in locating all these tractors. So he never stopped to organize an adequate searching party. "I am going to find those machines," he announced, "and I am going to find them in a hurry." And a moment later he and the lieutenant and the jeep disappeared up the road in the mud and the rain.

That was about five this afternoon. It is now nine in

the evening, and I have been whiling away the intervening hours eating a good supper at the local officers' mess and writing this letter to you at the local officers' club. The master of the ship has called and threatened that if the tractors do not come pretty soon, he will load up with other material here at the port and sail without us. These threats, however, do not scare me at all.

As no news has come from Colonel Daggett and the lieutenant, I can only speculate pleasantly on what may be happening out there in the forest in the wind and the rain and the fog. As the rain has probably obliterated the tractor tracks, and as there are a good many side roads, with innumerable ramifications, it will presumably take them a long time to find anything. So it is my guess that they are still aimlessly driving about in their open jeep, cold and wet and hungry and mad—all of which grieves me, especially in the case of the unfortunate lieutenant.

As for the tractor drivers, a good many if not all of them have doubtless become aware by this time that they are traveling in circles. But what can they do? The colonel has so incessantly dinned into them the principle of unquestioning obedience that they will naturally hesitate a long time before doing anything sensible that is against orders. Besides, they have plenty of K rations and extra fuel for their machines. So I feel sure they are still dutifully playing at follow-the-leader.

In other words, while Colonel Daggett drives frantically here and there, that enchanted ring of processionary tractors, in its remote sylvan sanctuary, is doggedly and interminably going round and round and round, everlastingly chasing its tail and getting nowhere.

And with this beautiful thought, I will close for the present, adding a postscript to let you know how this comes out.

Yours,
ALEXANDER BOTTS.

P.S.: Monday, October 1. It is all over. On Saturday morning, the day after the above was written, Colonel Daggett came back, wet and cold and raging. He had found nothing. He got hold of a plane. By this time the weather had cleared. He cruised for two hours, and finally spotted the tractors, still rotating faithfully in a counter-clockwise direction. A rescue party was dispatched. The tractors were brought in. But by this time it was Saturday night. The ship had taken on another cargo and sailed. And our new orders had arrived from Washington.

Thus I have been completely and gloriously successful in my tactics of delay, and you, Henderson, have been equally successful in stirring up the authorities in Washington. Unfortunately, however, through some ghastly error on the part of one of these armchair wonders in the War Department, what we have received is not the order to stay in this country—which you expected—but the previous order of August third, which had not, as you supposed, been canceled, and which directs us to proceed not to Honolulu, but to Manila. The result is that the entire outfit, after being promptly loaded onto another ship, is now steaming down Puget Sound, headed for a place much farther away than it was before we started our meddling. And all I can do about it is send this letter back by the pilot.

Moral: You and I can beat almost anything, but who can beat the United States Army?

Yours, and I still want to get out,
ALEXANDER BOTTS, MAJOR, AUS,
APO #4739, Care Postmaster,
San Francisco, California.

BOTTS IS BACK—WITH ALL
PAPERS IN ORDER

CARE OF DANIEL DENMAN,
EARTHWORM TRACTOR DEALER,
SEATTLE, WASHINGTON.
Thursday, August 22, 1946.

MR. GILBERT HENDERSON, PRESIDENT,
EARTHWORM TRACTOR COMPANY,
EARTHWORM CITY, ILLINOIS.

DEAR HENDERSON: It gives me great pleasure to announce that I am no longer Maj. Alexander Botts. I am back from the Pacific, the proud possessor of a splendid collection of war souvenirs. I am out of the Army, with my discharge and all other necessary documents in perfect order. I am full of ideas and energy.

The only thing I seem to lack right now is money. But that does not worry me, because I am resuming, as of today, my former identity as Mr. Alexander Botts, sales manager of the Earthworm Tractor Company. And you will be delighted to know that I have already started correcting some of the more serious mistakes that you people back home have been making while I have been off winning the war.

This morning I called on one of our oldest and most valued customers out here, Mr. Henry Stevenson, and at once uncovered a truly shocking state of affairs. Mr. Stevenson is now engaged in a big logging operation which is of tremendous importance in the housing program. His prewar Earthworm tractors are practically worn out. And he has

had ten of our 100 h.p. Earthworms on order for almost
a year—with no results whatever.

"If I don't get delivery on those machines by the end
of this month," said Mr. Stevenson, pounding on the desk,
"I'll cancel the whole order and buy myself a fleet of those
new Blue Ox tractors."

"What?" I said. "You aren't actually considering any
such hopeless monstrosity as the Blue Ox?"

"I know your Earthworms are better," admitted Mr.
Stevenson, "but I can't get delivery on them. These Blue
Oxen seem to be available. So I'm going to grab them.
What else can I do?"

"I'll tell you what you can do, Mr. Stevenson," I said.
"You can hand over all your troubles to Alexander Botts.
I am sorry you have been treated so badly during my ab-
sence. But, now that I am back, things are going to change.
You can trust me, Mr. Stevenson. I will see that you get
your ten Earthworm tractors by the end of the month."

"You really mean that, Mr. Botts?"

"It is a promise," I said.

I then wished Mr. Stevenson a cheery good-by and
called on our new Seattle dealer, Mr. Daniel Denman.

After introducing myself, I pounded on the desk even
more vigorously than Mr. Stevenson had done, and told the
man exactly what was the matter with him and what he
ought to do to correct it.

"I am astonished," I said, "at the neglect you have
shown in handling this important order from Mr. Stevenson. You will get in touch with the factory right now and
demand that those ten tractors be shipped at once by fast
freight."

I regret to say that Mr. Denman merely yawned in
my face. I yelled at him some more. Then I discovered
that he did not know who I am; he had been connected with
our organization such a short time that, incredible though
it may seem, he had never even heard the name "Alexander
Botts." Besides which, the poor muttonhead quite obviously

thinks he knows as much about the tractor business as I do. He not only refused to take orders; he would not even listen to suggestions. Apparently he has not yet learned that the war is over and it is once more fashionable to be polite. And that, Henderson, is why it becomes necessary for me to appeal to you.

First, I want you to ship those ten tractors to Mr. Stevenson at once. Second, I want you to instruct Mr. Denman that from now on he is to take orders from me . . . and without any back talk or monkey business. Third, you will tell the cashier at Earthworm City that I am once more on the pay roll and that he is to honor my expense accounts without any of the unnecessary quibbling which, I regret to say, has occasionally characterized his handling of such matters in the past.

Incidentally, you might ask him to wire me a couple of thousand dollars in advance expense money to relieve the financial stringency which I mentioned at the beginning of this letter.

In case you are still as inquisitive as you used to be about my private affairs, it might be well for me to explain that my present lack of ready cash is perfectly natural under the circumstances. I received my discharge early this year in the Philippines. For several months I remained overseas getting together and preparing for shipment the splendid collection of souvenirs to which I have previously referred. I landed in the United States about a month ago, since which time I have been awaiting the arrival of my souvenirs and enjoying a delightful holiday with my wife and children here on the Pacific Coast. All this I have kept confidential, because I felt that I needed a vacation, and I knew that if you learned I was out of the Army, you would immediately start pestering me to come back to work.

Now, however, my vacation is over. I am once more on the job. And as my activities grow in importance, the expenses will naturally expand.

As soon as I get things straightened out here in

Seattle, I plan to take off in a private plane on a grand tour of the United States for the purpose of stirring up all our dealers and modernizing their methods so that they can operate with greater effectiveness. In the course of two or three months I shall probably land at Earthworm City with a report on what I have done to the dealers and with suggestions for the reorganization and improvement of the factory and the home office.

Don't forget to have the cashier wire me the two thousand dollars.

Cordially yours,
ALEXANDER BOTTS,
Sales Manager, Earthworm Tractor Company.

P.S. To be on the safe side, make it three thousand.

EARTHWORM TRACTOR COMPANY
EARTHWORM CITY, ILLINOIS
OFFICE OF THE PRESIDENT

Saturday, August 24, 1946.

MR. ALEXANDER BOTTS,
CARE OF DANIEL DENMAN,
EARTHWORM TRACTOR DEALER,
SEATTLE, WASHINGTON.

DEAR BOTTS: Your letter is here, and I want you to know that the Earthworm Tractor Company is standing solidly behind its promise to take back all former employees who have been absent in the armed services. We are ready to do this regardless of added expense and inconvenience, and even though the returned veteran may have been away so long that his ability to carry on his former job has become considerably impaired.

To the end that matters may be handled with fairness to all, we have established in our Personnel Department a special Veterans' Division; adequately staffed with experienced psychiatrists and other experts who devote their entire time to assisting former soldiers, such as yourself, in the difficult problems of readjustment to civilian life.

Such being the case, I must ask that you come to Earthworm City at once for a refresher course in the principles of salesmanship, and for general consultation, reorientation and re-education. In the meantime, I must insist that you refrain from interfering in the affairs of our Sales Department.

Mr. Stevenson's tractors cannot be shipped for several months. Strikes and shortages have limited our production, and he will have to take his turn with our other customers. As I am not yet ready to put you on the pay roll as sales manager, I cannot give you any authority over Mr. Denman. I most certainly cannot grant you the sort of unlimited expense account that you seem to desire. And your plans for a grand tour in a private airplane are completely out of the question. I can sympathize with your feeling in this matter—I wish I had a private plane myself—but the Earthworm Tractor Company simply cannot afford to finance such luxuries.

Instead of the three thousand dollars requested, I am enclosing a check for one hundred dollars for advance expense money. This should be ample to bring you here to Earthworm City, where I hope to have the pleasure of seeing you in the immediate future.

Very sincerely yours,
GILBERT HENDERSON.

CARE OF DANIEL DENMAN,
EARTHWORM TRACTOR DEALER,
SEATTLE, WASHINGTON.
Tuesday, August 27, 1946.

DEAR HENDERSON: Your letter came yesterday. I am sorry that I cannot agree with your quaint idea that

I ought to come in to the factory to put on a vaudeville act with your trained psychiatrists and to submit myself to some vague course in reorientation and readjustment— whatever that means. The truth of the matter is that you, Henderson, ought to snap out of your swivel-chair lethargy and get out here in the great open spaces where you could learn a few of the facts of life about the tractor business in relation to the cash customers.

When your letter arrived, I must admit that I was considerably annoyed at your unenlightened attitude in refusing to ship the tractors, confirm my authority over Mr. Denman and supply me with adequate funds.

I spent most of yesterday evening composing a series of blistering telegrams which I had planned to send you every hour on the hour all day today. However, at nine o'clock this morning, before I got around to sending the first one, I received a piece of good news, which has made this whole telegraphic project unnecessary. The news dealt with an event which will make it possible for me to handle everything out here without any assistance from you or the home office. Mr. Stevenson is going to get his ten Earthworm tractors tomorrow, plus a lot of extra equipment. He has already kicked out the salesman for the Blue Ox tractor. In the meantime, I have Mr. Denman practically eating out of my hand. And I have plenty of money for all my immediate needs.

This happy situation has been brought about entirely because of the unusual collection of war souvenirs which I mentioned in my letter of last Thursday. As some of these souvenirs are now involved in a business transaction to which the Earthworm Tractor Company is a party, it seems reasonable that you, as president of the company, should be informed of the facts. This makes it necessary for me to trace the history of the great Botts collection.

As you probably know, almost all American soldiers are enthusiastic collectors of souvenirs. When they come home from overseas, they are apt to drag along Japanese swords, rifles, helmets and all manner of useless junk such as battle flags, uniforms, grass skirts, native carvings, and so forth and so on.

During my career in the Army I became interested in collecting souvenirs myself. Anything that I do at all I like to do well. So it is natural that I should have gone far beyond the sort of piker activities which characterize the average soldier.

One of the big problems of souvenir hunting in the Army overseas has been the difficulty of bringing the stuff home. On many Pacific islands, for instance, the entire terrain would be literally covered with trucks, jeeps, tanks, airplanes, tractors and similar matériel. On the beaches there would often be stranded landing craft and sometimes even larger vessels.

The average soldier was, of course, licked by the transportation problem. But not Alexander Botts. After my discharge from the Army in the Philippines, I got together with a small group of discharged Army and Navy officers and organized the Alexander Botts Salvage and Souvenir Co-operative, Inc. In the course of about two months, we were able to salvage two LST's from the beaches of an island called Yuk. After hiring crews to operate our craft, we spent another two months accumulating and loading our cargoes. We started for home about six weeks ago, loaded with probably the finest assortment of war relics ever assembled by any group of private collectors.

As I was in a hurry, I came ahead by plane. And all through my vacation with my family, I have been anxiously awaiting the arrival of the two LST's.

I did not say very much about all this in my first letter, because I was not sure when the stuff would arrive. But I am now delighted to report that the first LST came sailing into Puget Sound yesterday morning, and has now run its bow up on a beach which I had previously rented in a secluded cove on the Olympic Peninsula. This beach is cheaper than a pier at a regular port. It is also more private—which is a definite advantage for any project like this which might cause trouble with the authorities.

In addition to a large collection of the usual type of souvenirs, I have ten 100 h.p. Earthworm tractors, complete with bulldozers, winches and other miscellaneous equipment, all of which we had been able to pick up in surprisingly good condition.

These well-equipped tractors, as I have previously indicated, will be in Mr. Stevenson's hands by tomorrow. And I have already worked out the business and financial details so as to produce the greatest amount of good for the greatest number of people. First, acting as sales manager of the Alexander Botts Salvage and Souvenir Co-operative, Inc., I have made out a bill of sale transferring the machines to the Earthworm Tractor Company. Then, as sales manager of Earthworm, I have made out a bill of sale transferring the stuff to our dealer, Mr. Denman. Finally, I have had Mr. Denman make out a bill of sale passing everything along to Mr. Stevenson.

I quoted Mr. Stevenson a flat price of one hundred thousand dollars, or ten thousand dollars for each of the ten big tractors. Mr. Stevenson, after inspecting the stuff, eagerly closed the deal. Being a bona-fide big operator, he passed over his check for the full amount at once.

Following my basic principles of letting anybody who does business with me make a good profit, I am permitting Mr. Denman to hold out the standard 20 per cent commission. With this twenty thousand dollars' worth of pure gravy all set for him to lap up, it is no wonder that he is— as I previously remarked—practically eating out of my hand.

After deducting Mr. Denman's commission, there remains eighty thousand dollars, on which I am allowing the Earthworm Tractor Company a 10 per cent profit, or eight thousand dollars, which I feel is ample, considering how little work the company has done on this deal. This eight thousand dollars, incidentally, I am retaining out here as

expense money. This is a little more than the three thous-
and I asked for, but I can probably find a use for it.

The remaining seventy-two thousand dollars goes into
the treasury of the Alexander Botts Salvage and Souvenir
Co-operative, Inc., thus providing ample funds to pay off
the crews of our LST's, and also providing handsome cash
dividends for myself and my business associates, in addition to a liberal distribution of miscellaneous souvenirs.

In view of my sensational success in this deal, you will
naturally want me to keep right on as sales manager, without wasting any time in futile visits to the factory. In this
I heartily agree with you. It is also probable that you will
be tempted to start boasting to everybody about how good
I am. Ordinarily, this would be all right. But in this particular case, I have a very distinct feeling that silence might
be the better policy.

Do not get me wrong. I have done nothing dishonest.
My salvage operations were carried out with the knowledge
and consent of the authorities concerned. I even have documents which tend to prove this. These documents, however,
are not at the moment available. So I should much prefer,
for the time being, that my activities remain hidden from
the prying eyes of overzealous officials. As soon as I have
any more definite information I will let you know.

Cordially yours,
ALEXANDER BOTTS,
Sales Manager,
Earthworm Tractor Company.

TELEGRAM

EARTHWORM TRACTOR AGENCY,
WASHINGTON, D. C.,
AUGUST 30, 1946.

TO: ALEXANDER BOTTS,
CARE EARTHWORM TRACTOR AGENCY,
SEATTLE, WASHINGTON.

YOUR LETTER HAS BEEN FORWARDED TO ME HERE IN WASH-
INGTON WHERE I AM MAKING A BRIEF BUSINESS VISIT. YOUR
SALE OF SALVAGED ARMY EQUIPMENT SEEMS TO ME OF SUCH
DUBIOUS LEGALITY THAT I FEEL IT SHOULD BE CHECKED
AT ONCE BEFORE WE BECOME INVOLVED ANY MORE DEEPLY.
ACCORDINGLY I HAVE CONSULTED ARMY AND NAVY AUTHOR-
ITIES. THEY SAY ARMY AND NAVY EQUIPMENT SALVAGED ON
THE BATTLEFIELD IS STILL DEFINITELY GOVERNMENT PROP-
ERTY REGARDLESS OF ANY DOCUMENTS YOU MAY HAVE
WHICH "TEND TO PROVE" THAT YOUR SALVAGE OPERATIONS
WERE DONE WITH THE KNOWLEDGE AND CONSENT OF THE
AUTHORITIES CONCERNED. OBVIOUSLY, NOBODY IN THE
SOUTH PACIFIC WOULD HAVE THE AUTHORITY TO PRESENT
YOU WITH A LOT OF GOVERNMENT PROPERTY AS A FREE
GIFT. THIS MEANS THAT THE TRACTORS NEVER BELONGED
TO YOU, AND WHEN YOU SOLD THEM YOU COMMITTED A
SERIOUS CRIME. OFFICIALS HERE ARE WIRING WEST COAST
OFFICIALS TO INVESTIGATE AND TAKE WHATEVER STEPS
MAY BE NECESSARY. PLEASE ADVISE ME ON FUTURE DE-
VELOPMENTS, INCLUDING WHAT FURTHER ACTION YOU
ARE TAKING.

GILBERT HENDERSON,
PRESIDENT, EARTHWORM TRACTOR COMPANY.

SEATTLE, WASHINGTON,
Saturday, August 31, 1946.

DEAR HENDERSON: I am writing this after a long
and painful session with the Federal cops.

Honestly, Henderson, I can't understand why you act the way you do. When I courageously save you from your own folly and correct all your mistakes by refusing to desert my post, by skillfully talking this hitherto reluctant dealer into active co-operation, and by supplying the necessary tractors and putting through a deal by which we preserve the good will of our customer and set up a nice profit for both the company and our dealer—when I do all this, all you can think of is to go tattletaling to the Federal Government with such an ignorant and distorted version of the facts that you throw everything once more into confusion and fill the jails of our fair land with innocent persons.

It was yesterday morning that the Federal cops, egged on by your ill-advised chatter, descended upon us.

One group seized the ten tractors at the logging camp —thus throwing another monkey wrench into the already sadly impaired housing program. They also arrested Mr. Henry Stevenson on the absurd pretext that he was a receiver of goods stolen by the Earthworm Tractor Company. He was soon released on bail, but the incident must have dampened—at least temporarily—the enthusiasm for our organization which I had been working so hard to build up in his mind.

A second group of cops came swarming into the Earthworm Tractor Agency, arrested Mr. Denman and held him several hours until he could arrange bail. Apparently they were also after me. Fortunately, however, I had received your telegram a few minutes before the raid. As the officers came in the front door, I was already on my way out the back window.

I hurried to the cove, where I found that the second LST had just come in with the rest of the souvenirs, including several jeeps, peeps, trucks and a couple of C-47 transport planes. There was also a trunk full of documents, which I had been anxiously awaiting, and which I was fortunately able to take along when my pursuers caught up with me and dragged me back for questioning to the office of one of the assistant Federal attorneys here in Seattle.

The documents included all the different kinds of papers that are now required when you ship anything into this country from overseas. As I am always most meticulous in such matters, I had provided everything I knew was necessary, everything I thought was necessary, and everything I feared might be necessary. The trunk was jammed with an impressive array of affidavits, invoices, receipts, manifests, declarations, clearances, de-clearances, permits, releases, licenses, navicerts, bills of lading, bills of sale and dozens of other documents from the United States Bureau of Customs, Immigration Service, Bureau of Internal Revenue, Public Health Service, the Departments of Labor, State and Commerce, the War Shipping Administration and various other commissions, boards, services, bureaus, divisions, administrations and offices.

Ordinarily, this would have been enough for anybody. But the assistant district attorney before whom I had been haled was hopelessly prejudiced.

"There seems to be nothing wrong," he admitted grudgingly, "with the documents covering the actual shipment and landing of these goods. But that does not alter the fact that you are guilty of selling stolen property."

"It is not stolen," I said. I handed him a formal document, signed and sealed on the island of Yuk, by which His Gracious Majesty, the King of the Island, in consideration of the payment of one million dollars in lawful Yuk sea-shell money, transferred ownership of all former Army and Navy equipment on the island to the Alexander Botts Salvage and Souvenir Co-operative, Inc. "There you are," I said, "I bought the stuff perfectly honestly. You have no case against me at all."

Unfortunately, the man was still so dominated by the suspicions which you, Henderson, had so unwisely disseminated that he could no longer think straight.

"This is even more serious than I had supposed," he said ominously.

"How so?" I asked him.

"Our Government," he explained, "is naturally solicitous for the welfare of the inhabitants of islands which have been taken over by our forces in the course of the war. To the end that the simple-minded natives may be protected against exploitation by unscrupulous traders, an agency known as the Federal Office of Insular Economics has been set up, with powers to regulate commerce and trade, and to impose severe penalties against persons such as yourself who are guilty of swindling the natives by schemes such as purchasing valuable equipment for so-called money consisting of almost worthless sea shells."

"I know all about this Federal Office of Insular Economics," I said. "There was a FOOIE representative on the island of Yuk while I was there. We used to play gin rummy together. And—following the system, which I learned in the Army, of protecting myself at all times with adequate official papers—I procured a copy, on official FOOIE stationery, of this man's report on my operations."

I handed over the document—which told the whole story. For many generations—according to the report—the natives of Yuk had used for money a special kind of sea shell which occurs naturally only on an island many hundreds of miles away. During the war years there were no traders to bring in fresh supplies of these shells. The natives, in their frail canoes, had no way to get them. The amount of shell money gradually dwindled because of breakage and other factors. And a severe monetary depression resulted.

Then the Alexander Botts Salvage and Souvenir Cooperative, Inc., arrived. We sized up the situation and made a deal with the king. As soon as we had repaired one of the C-47 planes, we made a number of trips to a distant shell island and brought back several tons of seashell money— enough to equal one million dollars at the official rate of exchange set up by the king, myself and the FOOIE representative.

With all this money in the treasury, the king was able to establish a truly progressive regime patterned after our own Federal Administration in Washington. He promoted himself to the office of president, and then began pouring out money for social security, unemployment compensation, public works, subsidies to coconut farmers, public housing, education, hospitalization and hundreds of other worthy projects. All this spending so primed the pump of business activity that before I left the island they were enjoying a real boom. For some reason the cost of living began to go up, but the FOOIE representative was able to handle this problem very successfully by persuading the president to set up a price-control board, which began cracking down so vigorously on chiselers and black marketeers that all complaints against the government were silenced—at least for a while. The official conclusion of the FOOIE representative was that my timely action in expanding the money supply had saved the economic life of the entire island.

This should have satisfied the assistant Federal attorney. But it did not.

"This report," he admitted, "seems to clear you in the matter of cheating the natives. But it does not change the fact that the stuff is United States Government property, which the natives had no right to sell to you, and which you have no right to sell to Mr. Stevenson."

"Wrong again," I said.

Reaching into my precious pile of documents, I dragged out a certified copy of an official Army order, with a number of supporting affidavits, showing that when the United States forces had turned over the island of Yuk to the Australians, all Army supplies and matériel—including the two stranded LST's, the tractors, the airplanes and other equipment—were likewise turned over to the Australians. I also produced a formal treaty by which, in return for work done by the natives, the Australian commander, upon quitting the island, definitely transferred ownership in everything he was leaving behind to His Gracious Majesty, the King of the Island of Yuk.

This made the man angrier than ever. "When that stuff was transferred to the Australian Government," he said, "the transaction must have been under Lend-Lease. This means that the United States Government still has official title to the property. And you are guilty of selling stolen goods—just as I said in the beginning."

"Look," I said. "If I am guilty of selling stolen goods, so is His Majesty the King of Yuk. And what is more important, so is the Australian Government. If you arrest me for this, are you also going to arrest the Prime Minister of Australia and the Australian General Staff?"

"Don't be silly. You know I can't do that."

"All right then. I have the papers to prove that I bought these tractors in perfectly good faith. Do you actually think that you can get any jury over here to convict me on nothing more substantial than your unsupported claim that the goods were stolen, long ago and far away, by the Australian Government?"

This question seemed to be the last straw as far as the assistant United States attorney was concerned. Enmeshed in the net of paper work which I had woven about him, all he could do was sound off with helpless rage.

"Mr. Botts," he yelled, "I am thoroughly convinced that you are a crook! This time you have covered your tracks very successfully with this blizzard of documents! But I give you fair warning, if I ever catch you with your paper work down, I will prosecute you to the fullest extent of the law!"

"Not a chance," I said. "My years in the Army have taught me that in dealing with the Government it is always wise to remember that old Latin motto: 'Papyrus correctus, omnis correctus'—which means that if the paper work is okay, everything is okay."

"That will be enough out of you," said the attorney.

He called in a couple of mugs with badges on their vests. "The case against Stevenson, Denman and Botts is being dropped," he snarled. "The seized machinery is to be released. As for this character here"—he pointed at me—"you will eject him from this office at once. And I hope I never see him again."

I was promptly grabbed by the collar, hustled outside and deposited on the sidewalk along with my trunkful of papers. Later in the day I had a conference with Stevenson and Denman. I am pleased to report that both of them are now feeling fine. So everything is okay. And from now on, things are really going to happen.

The two LST's are proceeding by way of the Panama Canal to St. Louis, where I plan to sell them to our local dealer to be used in delivering tractors along the Mississippi River.

One of the C-47 transport planes is being flown to Earthworm City to be turned over to you, Henderson, absolutely free of charge and with my compliments. This ought to take care of that pathetic lament in your letter of several days ago: "I wish I had a private plane myself—but the Earthworm Tractor Company simply cannot afford to finance such luxuries."

I will soon take off in the other plane on my grand tour of inspection. My eight thousand dollars will probably last me until you have time to put me on the pay roll and set up a regular expense account for me. After all, my expenses will be quite moderate. The plane has been acquired without cost to the Earthworm Company, so future charges will be limited to gasoline, oil, maintenance, airport fees, hotel bills and salaries for pilot, copilot and hostess.

Yours enthusiastically,
ALEXANDER BOTTS.